W9-BMW-943

Contents

Hall • *Basic Biomechanics, Fifth Edition*

PREFACE

The fifth edition of *Basic Biomechanics* has been significantly updated and redesigned from the previous edition. As the interdisciplinary field of biomechanics grows in both breadth and depth, it is important that even introductory textbooks reflect the nature of the science. Accordingly, the text has been revised, expanded, and updated, with the objectives being to present relevant information from recent research findings and to prepare students to *analyze* human biomechanics.

The approach taken remains an integrated balance of qualitative and quantitative examples, applications, and problems designed to illustrate the principles discussed. The fifth edition also retains the important sensitivity to the fact that some beginning students of biomechanics possess weak backgrounds in mathematics. For this reason, it includes numerous sample problems and applications, along with practical advice on approaching quantitative problems.

ORGANIZATION

Each chapter follows a logical and readable format, with the introduction of new concepts consistently accompanied by practical human movement examples and applications from across the life span and across sport, clinical, and daily living activities.

NEW CONTENT HIGHLIGHTS

New content has been added to provide updated scientific information on relevant topics. All chapters have been revised to incorporate the latest information from the biomechanics research literature, and numerous new sport and clinical applications and examples are included. Topics added or significantly expanded include bone modeling and remodeling, osteoporosis, bone changes during spaceflight, articular cartilage function, osteoarthritis, muscle fiber–type conversion, the stretch-shortening cycle, neuromuscular fatigue and injuries, ACL rupture, balance and falling, and gait economy.

Balanced Coverage

The Biomechanics Academy of AAHPERD recommends that undergraduate students in biomechanics devote approximately one-third of study time to anatomical considerations, one-third to mechanical considerations, and the remainder to applications. The integrated approach to coverage of these areas taken in previous editions is continued in this fifth edition.

Applications Oriented

All chapters in this new edition contain discussion of a broad range of updated human movement applications, many of which are taken from the recent biomechanics research literature. Special emphasis has been placed on examples that span all ages and address clinical and daily living issues, as well as sport applications.

The Use of Problems

Problems and laboratory exercises are incorporated throughout the text, with some references to the *Dynamic Human* CD-ROM and e-Human software, which can be bundled with the book on an optional basis.

Laboratory Experiences

The integrated laboratory manual appears at the end of each chapter with references to simulations on the text's Online Learning Center. The soft-cover design with perforation allows laboratory manual pages to be completed and turned in to instructors.

Integrated Technology

Technology is integrated throughout the text, with an Online Learning Center box appearing on every chapter-opening page and directing students to resources online, while lists of related Websites at the end of each chapter offer pertinent sources to students. Problems and laboratory experiences are incorporated throughout the text and updated to reference the Online Learning Center.

PEDAGOGICAL FEATURES

In addition to the sample problems, problem sets, laboratory experiences, Online Learning Center boxes, end-of-chapter key terms lists, and lists of Websites, the book contains other pedagogical features from previous editions. These include **key concepts, marginal definitions, sample problems, chapter summaries, introductory and additional problems, references,** and **appendices.**

ANCILLARIES

Online Learning Center

www.mhhe.com/hall5e
This Website offers resources to students and instructors. It includes downloadable ancillaries, Web links, student quizzing, additional information on topics of interest, and much more.
Resources for the instructor include:

* Downloadable PowerPoint presentation with annotated lecture notes

* Online instructor's manual (developed by Darla Smith, University of Texas at El Paso)

* Test bank, available as Word files and with EZ Test computerized testing software
* Interactive links
* Links to professional resources
* Online laboratory manual with simulations

  Resources for the student include:

* Flashcards of chapter key terms
* Downloadable PowerPoint presentation
* Interactive activities
* Self-grading quizzes
* Online laboratory manual with simulations

ACKNOWLEDGMENTS

I would like to thank developmental editor Erin Strathmann for her quality work on the new edition of this book. Many thanks also to copy editor Tom Briggs and senior production editor Mel Valentin for their very capable and professional work on this revision. I also wish to extend appreciation to the following reviewers:

Gail B. Arnold
University of Massachusetts - Boston

Jeffery Barto
University of North Carolina - Charlotte

Brian Church
Arkansas State University

Robert D. Clark
California Polytechnic State University

Declan Connolly
University of Vermont

David J. Kean
Kent State University

William A. Kuehl
Grand Canyon University

Steven T. McCaw
Illinois State University

John A. Mercer
University of Nevada - Las Vegas

Mark H. Rescino
Rivier College

Darla R. Smith
University of Texas-El Paso

Daniel Too
State University of New York at Brockport

Ross E. Vaughn
Boise State University

Tony Zaloga
Frostburg State University

Carole J. Zebras
University of Kansas

Finally, I also very much appreciate the excellent suggestions I have received over the five editions of this book from numerous students and colleagues.

Susan J. Hall

Professor and Chair,
Department of Health, Nutrition, and Exercise Sciences,
College of Health Sciences
University of Delaware

1

What Is Biomechanics?

After completing this chapter, you will be able to:

Define the terms *biomechanics*, *statics*, *dynamics*, *kinematics*, and *kinetics*, and explain the ways in which they are related.

Describe the scope of scientific inquiry addressed by biomechanists.

Distinguish between qualitative and quantitative approaches for analyzing human movement.

Explain how to formulate questions for qualitative analysis of human movement.

Use the 11 steps identified in the chapter to solve formal problems.

ONLINE LEARNING CENTER RESOURCES

www.mhhe.com/hall5e

Log on to our Online Learning Center (OLC) for access to these additional resources:

* Online Lab Manual
* Flashcards with definitions of chapter key terms
* Chapter objectives
* Chapter lecture PowerPoint presentation
* Self-scoring chapter quiz
* Additional chapter resources
* Web links for study and exploration of chapter-related topics

2 BASIC BIOMECHANICS

Learning to walk is an ambitious task from a biomechanical perspective.

● *Courses in anatomy, physiology, mathematics, physics, and engineering provide background knowledge for biomechanists.*

biomechanics
application of mechanical principles in the study of living organisms

mechanics
branch of physics that analyzes the actions of forces on particles and mechanical systems

Anthropometric characteristics may predispose an athlete to success in one sport and yet be disadvantageous for participation in another.

W hy do some golfers slice the ball? How can workers avoid developing low back pain? What cues can a physical education teacher provide to help students learn the underhand volleyball serve? Why do some elderly individuals tend to fall? We have all admired the fluid, graceful movements of highly skilled performers in various sports. We have also observed the awkward first steps of a young child, the slow progress of an injured person with a walking cast, and the hesitant, uneven gait of an elderly person using a cane. Virtually every activity class includes a student who seems to acquire new skills with utmost ease and a student who trips when executing a jump or misses the ball when attempting to catch, strike, or serve. What enables some individuals to execute complex movements so easily, while others appear to have difficulty with relatively simple movement skills?

Although the answers to these questions may be rooted in physiological, psychological, or sociological issues, the problems identified are all biomechanical in nature. This book will provide a foundation for identifying, analyzing, and solving problems related to the biomechanics of human movement.

BIOMECHANICS: DEFINITION AND PERSPECTIVE

During the early 1970s, the international community adopted the term biomechanics to describe the science involving the study of biological systems from a mechanical perspective (42). Biomechanists use the tools of mechanics, the branch of physics involving analysis of the actions of forces, to study the anatomical and functional aspects of living

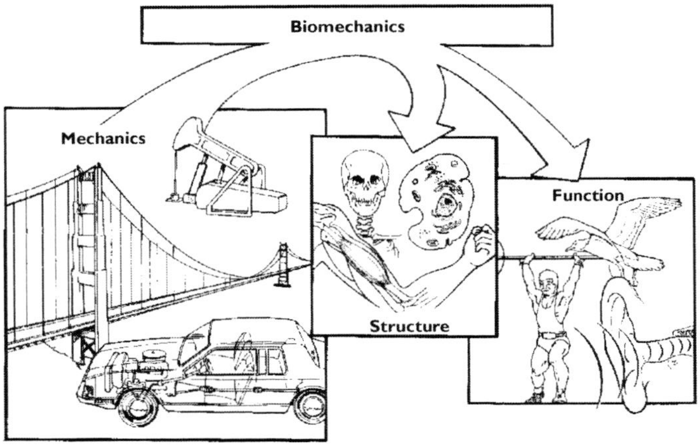

FIGURE 1-1

Biomechanics uses the principles of mechanics for solving problems related to the structure and function of living organisms.

organisms (Figure 1-1). Statics and dynamics are two major subbranches of mechanics. Statics is the study of systems that are in a state of constant motion, that is, either at rest (with no motion) or moving with a constant velocity. Dynamics is the study of systems in which acceleration is present.

Kinematics and kinetics are further subdivisions of biomechanical study. Kinematics is the description of motion, including the pattern and speed of movement sequencing by the body segments that often translates to the degree of coordination an individual displays. Whereas kinematics describes the appearance of motion, kinetics is the study of the forces associated with motion. The study of human biomechanics may include questions such as whether the amount of force the muscles are producing is optimal for the intended purpose of the movement. Anthropometric factors, including the size, shape, and weight of the body segments, are other important considerations in a kinetic analysis.

Although biomechanics is relatively young as a recognized field of scientific inquiry, biomechanical considerations are of interest in several different scientific disciplines and professional fields. Biomechanists may have academic backgrounds in zoology; orthopedic, cardiac, or sports medicine; biomedical or biomechanical engineering; physical therapy; or kinesiology, with the commonality being an interest in the biomechanical aspects of the structure and function of living things.

The biomechanics of human movement is one of the subdisciplines of kinesiology, the study of human movement (Figure 1-2). Although some biomechanists study topics such as ostrich locomotion, blood flow through constricted arteries, or micromapping of dental cavities, this book focuses primarily on the biomechanics of human movement from the perspective of the movement analyst.

As shown in Figure 1-3, biomechanics is also a scientific branch of sports medicine. Sports medicine has been defined by Lamb as "an umbrella term that encompasses both clinical and scientific aspects of exercise and sport" (34). The American College of Sports Medicine is an example of an organization that promotes interaction between scientists and clinicians with interests in sports medicine–related topics.

statics
branch of mechanics dealing with systems in a constant state of motion

dynamics
branch of mechanics dealing with systems subject to acceleration

kinematics
study of the description of motion, including considerations of space and time

kinetics
study of the action of forces

anthropometric
related to the dimensions and weights of body segments

kinesiology
study of human movement

sports medicine
clinical and scientific aspects of sports and exercise

FIGURE 1-2

The subdisciplines of kinesiology.

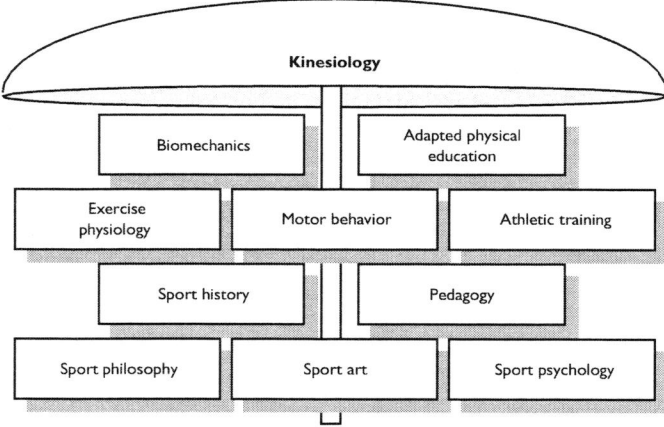

FIGURE 1-3

The branches of sports medicine.

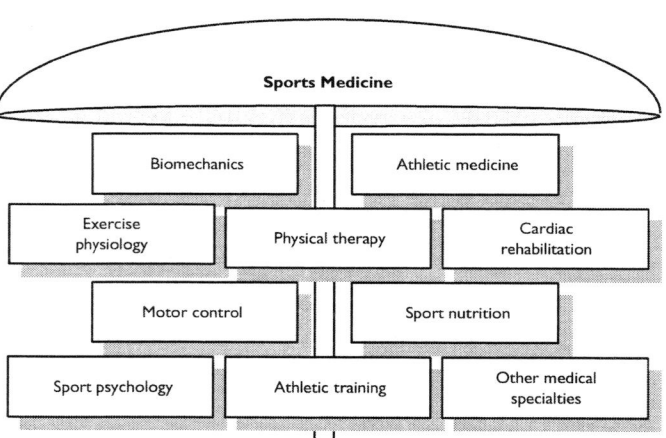

What Problems Are Studied by Biomechanists?

As expected given the different scientific and professional fields represented, biomechanists study questions or problems that are topically diverse. For example, zoologists have examined the locomotion patterns of dozens of species of animals walking, running, trotting, and galloping at controlled speeds on a treadmill to determine why animals choose a particular stride length and stride rate at a given speed. They concluded that most vertebrates, including humans, select a gait that optimizes economy, or metabolic energy consumption, at a given speed (46). Research suggests that it is the cost of muscular force production that primarily governs the energy cost of running (50). Interestingly, this means that if a biped, such as a turkey, and a quadruped, such as a dog, are of similar body weights, they use about the same amount of energy when running, in spite of the apparent differences in body size and shape and running mechanics (51). This is true because although bipeds, compared to quad-

● In research, each new study, investigation, or experiment is usually designed to address a particular question or problem.

FIGURE I-4

Research on the biomechanics of animal gaits poses some interesting problems.

rupeds, tend to have the advantage of longer legs and the ability to take longer steps, they must recruit more muscle to support body weight. One of the challenges of this type of research is determining how to persuade a cat, a dog, or a turkey to run on a treadmill (Figure 1-4).

Among humans, although the energy cost of running increases with running speed, there are sizable differences in energy cost between individuals that become even larger as running speed increases (32). Although some individuals appear to run more smoothly and comfortably than others, no particular biomechanical factors have been associated with either good or poor running economy (32). Differences in muscle fiber type composition appear to translate into differences in energy utilization during running (see Chapter 6) (33). Strength training and high-altitude training have been shown to improve running economy by promoting better utilization of elastic energy and oxygen within the working muscles (55).

There are also changes in the energy cost of running and walking among growing children as their bodies undergo developmental changes in body proportions and motor skills. Between early childhood and young adulthood, there is a decrease in the amount of energy required for standing, walking, and running, with children expending 70% more energy to walk at a fast pace than adults (17).

The U.S. National Aeronautics and Space Administration (NASA) sponsors another multidisciplinary line of biomechanics research to promote understanding of the effects of microgravity on the human musculoskeletal system. Of concern is the fact that astronauts who have been out of the earth's gravitational field for just a few days have returned with muscle atrophy, cardiovascular and immune system changes, and reduced bone density, mineralization, and strength, especially in the lower extremities (20). The issue of bone loss, in particular, is currently a limiting factor for long-term space flights, with bone lost at a rate of about 1% per month from the lumbar spine and 1.5% per month from the hips (39). Both increased

6   BASIC BIOMECHANICS

bone resorption and decreased calcium absorption appear to be responsible (see Chapter 4) (56).

Since those early days of space flight, biomechanists have designed and built a number of exercise devices for use in space to take the place of normal bone-maintaining activities on earth. Some of this research has focused on the design of treadmills for use in space that load the bones of the lower extremity with deformations and strain rates that are optimal for stimulating new bone formation (14). Scientists have discovered that applying an anteriorly directed horizontal force to individuals running in low-gravity environments generates impact forces that are much more similar to those sustained when running on earth (11). This is an important finding, since lower-extremity bone strain, which is believed to be a critical link in the mechanical stimulation of bone growth and maintenance, is directly related to the magnitude of the ground reaction forces sustained (47). So far, however, no adequate substitute has been found for weight bearing for the prevention of bone loss in space (20).

Maintaining sufficient bone-mineral density is also a topic of concern here on earth. Osteoporosis is a condition in which bone mineral mass and strength are so severely compromised that daily activities can cause bone pain and fracturing (23). This condition is found in most elderly individuals, with earlier onset in women, and is becoming increasingly prevalent throughout the world with the increasing mean age of the population (31). Today, approximately 40% of women experience one or more osteoporotic fractures after age 50, and after age 60, about 90% of all fractures in both men and women are osteoporosis-related (35, 49). The most common fracture site is the vertebrae, with the presence of one fracture indicating increased risk for future vertebral and hip fractures (25).

Osteoporosis is neither a disease with acute onset nor an inevitable accompaniment of aging, but the result of a lifetime of habits that are erosive to the skeletal system (5). Among women, in particular, low levels of physical activity during adolescence have been positively correlated with increased risk for osteoporosis later in life (53). Other known risk factors for developing osteoporosis include physical inactivity over a lifetime; cigarette smoking; deficiencies in estrogen, calcium, and vitamin D; and excessive consumption of protein, caffeine, and alcohol (16). The two key strategies for preventing osteoporotic fractures are maximizing peak bone mass during adolescence and early adulthood and preventing bone loss at menopause (31). Importantly, studies show that a regular program of weight-bearing exercise, such as walking, among individuals with osteoporosis can increase bone health and strength (3).

Another problem area challenging biomechanists who study the elderly is mobility impairment. Age is associated with decreased ability to balance, and older adults both sway more and fall more than young adults, although the reasons for these changes are not well understood (45). Falls, and particularly fall-related hip fractures, are extremely serious, common, and costly medical problems among the elderly. Each year, falls cause large percentages of the wrist fractures, head injuries, vertebral fractures, and lacerations, as well as over 90% of the hip fractures, occurring in the United States (52). Biomechanical research teams are investigating the biomechanical factors that enable individuals to avoid falling, the characteristics of safe landings from falls, the forces sustained by different parts of the body during falls, and the ability of protective clothing and floors to prevent falling injuries (52). Promising work in the development of intervention strategies has shown that exercise walking can be effective in improving balance and reducing the likelihood of falling among sedentary older adults (6).

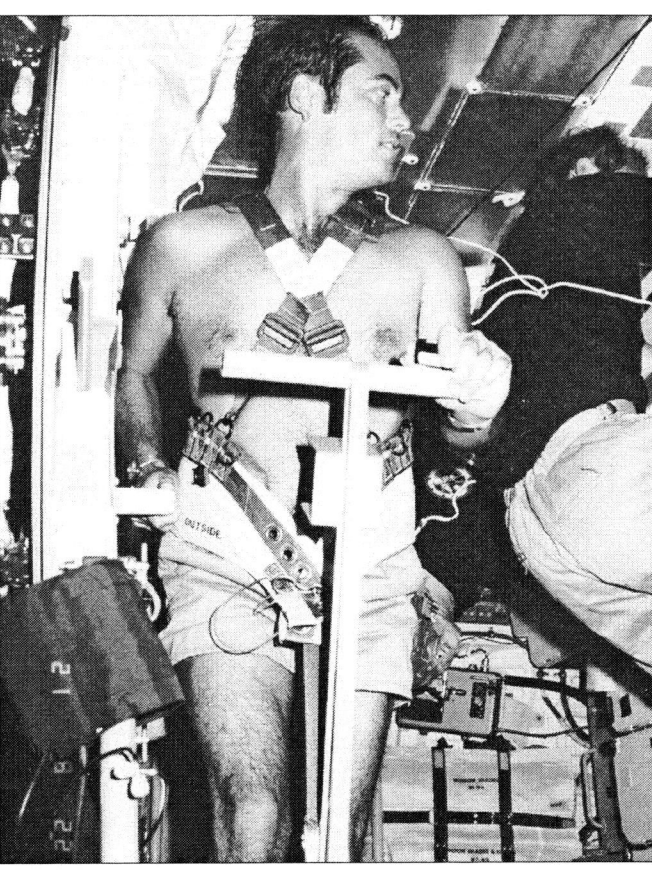

Exercise in space is critically important for preventing loss of bone mass among astronauts, as demonstrated by astronaut Bob Crippen on shuttle flight STS-7. Photo courtesy of NASA.

Research by clinical biomechanists has resulted in improved gait among children with cerebral palsy, a condition involving high levels of muscle tension and spasticity. The gait of the cerebral palsy individual is characterized by excessive knee flexion during stance. This problem is treated by surgical lengthening of the hamstring tendons to improve knee extension during stance. In some patients, however, the procedure also diminishes knee flexion during the swing phase of gait, resulting in dragging of the foot. After research showed that patients with this problem exhibited significant co-contraction of the rectus femoris with the hamstrings during the swing phase, orthopedists began treating the problem by surgically attaching the rectus femoris to the sartorius insertion (24). This creative, biomechanics research–based approach has enabled a major step toward gait normalization for children with cerebral palsy.

Research by biomedical engineers has also resulted in improved gait for children and adults with below-knee amputations. Ambulation with a prosthesis creates an added metabolic demand, which can be particularly significant for elderly amputees and for young active amputees who participate in sports requiring aerobic conditioning. In response to this problem, researchers have developed an array of lower-limb and foot

8   BASIC BIOMECHANICS

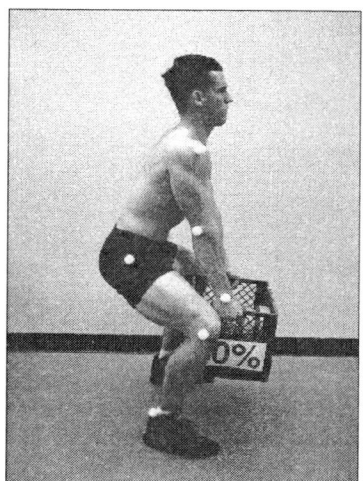

Occupational biomechanics involves study of safety factors in activities such as lifting.

carpal tunnel syndrome
overuse condition caused by compression of the median nerve in the carpal tunnel and involving numbness, tingling, and pain in the hand

The aerodynamic cycling equipment introduced in the 1984 Olympic Games contributed to the new world records set.

prostheses that store and return mechanical energy during gait, thereby reducing the metabolic cost of locomotion (2, 22, 40, 58). Studies have shown that the more compliant prostheses are better suited for active and fast walkers, whereas prostheses that provide a more stable base of support are generally preferred for the elderly population (8). Microchip-controlled "Intelligent Prostheses" show promise for reducing the energy cost of walking at a range of speeds (13).

Occupational biomechanics is a field that focuses on the prevention of work-related injuries and the improvement of working conditions and worker performance (10). Researchers in this field have learned that work-related low back pain can derive not only from the handling of heavy materials but from unnatural postures, sudden and unexpected motions, and the characteristics of the individual worker (63). Occupational biomechanists are also recognizing how important it is for workers to be both physically and mentally prepared for jobs in industry in order to prevent low back pain (63). Sophisticated biomechanical models of the trunk are now being used in the design of materials-handling tasks in industry to enable minimizing potentially injurious stresses to the low back (9).

In recent years, although the number of overall workplace injuries has decreased, carpal tunnel syndrome, a neurological impairment at the wrist often associated with occupational overuse, has steadily increased in frequency (7). Because carpal tunnel syndrome is particularly associated with repetitive keyboard use, studies are being conducted to explore novel keyboard designs that may be more biomechanically optimal than the traditional keyboard (41). Interesting new designs being tested include a keyboard split into left and right halves, with each half positioned directly in front of a shoulder, and split, vertically aligned keyboards that allow maintaining the wrists in neutral position (37).

Biomechanists have also contributed to performance improvements in selected sports through the design of innovative equipment. One excellent example of this is the Klapskate, the speed skate equipped with a hinge near the toes that allows the skater to plantar flex at the ankle during push-off, resulting in up to 5% higher skating velocities than were obtainable with traditional skates (27). The Klapskate was designed by van Ingen Schenau and de Groot, based on study of the gliding push-off technique in speed skating by van Ingen Schenau and Baker, as well as work on the intermuscular coordination of vertical jumping by Bobbert and van Ingen Schenau (15). When the Klapskate was used for the first time by competitors in the 1998 Winter Olympic Games, speed records were shattered in every event.

Numerous innovations in sport equipment and apparel have also resulted from findings of experiments conducted in experimental chambers called *wind tunnels* that involved controlled simulation of the air resistance actually encountered during particular sports. Examples include the aerodynamic helmets, clothing, and cycle designs used in competitive cycling, and the ultrasmooth suits worn in other competitive speed-related events, such as swimming, track, skating, and skiing. Wind tunnel experiments have also been conducted to identify optimal body configuration during events such as ski jumping (60).

Sport biomechanists have also directed efforts at improving the biomechanical, or technique, components of athletic performance. They have learned, for example, that factors contributing to superior performance in the long jump, high jump, and pole vault include high horizontal velocity going into takeoff and a shortened last step that facilitates continued elevation of the total-body center of mass (12, 26). Study of baseball pitchers has determined that high-velocity pitchers display greater external rotation

Biomechanists Develop a Revolutionary New Figure Skate

What do 1996 U.S. figure skating champion Rudy Galindo and 1998 Olympic gold medal winner Tara Lipinski have in common besides figure skating success? They have both had double hip replacements, Galindo at age 32 and Lipinski at age 18.

Overuse injuries among figure skaters are on the rise at an alarming rate, with most involving the lower extremities and lower back (4, 21). With skaters performing more and more technically demanding programs including multirotation jumps, on-ice training time for elite skaters now typically includes over 100 jumps per day, six days per week, year after year.

Yet unlike most modern sports equipment, the figure skate has undergone only very minor modifications since 1900. The soft-leather, calf-high boots of the nineteenth century are now made of stiffer leather to promote ankle stability and are not quite as high to allow a small amount of ankle motion. However, the basic design of the rigid boot with a screwed-on steel blade has not changed.

The problem with the traditional figure skate is that when a skater lands after a jump, the rigid boot severely restricts motion at the ankle, forcing the skater to land nearly flat-footed and preventing motion at the ankle that could help attenuate the landing shock that gets translated upwards through the musculoskeletal system. Not surprisingly, the incidence of overuse injuries in figure skating is mushrooming due to the increased emphasis on performing jumps, the increase in training time, and the continued use of outdated equipment.

To address this problem, biomechanist Jim Richards and graduate student Dustin Bruening, working at the University of Delaware's Human Performance Lab, have designed and tested a new figure skating boot. Following the design of modern-day Alpine skiing and in-line skating boots, the new boot incorporates an articulation at the ankle that permits flexion movement but restricts potentially injurious sideways movement.

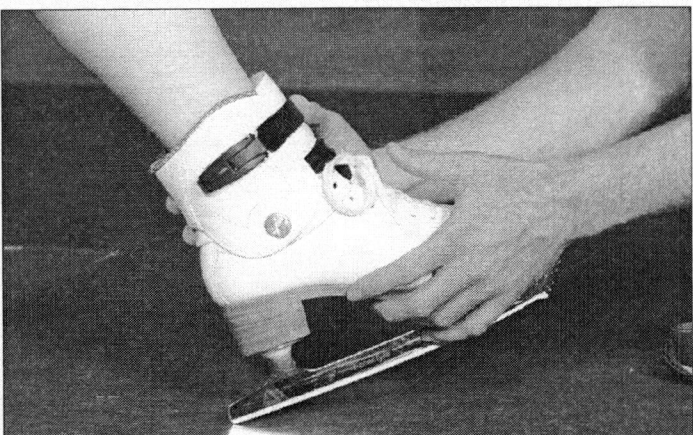

New figure skating boot with an articulation at the ankle designed by biomechanists at the University of Delaware.

The boot enables skaters to land toe-first, with the rest of the foot hitting the ice more slowly. This extends the landing time, thereby spreading the impact force over a longer time and dramatically diminishing the peak force translated up through the body. As shown in the graph, the new boot attenuates the peak landing force on the order of 30%.

Although the new figure skating boot design was motivated by a desire to reduce the incidence of stress injuries in skating, it may also promote performance. The ability to move through a larger range of motion at the ankle may well enable higher jump heights and concomitantly more rotations while the skater is in the air.

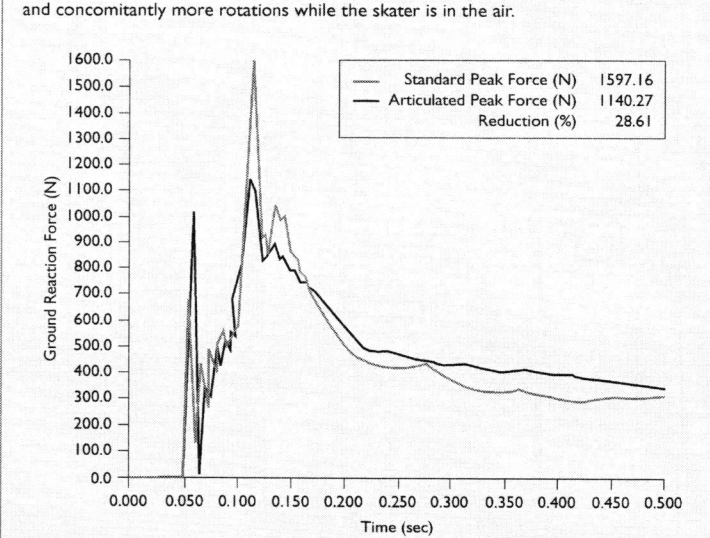

	Standard Peak Force (N)	1597.16
	Articulated Peak Force (N)	1140.27
	Reduction (%)	28.61

The new figure skating boot with an articulation at the ankle reduces peak impact forces during landing from a jump on the order of 30%.
Graph courtesy of D. Bruening and J. Richards.

Skaters who adopt the new boot are finding that using it effectively requires a period of acclimatization. Those who have been skating in the traditional boot for many years tend to have reduced strength in the musculature surrounding the ankle. Improving ankle strength is likely to be necessary for optimal use of a boot that now allows ankle motion.

at the shoulder, more forward trunk tilt at ball release, higher-extension angular velocity at the lead knee, and greater angular velocity of the pelvis and upper torso than lower-velocity pitchers (38, 57).

One rather dramatic example of performance improvement partially attributable to biomechanical analysis is the case of four-time Olympic discus champion Al Oerter. Mechanical analysis of the discus throw requires precise evaluation of the major mechanical factors affecting the flight of the discus. These factors are:

1. The speed of the discus when it is released by the thrower
2. The projection angle at which the discus is released
3. The height above the ground at which the discus is released
4. The angle of attack (the orientation of the discus relative to the prevailing air current)

By using computer simulation techniques, researchers can predict the needed combination of values for these four variables that will result in a throw of maximum distance for a given athlete (28). High-speed cameras can record performances in great detail, and when the film or video is analyzed, the actual projection height, velocity, and angle of attack can be compared to the computer-generated values required for optimal performance. At the age of 43, Oerter bettered his best Olympic performance by

8.2 m. Although it is difficult to determine the contributions of motivation and training to such an improvement, some part of Oerter's success was a result of enhanced technique following biomechanical analysis (54). Most adjustments to skilled athletes' techniques produce relatively modest results because their performances are already characterized by above-average technique.

Some of the research produced by sport biomechanists has been done in conjunction with the Sports Medicine Division of the United States Olympic Committee (USOC). The general goal of USOC research is to examine the ways in which mechanical factors limit the performances of elite American athletes training for Olympic and other international competition (19). Typically, this work is done in direct cooperation with the national coach of the sport to ensure the practicality of results. USOC-sponsored research has yielded much new information about the mechanical characteristics of elite performance in various sports. Because of continuing advances in scientific analysis equipment, the role of sport biomechanists in contributing to performance improvements is likely to be increasingly important in the future.

●*The USOC began funding sports medicine research in 1981. Other countries began sponsoring research to boost the performance of elite athletes in the early 1970s.*

The influence of biomechanics is also being felt in sports popular with both nonathletes and athletes, such as golf. Computerized video analyses of golf swings designed by biomechanists are commonly available at golf courses and equipment shops. The science of biomechanics can play a role in optimizing the distance and accuracy of all golf shots, including putting, through analysis of body angles, joint forces, and muscle activity patterns (29). A common technique recommendation is to maintain a single fixed center of rotation to impart force to the ball (29).

Other concerns of sport biomechanists relate to minimizing sport injuries through both identifying dangerous practices and designing safe equipment and apparel. In recreational runners, for example, research shows that the most serious risk factors for overuse injuries are training errors such as a sudden increase in running distance or intensity, excess cumulative mileage, running on cambered surfaces, and improper footwear (43). The complexity of safety-related issues increases when the sport is equipment-intensive. Evaluation of protective helmets involves ensuring not only that the impact characteristics offer reliable protection but also that the helmet does not overly restrict wearers' peripheral vision.

●*Impact testing of protective sport helmets is carried out scientifically in engineering laboratories.*

An added complication is that equipment designed to protect one part of the body may actually contribute to the likelihood of injury in another part of the musculoskeletal system. Modern ski boots and bindings, while effective in protecting the ankle and lower leg against injury, unfortunately contribute to severe bending moments at the knee when the skier loses balance. This factor has contributed to the nearly threefold increase in the incidence of knee injuries in skiing since 1972 (30). Injuries in snowboarding are also more frequent with rigid, as compared to pliable, boots, although more than half of all snowboarding injuries are to the upper extremity (36, 48).

Another challenging area of research for biomechanists in the realm of sport safety is investigation of the efficacy of prophylactic knee braces designed to protect the knees from valgus stresses that could damage the medial collateral ligaments. The wearing of such braces by healthy individuals has been a contentious issue since the American Academy of Orthopaedics issued a position statement against their use in 1987 (35). Research shows that knee braces can contribute 20–30% added resistance against lateral blows to the knee, with custom-fitted braces providing the best protection (1). A possible concern, however, is that knee braces act to change the pattern of lower-extremity muscle activity during gait, with less work performed at the knee and more at the hip (18). Other documented problems that appear to affect some athletes more than others and may be brace-specific include reduced sprinting speed and earlier onset of fatigue (1).

An area of biomechanics research with implications for both safety and performance is sport shoe design. Today sport shoes are designed both to prevent excessive loading and related injuries and to enhance performance. Because the ground or playing surface, the shoe, and the human body compose an interactive system, athletic shoes are specifically designed for particular sports, surfaces, and anatomical considerations. Aerobic dance shoes are constructed to cushion the metatarsal arch. Football shoes to be used on artificial turf are designed to minimize the risk of knee injury. Running shoes are available for training and racing on snow and ice. In fact, sport shoes today are so specifically designed for designated activities that wearing an inappropriate shoe can contribute to the likelihood of injury (59, 62).

These examples illustrate the diversity of topics addressed in biomechanics research, including some examples of success and some areas of continuing challenge. Clearly, biomechanists are contributing to the knowledge base on the full gamut of human movement, from the gait of the physically challenged child to the technique of the elite athlete. Although varied, all of the research described is based on applications of mechanical principles in solving specific problems in living organisms. This book is designed to provide an introduction to many of those principles and to focus on some of the ways in which biomechanical principles may be applied in the analysis of human movement.

Why Study Biomechanics?

As is evident from the preceding section, biomechanical principles are applied by scientists and professionals in a number of fields to problems related to human health and performance. Knowledge of basic biomechanical concepts is also essential for the competent physical education teacher, physical therapist, physician, coach, personal trainer, or exercise instructor.

An introductory course in biomechanics provides foundational understanding of mechanical principles and their applications in analyzing movements of the human body. The knowledgeable human movement analyst should be able to answer the following types of questions related to biomechanics: Why is swimming *not* the best form of exercise for individuals with osteoporosis? What is the biomechanical principle behind variable-resistance exercise machines? What is the safest way to lift a heavy object? Is it possible to judge what movements are more/less economical from visual observation? At what angle should a ball be thrown for maximum distance? From what distance and angle is it best to observe a patient walk down a ramp or a volleyball player execute a serve? What strategies can an elderly person or a football lineman employ to maximize stability? Why are some individuals unable to float?

Perusing the objectives at the beginning of each chapter of this book is a good way to highlight the scope of biomechanical topics to be covered at the introductory level. For those planning careers that involve visual observation and analysis of human movement, knowledge of these topics will be invaluable.

PROBLEM-SOLVING APPROACH

Scientific research is usually aimed at providing a solution for a particular problem or answering a specific question. Even for the nonresearcher, however, the ability to solve problems is a practical necessity for functioning in modern society. The use of specific problems is also an effective approach for illustrating basic biomechanical concepts.

Quantitative versus Qualitative Problems

Analysis of human movement may be either *quantitative* or *qualitative*. *Quantitative* implies that numbers are involved, and *qualitative* refers to a description of quality without the use of numbers. After watching the performance of a standing long jump, an observer might qualitatively state, "That was a very good jump." Another observer might quantitatively announce that the same jump was 2.1 m in length. Other examples of qualitative and quantitative descriptors are displayed in Figures 1-5 and 1-6.

It is important to recognize that *qualitative* does not mean *general*. Qualitative descriptions may be general, but they may also be extremely

quantitative
involving the use of numbers

qualitative
involving nonnumeric description of quality

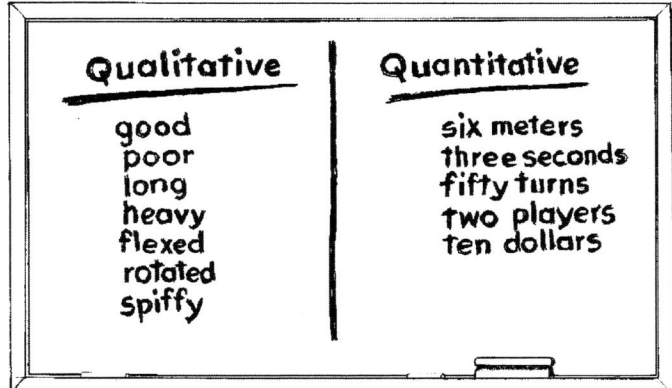

Examples of qualitative and quantitative descriptors.

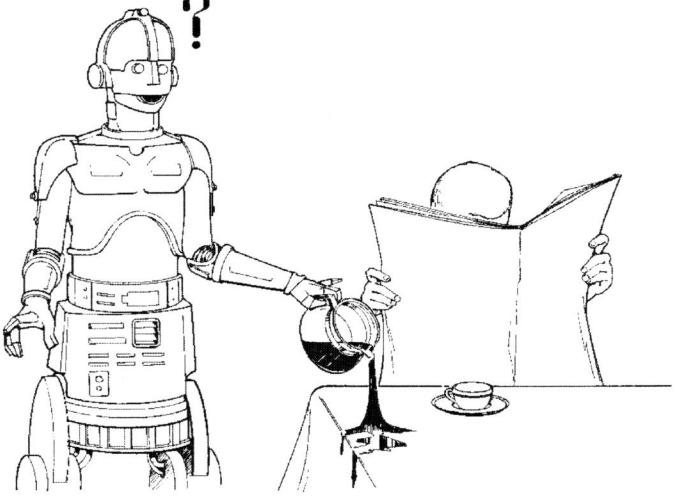

Quantitatively, the robot missed the coffee cup by 15 cm. Qualitatively, he malfunctioned.

detailed. It can be stated qualitatively and generally, for example, that a man is walking down the street. It might also be stated that the same man is walking very slowly, appears to be leaning to the left, and is bearing weight on his right leg for as short a time as possible. The second description is entirely qualitative but provides a more detailed picture of the movement.

Both qualitative and quantitative descriptions play important roles in the biomechanical analysis of human movement. Biomechanical researchers rely heavily on quantitative techniques in attempting to answer specific questions related to the mechanics of living organisms. Clinicians, coaches, and teachers of physical activities regularly employ qualitative observations of their patients, athletes, or students to formulate opinions or give advice.

Solving Qualitative Problems

Qualitative problems commonly arise during daily activities. Questions such as what clothes to wear, whether to major in botany or English, and whether to study or watch television are all problems in the sense that they are uncertainties that may require resolution. Thus, a large portion of our daily lives is devoted to the solution of problems.

Analyzing human movement, whether to identify a gait anomaly or to refine a technique, is essentially a process of problem solving. Whether the analysis is qualitative or quantitative, this involves identifying, then studying or analyzing, and finally answering a question or problem of interest.

Coaches rely heavily on qualitative observations of athletes' performances in formulating advice about technique.

To effectively analyze a movement, it is essential first to formulate one or more questions regarding the movement. Depending on the specific purpose of the analysis, the questions to be framed may be general or specific. General questions, for example, might include the following:

1. Is the movement being performed with adequate (or optimal) force?
2. Is the movement being performed through an appropriate range of motion?
3. Is the sequencing of body movements appropriate (or optimal) for execution of the skill?
4. Why does this elderly woman have a tendency to fall?
5. Why is this shot putter not getting more distance?

More specific questions might include these:

1. Is there excessive pronation taking place during the stance phase of gait?
2. Is release of the ball taking place at the instant of full elbow extension?
3. Does selective strengthening of the vastus medialis obliquus alleviate mistracking of the patella for this person?

Once one or more questions have been identified, the next step in analyzing a human movement is to collect data. The form of data most commonly collected by teachers, therapists, and coaches is qualitative visual observation data. That is, the movement analyst carefully observes the movement being performed and makes either written or mental notes. To acquire the best observational data possible, it is useful to plan ahead as to the optimal distance(s) and perspective(s) from which to make the observations. These and other important considerations for qualitatively analyzing human movement are discussed in detail in Chapter 2.

Formal versus Informal Problems

When confronted with a stated problem taken from an area of mathematics or science, many individuals believe they are not capable of finding a solution. Clearly, a stated math problem is different from a problem such as what to wear to a particular social gathering. In some ways, however, the informal type of problem is the more difficult one to solve. According to Wickelgren (61), a formal problem (such as a stated math problem) is characterized by three discrete components:

1. A set of given information
2. A particular goal, answer, or desired finding
3. A set of operations or processes that can be used to arrive at the answer from the given information

In dealing with informal problems, however, individuals may find the given information, the processes to be used, and even the goal itself to be unclear or not readily identifiable.

Solving Formal Quantitative Problems

Formal problems are effective vehicles for translating nebulous concepts into well-defined, specific principles that can be readily understood and applied in the analysis of human motion. People who believe themselves incapable of solving formal stated problems do not recognize that, to a large extent, problem-solving skills can be learned. Entire books on problem-solving approaches and techniques are available. However, most students are not exposed to coursework involving general strategies of the problem-solving process. A simple procedure for approaching and solving problems involves 11 sequential steps:

1. Read the problem *carefully*. It may be necessary to read the problem several times before proceeding to the next step. Only when you clearly understand the information given and the question(s) to be answered should you undertake step 2.
2. Write down the given information in list form. It is acceptable to use symbols (such as v for velocity) to represent physical quantities if the symbols are meaningful.
3. Write down what is wanted or what is to be determined, using list form if more than one quantity is to be solved for.
4. Draw a diagram representing the problem situation, clearly indicating all known quantities and representing those to be identified with question marks. (Although certain types of problems may not easily be represented diagrammatically, it is critically important to carry out this step whenever possible to accurately visualize the problem situation.)
5. Identify and write down the relationships or formulas that might be useful in solving the problem. (More than one formula may be useful and/or necessary.)
6. From the formulas that you wrote down in step 5, select the formula(s) containing both given variables (from step 2) and the variables that are desired unknowns (from step 3). If a formula contains only one unknown variable that is the variable to be determined, skip step 7 and proceed directly to step 8.
7. If you cannot identify a workable formula (in more difficult problems), certain essential information was probably not specifically stated but can be determined by inference and by further thought on and analysis of the given information. If this occurs, it may be necessary to repeat step 1 and review the pertinent information relating to the problem presented in the text.

inference
process of forming deductions from available information

8. Once you have identified the appropriate formula(s), write the formula(s) and carefully substitute the known quantities given in the problem for the variable symbols.

FIGURE 1-7

Using the systematic process helps simplify problem solving.

Summary of Steps for Solving Formal Problems

1. Read the problem carefully.
2. List the given information.
3. List the desired (unknown) information for which you are to solve.
4. Draw a diagram of the problem situation showing the known and unknown information.
5. Write down formulas that may be of use.
6. Identify the formula to use.
7. If necessary, reread the problem statement to determine whether any additional needed information can be inferred.
8. Carefully substitute the given information into the formula.
9. Solve the equation to identify the unknown variable (the desired information).
10. Check that the answer is both reasonable and complete.
11. Clearly box in the answer.

9. Using the simple algebraic techniques reviewed in Appendix A, solve for the unknown variable by (a) rewriting the equation so that the unknown variable is isolated on one side of the equals sign and (b) reducing the numbers on the other side of the equation to a single quantity.

10. Do a commonsense check of the answer derived. Does it seem too small or too large? If so, recheck the calculations. Also check to ensure that *all* questions originally posed in the statement of the problem have been answered.

11. Clearly box in the answer and include the correct units of measurement.

Figure 1-7 provides a summary of this procedure for solving formal quantitative problems. These steps should be carefully studied, referred to, and applied in working the quantitative problems included at the end of each chapter. Sample Problems 1.1 and 1.2 illustrate the use of this procedure.

Units of Measurement

Providing the correct units of measurement associated with the answer to a quantitative problem is important. Clearly, an answer of 2 cm is quite different from an answer of 2 km. It is also important to recognize the units of measurement associated with particular physical quantities. Ordering 10 km of gasoline for a car when traveling in a foreign country would clearly not be appropriate.

The predominant system of measurement still used in the United States is the English system. The English system of weights and measures arose over the course of several centuries primarily for purposes of commerce and land parceling. Specific units came largely from royal decrees. For example, a yard was originally defined as the distance from the end of the nose of King Henry I to the thumb of his extended arm. The English system of measurement displays little logic. There are 12 inches to the foot, 3 feet to the yard, 5280 feet to the mile, 16 ounces to the pound, and 2000 pounds to the ton.

The system of measurement that is presently used by every major country in the world except the United States is Le Système International d'Unites (the International System of Units), which is commonly known as the S.I. or the metric system. The metric system originated as the result of a request of King Louis XVI to the French Academy of Sciences in the 1790s. Although the system fell briefly from favor in France,

English system
system of weights and measures originally developed in England and used in the United States today

metric system
system of weights and measures used internationally in scientific applications and adopted for daily use by every major country except the United States

SAMPLE PROBLEM 1.1

A baseball player hits a triple to deep center field. As he is approaching third base, he notices that the incoming throw to the catcher is wild, and he decides to break for home plate. The catcher retrieves the ball 10 m from the plate and runs back toward the plate at a speed of 5 m/s. As the catcher starts running, the base runner, who is traveling at a speed of 9 m/s, is 15 m from the plate. Given that time = distance/speed, who will reach the plate first?

Solution

Step 1   Read the problem carefully.

Step 2   Write down the given information:

$$\text{base runner's speed} = 9 \text{ m/s}$$
$$\text{catcher's speed} = 5 \text{ m/s}$$
$$\text{distance of base runner from plate} = 15 \text{ m}$$
$$\text{distance of catcher from plate} = 10 \text{ m}$$

Step 3   Write down the variable to be identified: Find which player reaches home plate in the shortest time.

Step 4   Draw a diagram of the problem situation.

Step 5   Write down formulas of use:

$$\text{time} = \text{distance/speed}$$

Step 6   Identify the formula to be used: It may be assumed that the formula provided is appropriate because no other information relevant to the solution has been presented.

Step 7   Reread the problem if all necessary information is not available: It may be determined that all information appears to be available.

Step 8   Substitute the given information into the formula:

$$\text{time} = \frac{\text{distance}}{\text{speed}}$$

Catcher:

$$\text{time} = \frac{10 \text{ m}}{5 \text{ m/s}}$$

Base runner:

$$\text{time} = \frac{15 \text{ m}}{9 \text{ m/s}}$$

Step 9   Solve the equations:

Catcher:

$$\text{time} = \frac{10 \text{ m}}{5 \text{ m/s}}$$
$$\text{time} = 2 \text{ s}$$

Base runner:

$$\text{time} = \frac{15 \text{ m}}{9 \text{ m/s}}$$
$$\text{time} = 1.67 \text{ s}$$

Step 10   Check that the answer is both reasonable and complete.

Step 11   Box in the answer:

The base runner arrives at home plate first, by 0.33 s.

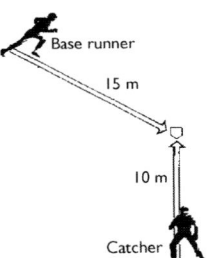

Base runner

15 m

10 m

Catcher

18   BASIC BIOMECHANICS

SAMPLE PROBLEM 1.2

A man sits in a 20 kg wheelchair at the top of a short ramp. When the brakes on the wheelchair are suddenly released, the wheelchair begins to roll down the ramp, accelerating at a rate of 0.5 m/s². If the net force causing the wheelchair to roll down the ramp is 45 Newtons (N), what is the mass of the man in the wheelchair? (*Hint:* The relationship to be used in solving this problem is force = mass × acceleration. For more information on the metric units of kilograms, meters, and Newtons, refer to Appendix C.) *This time, work through the 11 steps on your own.*

Step 2
$$\text{net force} = 45 \text{ N}$$
$$\text{wheelchair mass} = 20 \text{ kg}$$
$$\text{acceleration} = 0.5 \text{ m/s}^2$$

Step 3   Find: mass of man

Step 4
$$\text{mass}_{total} = \text{mass}_{chair} + \text{mass}_{man}$$

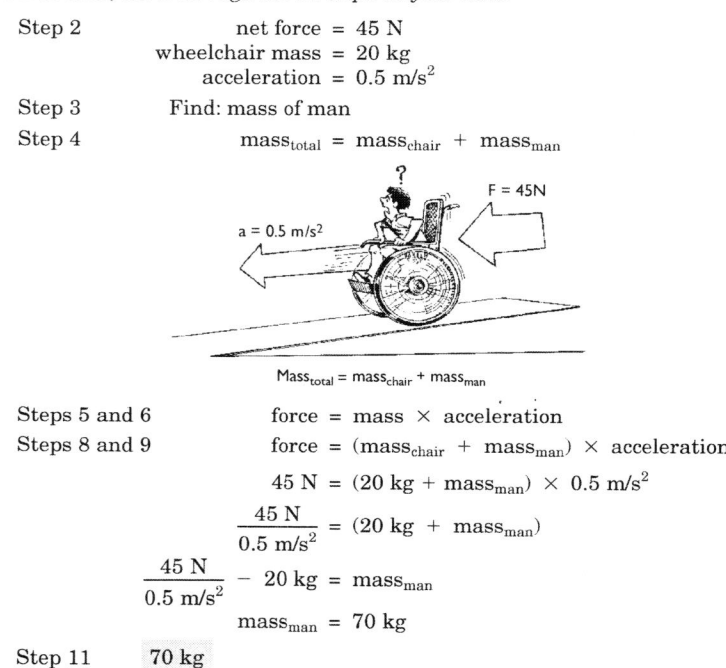

$$\text{Mass}_{total} = \text{mass}_{chair} + \text{mass}_{man}$$

Steps 5 and 6
$$\text{force} = \text{mass} \times \text{acceleration}$$

Steps 8 and 9
$$\text{force} = (\text{mass}_{chair} + \text{mass}_{man}) \times \text{acceleration}$$
$$45 \text{ N} = (20 \text{ kg} + \text{mass}_{man}) \times 0.5 \text{ m/s}^2$$
$$\frac{45 \text{ N}}{0.5 \text{ m/s}^2} = (20 \text{ kg} + \text{mass}_{man})$$
$$\frac{45 \text{ N}}{0.5 \text{ m/s}^2} - 20 \text{ kg} = \text{mass}_{man}$$
$$\text{mass}_{man} = 70 \text{ kg}$$

Step 11   70 kg

it was readopted in 1837. In 1875, the Treaty of the Meter was signed by 17 countries agreeing to adopt the metric system.

Since that time the metric system has enjoyed worldwide popularity for several reasons. First, it entails only four base units—the meter, of length; the kilogram, of mass; the second, of time; and the degree Kelvin, of temperature. Second, the base units are precisely defined, reproducible quantities that are independent of factors such as gravitational force. Third, all units excepting those for time relate by factors of 10, in contrast to the numerous conversion factors necessary in converting English units of measurement. Last, the system is used internationally.

For these reasons, as well as the fact that the metric system is used almost exclusively by the scientific community, it is the system used in this book. For those who are not familiar with the metric system, it is useful to be able to recognize the approximate English system equivalents of metric quantities. Two conversion factors that are particularly valuable are 2.54 cm for every inch and approximately 4.45 N for every pound. All of the relevant units of measurement in both systems and common English-metric conversion factors are presented in Appendix C.

SUMMARY

Biomechanics is a multidisciplinary science involving the application of mechanical principles in the study of the structure and function of living organisms. Because biomechanists come from different academic backgrounds and professional fields, biomechanical research addresses a spectrum of problems and questions.

Basic knowledge of biomechanics is essential for competent professional analysts of human movement, including physical education teachers, physical therapists, physicians, coaches, personal trainers, and exercise instructors. The structured approach presented in this book is designed to facilitate the identification, analysis, and solution of problems or questions related to human movement.

INTRODUCTORY PROBLEMS

1. Locate and read three articles from the scientific literature that report the results of biomechanical investigations. (*The Journal of Biomechanics, the Journal of Applied Biomechanics,* and *Medicine and Science in Sports and Exercise* are possible sources.) Write a one-page summary of each article, and identify whether the investigation involved statics or dynamics and kinetics or kinematics.
2. List 8–10 websites that are related to biomechanics, and write a paragraph describing each site.
3. Write a brief discussion about how knowledge of biomechanics may be useful in your intended profession or career.
4. Choose three jobs or professions, and write a discussion about the ways in which each involves quantitative and qualitative work.
5. Write a summary list of the problem-solving steps identified in the chapter, using your own words.
6. Write a description of one informal problem and one formal problem.
7. Step by step, show how to arrive at a solution to one of the problems you described in Problem 6.
8. Solve for x in each of the equations below. Refer to Appendix A for help if necessary.

    a. $x = 5^3$ e. $x^2 = 27 + 35$ h. $7 \times 5 = -40 + x$
    b. $7 + 8 = x/3$ f. $x = \sqrt{79}$ i. $3^3 = x/2$
    c. $4 \times 3^2 = x \times 8$ g. $x + 3 = \sqrt{38}$ j. $15 - 28 = x \times 2$
    d. $-15/3 = x + 1$

    (Answers: a. 125; b. 45; c. 4.5; d. -6; e. 7.9; f. 8.9; g. 3.2; h. 75; i. 54; j. -6.5)
9. Two schoolchildren race across a playground for a ball. Tim starts running at a distance of 15 m from the ball, and Jan starts running at a distance of 12 m from the ball. If Tim's average speed is 4.2 m/s and Jan's average speed is 4.0 m/s, which child will reach the ball first? Show how you arrived at your answer. (See Sample Problem 1.1.) (Answer: Jan reaches the ball first.)
10. A 0.5 kg ball is kicked with a force of 40 N. What is the resulting acceleration of the ball? (See Sample Problem 1.2.) (Answer: 80 m/s^2)

ADDITIONAL PROBLEMS

1. Select a specific movement or sport skill of interest, and read two or three articles from the scientific literature that report the results of biomechanical investigations related to the topic. Write a short paper that integrates the information from your sources into a scientifically based description of your chosen movement.

2. When attempting to balance your checkbook, you discover that your figures show a different balance in your account than was calculated by the bank. List an ordered, logical set of procedures that you may use to discover the error. You may use list, outline, or block diagram format.

3. Sarah goes to the grocery store and spends half of her money. On the way home, she stops for an ice cream cone that costs $0.78. Then she stops and spends one-fourth of her remaining money to settle a $5.50 bill at the dry cleaners. How much money did Sarah have originally? (Answer: $45.56)

4. Wendell invests $10,000 in a stock portfolio made up of Petroleum Special at $30 per share, Newshoe at $12 per share, and Beans & Sprouts at $2.50 per share. He places 60% of the money in P.S., 30% in N, and 10% in B & S. With market values changing (P.S. down $3.12, N up 80%, and B & S up $0.20), what is his portfolio worth six months later? (Answer: $11,856)

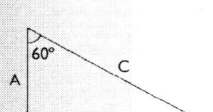

5. The hypotenuse of right triangle *ABC* (shown here) is 4 cm long. What are the lengths of the other two sides? (Answer: *A* = 2 cm; *B* = 3.5 cm)

6. In triangle *DEF,* side *E* is 4 cm long and side *F* is 7 cm long. If the angle between sides *E* and *F* is 50 degrees, how long is side *D?* (Answer: 5.4 cm)

7. An orienteer runs 300 m north and then 400 m to the southeast (at a 45° angle to north). If he has run at a constant speed, how far away is he from the starting position? (Answer: 283.4 m)

8. John is out for his daily noontime run. He runs 2 km west, then 2 km south, and then runs on a path that takes him directly back to the place he started at.
   a. How far did John run?
   b. If he has run at an average speed of 4 m/s, how long did the entire run take?
   (Answers: a. 6.83 km; b. 28.5 min)

9. John and Al are in a 15 km race. John averages 4.4 m/s during the first half of the race and then runs at a speed of 4.2 m/s until the last 200 m, which he covers at 4.5 m/s. At what average speed must Al run to beat John? (Answer: > 4.3 m/s)

10. A sailboat heads north at 3 m/s for 1 hour and then tacks back to the southeast (at 45° to north) at 2 m/s for 45 minutes.
    a. How far has the boat sailed?
    b. How far is it from its starting location?
    (Answers: a. 16.2 km; b. 8.0 km)

NAME _____

DATE _____

LABORATORY EXPERIENCES

1. Working in a group of 3–5 students, choose three human movements or motor skills with which you are all familiar. (A vertical jump is an example.) For each movement, list at least three general questions and three specific questions that an analyst might choose to answer.

Movement/Skill 1: _____

General Questions

1. _____

2. _____

3. _____

Specific Questions

1. _____

2. _____

3. _____

Movement/Skill 2: _____

General Questions

1. _____

2. _____

3. _____

Specific Questions

1. _____

22   BASIC BIOMECHANICS

2. _____
_____

3. _____
_____

Movement/Skill 3: _____

General Questions

1. _____
_____

2. _____
_____

3. _____
_____

Specific Questions

1. _____
_____

2. _____
_____

3. _____
_____

2. Working in a group of 3–5 students, choose a human movement or motor skill with which you are all
familiar, and have two members of the group simultaneously perform the movement several times
as the group observes. Based on your comparative observations, list any differences and similarities that you can detect. Which of these are of potential importance and which are more a matter of
personal style?

Movement Differences   **Important? (Y/N)**

_____   _____

_____   _____

_____   _____

_____   _____

_____   _____

_____   _____

_____   _____

Movement Similarities	**Important? (Y/N)**

3. Working in a group of 3–5 students, view a previously taken video or film of a human movement or motor skill performance. After viewing the movement several times, list at least three general questions and three specific questions that an analyst might choose to answer regarding the movement.

General Questions

1. _____

2. _____

3. _____

Specific Questions

1. _____

2. _____

3. _____

4. Having completed Laboratory Experiences 1–3, discuss in your group the relative advantages and disadvantages of each of the three exercises in terms of your ability to formulate meaningful questions.
5. Have one member of your group perform several trials of walking as the group observes from front, side, and rear views. The subject may walk either on a treadmill or across the floor. What observations can be made about the subject's gait from each view that are not visible or apparent from the other views?

Front View Observations

_____

_____

24   BASIC BIOMECHANICS

_____

_____

_____

Side View Observations

_____

_____

_____

_____

_____

Rear View Observations

_____

_____

_____

_____

_____

REFERENCES

1. Albright JP, Saterbak A, and Stokes J: Use of knee braces in sport. Current recommendations, Sports Med 20:281, 1995.

2. Arya AP, Lees A, Nirula HC, and Klenerman L: A biomechanical comparison of the SACH, Seattle and Jaipur feet using ground reaction forces, Prosthet Orthot Int 19:37, 1995.

3. Barlet JP, Coxam V, and Davicco MJ: Physical exercise and the skeleton, Arch Physiol Biochem 103:681, 1995.

4. Block RM: Figure skating injuries, Phys Med Rehabil Clin N Am 10:177, 1999.

5. Bockman RS: Osteoporosis and its management in older women, J Am Med Women's Assoc 52:121, 1997.

6. Bucher DM, Cres ME, deLateur BJ, Esselman PC, Margherita AJ, Price R, and Wagner EH: A comparison of the effects of three types of endurance training on balance and other risk factors in older adults, Aging (Milano) 9:112, 1997.

7. Carneiro RS: Carpal tunnel syndrome: the cause dictates the treatment, Cleve Clin J Med 66:159, 1999.

8. Casillas JM, Dulieu V, Cohen M, Marcer I, and Didier JP: Bioenergetic comparison of a new energy-storing foot and SACH foot in traumatic below-knee vascular amputations, Arch Phys Med Rehabil 76:39, 1995.

9. Chaffin DB: Primary prevention of low back pain through the application of biomechanics in manual materials handling tasks, G Ital Med Lav Ergon 27:40, 2005.

10. Chaffin DB, Martin BJ, and Andersson GBJ: *Occupational biomechanics* (3rd ed) New York, 1999, John Wiley & Sons.

11. Chang YH, Hamerski CM, and Kram R: Applied horizontal force increases impact loading in reduced-gravity running, J Biomech 34:679, 2001.

12. Dapena J and Chung CS: Vertical and radial motions of the body during the take-off phase of high jumping, Med Sci Sports Exerc 20:290, 1988.

13. Datta D, Heller B, and Howitt J: A comparative evaluation of oxygen consumption and gait pattern in amputees using Intelligent Prostheses and conventionally damped knee swing-phase control, Clin Rehabil 19:398, 2005.

14. Davis BL, Cavanagh PR, Sommer HJ 3rd, and Wu, G: Ground reaction forces during locomotion in simulated microgravity, Aviat Space Environ Med 67:235, 1996.

15. De Koning JJ, Houdijk H, de Groot G, and Bobbert MF: From biomechanical theory to application in top sports: the Klapskate story, J Biomech 33:1225, 2000.

16. Deal CL: Osteoporosis: prevention, diagnosis, and management. Am J Med 102:35S, 1997.

17. DeJaeger D, Willems PA, and Heglund NC: The energy cost of walking in children, Pflugers Arch 441:538, 2001.

18. DeVita P, Torry M, Glover KL, and Speroni DL: A functional knee brace alters joint torque and power patterns during walking and running, J Biomech 29:583, 1996.

19. Dillman CJ: Overview of the United States Olympic Committee sports medicine biomechanics program. In Butts NK, Gushiken TT, and Zarins B, eds: *The elite athlete,* New York, 1985, Spectrum Publications.

20. Doty SB: Space flight and bone formation, Materwiss Werksttech 35:951, 2004.

21. Dubravcic-Simunjak S, Pecina M, Kuipers H, Moran J, and Haspl M: The incidence of injuries in elite junior figure skaters, Am J Sports Med 31:511, 2003.

22. Farber BS and Jacobson JS: An above-knee prosthesis with a system of energy recovery: a technical note, J Rehabil Res Dev 32:337, 1995.

23. Frost HM: Osteoporosis: a rationale for further definitions? Calcif Tissue Int 62:89, 1998.

26   BASIC BIOMECHANICS

24. Gage JR, Perry J, Hicks RR, Koop S, and Werntz JR: Rectus femoris transfer to improve knee function of children with cerebral palsy. Develop Med Child Neur 29:159, 1987.

25. Greenblatt D: Treatment of postmenopausal osteoporosis, Pharmacotherapy 25:574, 2005.

26. Hay JG and Nohara H: The techniques used by elite long jumpers in preparation for take-off, J Biomech 23:229, 1990.

27. Houdijk H, de Koning JJ, de Groot G, Bobbert MF, and van Ingen Schenau GJ: Push-off mechanics in speed skating with conventional skates and klapskates, Med Sci Sprt Exerc 32:635, 2000.

28. Hubbard M, de Mestre NJ, and Scott J: Dependence of release variables in the shot put, J Biomech 34:449, 2001.

29. Hume PA, Keogh K, and Reid D: The role of biomechanics in maximizing distance and accuracy of golf shots, Sports Med 35:429, 2005.

30. Johnson SC: Anterior cruciate ligament injury in elite Alpine competitors, Med Sci Sports Exerc 27:323, 1995.

31. Kleerekoper M: Prevention of postmenopausal bone loss and treatment of osteoporosis, Semin Reprod Med 23:141, 2005.

32. Kyröläinen H, Belli A, and Komi P: Biomechanical factors affecting running economy, Med Sci Sports Exer 33:1330, 2001.

33. Kyröläinen H, Kivela R, Koskinen S, McBride J, Andersen JL, Takala T, Sipila S, and Komi PV: Interrelationships between muscle structure, muscle strength, and running economy, Med Sci Sports Exerc 35:45, 2003.

34. Lamb DR: The sports medicine umbrella, Sports Med Bull 5:8, 1984.

35. Lips P: Epidemiology and predictors of fractures associated with osteoporosis, Am J Med 103:3S, 1997.

36. Machold W, Kwansy O, Gässler P, Kolonja A, Reddy B, Bauer E, and Lehr S: Risk of injury through snowboarding, J Trauma 48: 1109, 2000.

37. Marklin RW, Simoneau GG, and Monroe JF: The effect of split and vertically-inclined computer keyboards on wrist and forearm posture, Proceedings of the Human Factors and Ergonomics Society 41st Annual Meeting, Albuquerque, NM, 642–46, 1997.

38. Matsuo T, Escamilla RF, Fleisig GS, Barrentine SW, and Andrews JR: Comparison of kinematic and temporal parameters between different pitch velocity groups, J Appl Biomech 17:1, 2001.

39. McCarthy ID: Fluid shifts due to microgravity and their effects on bone: a review of current knowledge, Ann Biomed Eng 33:95, 2005.

40. Miller LA and Childress DS: Analysis of a vertical compliance prosthetic foot, J Rehabil Res Dev 34:52, 1997.

41. Nelson JE, Treaster DE, and Marras WS: Finger motion, wrist motion and tendon travel as a function of keyboard angles, Clin Biomech 15:489, 2000.

42. Nelson RC: Biomechanics: past and present. In Cooper JM and Haven B, eds: Proceedings of the Biomechanics Symposium, Bloomington, IN, 1980.

43. O'Toole ML: Prevention and treatment of injuries to runners, Med Sci Sports Exerc 24:S360, 1992.

44. Paluska SA and McKeag DB: Knee braces: current evidence and clinical recommendations for their use, Am Fam Physician 61:411, 2000.

45. Perrin PP, Jeandel C, Perrin CA, and Béné MC: Influence of visual control, conduction, and central integration on static and dynamic balance in healthy older adults, Gerontology 43:223, 1997.

46. Perry AK, Blickhan R, Biewener AA, Heglund NC, and Taylor CR: Preferred speeds in terrestrial vertebrates: are they equivalent? J Exp Biol 137:207, 1988.

47. Peterman MM, Hamel AJ, Cavanagh PR, Paizza SJ, and Shrakey NA: In vitro modeling of human tibial strains during exercise in micro-gravity, J Biomech 34:693, 2001.

48. Pigozzi F, Santori N, Di Salvo V, Parisi A, and Di-Luigi L: Snowboard traumatology: an epidemiological study, Orthopedics 20:505, 1997.

49. Recker RR: Osteoporosis, Contemp Nutr 8:1, 1983.

50. Roberts TJ, Chen MS, and Taylor CR: Limb design and running mechanics, J Exp Biol 201:Pt 19:2753, 1998.

51. Roberts TJ, Kram R, Weyand PG, and Taylor CR: Metabolic cost of generating force, J Exp Biol 201:Pt 19:2745, 1998.
52. Robinovitch SN, Hsiao ET, Sandler R, Cortez J, Liu Q, and Paiement GD: Prevention of falls and fall-related fractures through biomechanics, Exer Sprt Sci Rev 28:74, 2000.
53. Rubin LA, Hawker GA, Peltekova VD, Fielding LJ, Ridout R, and Cole DE: Determinants of peak bone mass: clinical and genetic analyses in a young female Canadian cohort, J Bone Miner Res 14:633, 1999.
54. Ruby D: Biomechanics—how computers extend athletic performance to the body's far limits, Popular Science p 58, Jan 1982.
55. Saunders PU, Pyne DB, Telford RD, and Hawley JA: Factors affecting running economy in trained distance runners, Sports Med 34:465, 2004.
56. Smith SM, Wastney ME, O'Brien KO, Morukov BV, Larina IM, Abrams SA, Davis-Street JE, Oganov V, and Shackelford LC: Bone markers, calcium metabolism, and calcium kinetics during extended-duration space flight on the mir space station, J Bone Miner Res 20:208, 2004.
57. Stodden DF, Fleisig GS, McLean SP, Lyman SL, and Andrews JR: Relationship of pelvis and upper torso kinematics to pitched baseball velocity, J Appl Biomech 17:164, 2001.
58. Torburn L, Powers CM, Guiterrez, and Perry J: Energy expenditure during ambulation in dysvascular and traumatic below-knee amputees: a comparison of five prosthetic feet, J Rehabil Res Dev 32:111, 1995.
59. Van Gheluwe BV, Kerwin D, Roosen P, and Tielemans R: The influence of heel fit on rearfoot motion in running shoes, J Appl Biomech 15:361, 1999.
60. Virmavirta M, Kivekäs J, and Komi P: Take-off aerodynamics in ski jumping, J Biomech 34:465, 2001.
61. Wickelgren WA: How to solve problems, San Francisco, 1974, WH Freeman.
62. Wilk BR, Fisher KL, and Gutierrez W: Defective running shoes as a contributing factor in plantar fasciitis in a triathlete, J Orthop Sports Phys Ther 30:21, 2000.
63. Yamamoto S: A new trend in the study of low back pain in workplaces, Ind Health 35:173, 1997.

ANNOTATED READINGS

Bartlett RM: Current issues in the mechanics of athletic activities. A position paper, J Biomech 30:477, 1997.
Reviews important or contentious current issues in the study of the biomechanics of athletic activities.

Chaffin DB and Andersson GBJ: *Occupational biomechanics* (3rd ed), New York, 1999, John Wiley & Sons.
Serves as a comprehensive text on occupational biomechanics.

Elliott B: Biomechanics: an integral part of sport science and sport medicine, J Sci Med Sport 2:299, 1999.
Provides an overview of clinical biomechanics and occupational biomechanics, as well as the role of biomechanics in sports science and sports medicine, in a review format.

Zeitz, P: *The art and craft of problem solving,* New York, 1999, John Wiley & Sons.
Provides general strategies, as well as specific tools and techniques, for solving quantitative problems.

RELATED WEB SITES

American College of Sports Medicine—Biomechanics Interest Group
www.acsm.org
Provides a link to the American College of Sports Medicine Member Service Center, which links to the ACSM Interest Groups, including the Biomechanics Interest Group.

American Society of Biomechanics
asb-biomech.org/
> *Home page of the American Society of Biomechanics; provides information about the organization, conference abstracts, and graduate programs in biomechanics.*

Biomch-L Newsgroup
isb.ri.ccf.org/biomch-l/
> *Provides information about an e-mail discussion group for biomechanics and human/animal movement science.*

Biomechanics Classes on the Web
www.uoregon.edu/~karduna/biomechanics/
> *Contains links to over 100 biomechanics classes with web-based instructional components.*

Biomechanics World Wide
www.per.ualberta.ca/biomechanics/
> *A comprehensive site with links to other websites for a wide spectrum of topics related to biomechanics.*

Biomechanics Yellow Pages
www.isbweb.org/~byp/
> *Provides information on technology used in biomechanics-related work and includes a number of downloadable video clips.*

International Society of Biomechanics
www.isbweb.org/
> *Home page of the International Society of Biomechanics (ISB); provides information on ISB, biomechanical software and data, and pointers to other sources of biomechanics-related information.*

KEY TERMS

anthropometric	related to the dimensions and weights of body segments
biomechanics	application of mechanical principles in the study of living organisms
carpal tunnel syndrome	overuse condition caused by compression of the median nerve in the carpal tunnel and involving numbness, tingling, and pain in the hands
dynamics	branch of mechanics dealing with systems subject to acceleration
English system	system of weights and measures originally developed in England and used in the United States today
inference	process of forming deductions from available information
kinematics	study of the description of motion, including considerations of space and time
kinesiology	study of human movement
kinetics	study of the action of forces
mechanics	branch of physics that analyzes the actions of forces on particles and mechanical systems
metric system	system of weights and measures used internationally in scientific applications and adopted for daily use by every major country except the United States
qualitative	involving nonnumeric description of quality
quantitative	involving the use of numbers
sports medicine	clinical and scientific aspects of sports and exercise
statics	branch of mechanics dealing with systems in a constant state of motion

CHAPTER

Kinematic Concepts For Analyzing Human Motion

After completing this chapter, you will be able to:

Provide examples of linear, angular, and general forms of motion.

Identify and describe the reference positions, planes, and axes associated with the human body.

Define and appropriately use directional terms and joint movement terminology.

Explain how to plan and conduct an effective qualitative human movement analysis.

Identify and describe the uses of available instrumentation for measuring kinematic quantities.

Visit the Online Learning Center at www.mhhe.com/hall5e to access the Online Lab Manual and many additional resources.

I s it best to observe walking gait from a side view, front view, or back view? From what distance can a coach best observe a pitcher's throwing style? What are the advantages and disadvantages of analyzing a movement captured on video? To the untrained observer, there may be no differences in the forms displayed by an elite hurdler and a novice hurdler or in the functioning of a normal knee and an injured, partially rehabilitated knee. What skills are necessary and what procedures are used for effective analysis of human movement kinematics?

One of the most important steps in learning a new subject is mastering the associated terminology. Likewise, learning a general analysis protocol that can be adapted to specific questions or problems within a field of study is invaluable. In this chapter, human movement terminology is introduced, and the problem-solving approach is adapted to provide a template for qualitative solving of human movement analysis problems.

FORMS OF MOTION

general motion
involving translation and rotation simultaneously

Most human movement is general motion, a complex combination of linear and angular motion components. Since linear and angular motion are "pure" forms of motion, it is sometimes useful to break complex movements down into their linear and angular components when performing an analysis.

linear
along a line that may be straight or curved, with all parts of the body moving in the same direction at the same speed

Linear Motion

angular
involving rotation around a central line or point

translation
linear motion

Pure linear motion involves uniform motion of the system of interest, with all system parts moving in the same direction at the same speed. Linear motion is also referred to as translatory motion, or translation. When a body experiences translation, it moves as a unit, and portions of the body do not move relative to each other. For example, a sleeping passenger on a smooth airplane flight is being translated through the air. If the passenger awakens and reaches for a magazine, however, pure translation is no longer occurring because the position of the arm relative to the body has changed.

rectilinear
along a straight line

curvilinear
along a curved line

Linear motion may also be thought of as motion along a line. If the line is straight, the motion is rectilinear; if the line is curved, the motion is curvilinear. A motorcyclist maintaining a motionless posture as the bike moves along a straight path is moving rectilinearly. If the motorcyclist jumps the bike and the frame of the bike does not rotate, both rider and bike (with the exception of the spinning wheels) are moving curvilinearly while airborne. Likewise, a Nordic skier coasting in a locked static position down a short hill is in rectilinear motion. If the skier jumps over a gully with all body parts moving in the same direction at the same speed along a curved path, the motion is curvilinear. When a motorcyclist or skier goes over the crest of a hill, the motion is *not* linear, because the top of the body is moving at a greater speed than lower body parts. Figure 2-1 displays a gymnast in rectilinear, curvilinear, and rotational motion.

Angular Motion

axis of rotation
imaginary line perpendicular to the plane of rotation and passing through the center of rotation

Angular motion is rotation around a central imaginary line known as the axis of rotation, which is oriented perpendicular to the plane in which the rotation occurs. When a gymnast performs a giant circle on a bar, the entire body rotates, with the axis of rotation passing through the center of the bar. When a springboard diver executes a somersault in midair, the

Rotation of a body segment at a joint occurs around an imaginary line known as the axis of rotation that passes through the joint center.

entire body is again rotating, this time around an imaginary axis of rotation that moves along with the body. Almost all volitional human movement involves rotation of a body segment around an imaginary axis of rotation that passes through the center of the joint to which the segment attaches. When angular motion or rotation occurs, portions of the body in motion are constantly moving relative to other portions of the body.

General Motion

When translation and rotation are combined, the resulting movement is general motion. A football kicked end over end translates through the air as it simultaneously rotates around a central axis (Figure 2-2). A runner is translated along by angular movements of body segments at the hip, knee, and ankle. Human movement usually consists of general motion rather than pure linear or angular motion.

● *Most human movement activities are categorized as general motion.*

Mechanical Systems

Before determining the nature of a movement, the mechanical system of interest must be defined. In many circumstances, the entire human body is chosen as the system to be analyzed. In other circumstances, however, the system might be defined as the right arm or perhaps even a ball being projected by the right arm. When an overhand throw is executed, the body as a whole displays general motion, the motion of the throwing arm is primarily angular, and the motion of the released ball is linear. The mechanical system to be analyzed is chosen by the movement analyst according to the focus of interest.

system
object or group of objects chosen by the analyst for study

32   BASIC BIOMECHANICS

Examples of rectilinear, curvilinear, and rotational motion.

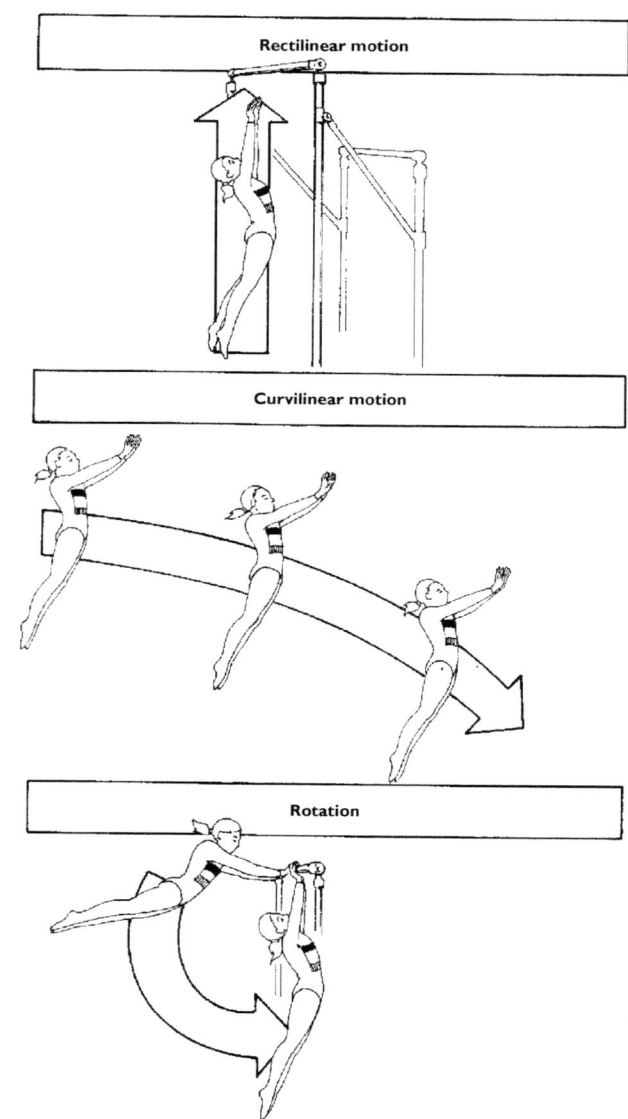

STANDARD REFERENCE TERMINOLOGY

Communicating specific information about human movement requires specialized terminology that precisely identifies body positions and directions.

Anatomical Reference Position

Anatomical reference position is an erect standing position with the feet slightly separated and the arms hanging relaxed at the sides, with the

anatomical reference position

erect standing position with all body parts, including the palms of the hands, facing forward; considered the starting position for body segment movements

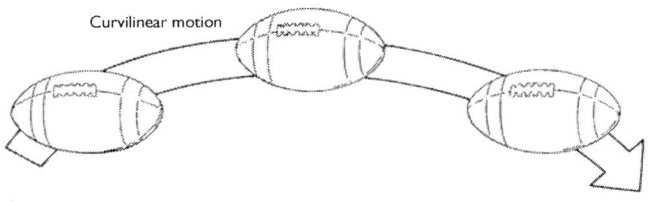

Curvilinear motion

FIGURE 2-2

General motion is a combination of linear and angular motion.

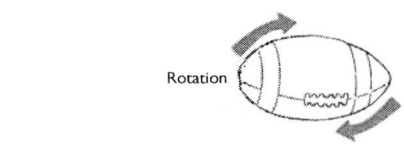

Rotation

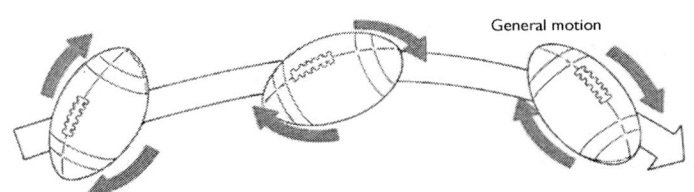

General motion

palms of the hands facing forward. It is not a natural standing position, but is the body orientation conventionally used as the reference position or starting place when movement terms are defined.

Directional Terms

In describing the relationship of body parts or the location of an external object with respect to the body, the use of directional terms is necessary. The following are commonly used directional terms:

Superior: closer to the head (In zoology, the synonymous term is *cranial*.)

Inferior: farther away from the head (In zoology, the synonymous term is *caudal*.)

Anterior: toward the front of the body (In zoology, the synonymous term is *ventral*.)

Posterior: toward the back of the body (In zoology, the synonymous term is *dorsal*.)

Medial: toward the midline of the body

Lateral: away from the midline of the body

Proximal: closer in proximity to the trunk (For example, the knee is proximal to the ankle.)

Distal: at a distance from the trunk (For example, the wrist is distal to the elbow.)

Superficial: toward the surface of the body

Deep: inside the body and away from the body surface

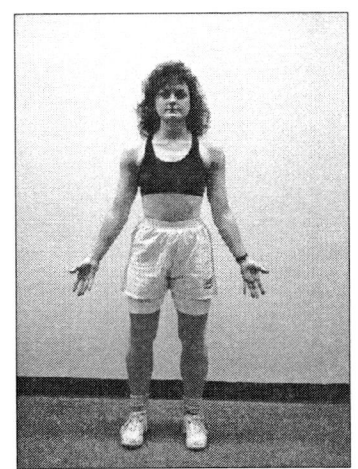

Anatomical reference position.

34 BASIC BIOMECHANICS

●*Reference planes and axes are useful in describing gross body movements and in defining more specific movement terminology.*

cardinal planes
three imaginary perpendicular reference planes that divide the body in half by mass

sagittal plane
plane in which forward and backward movements of the body and body segments occur

frontal plane
plane in which lateral movements of the body and body segments occur

transverse plane
plane in which horizontal body and body segment movements occur when the body is in an erect standing position

●*Although most human movements are not strictly planar, the cardinal planes provide a useful way to describe movements that are primarily planar.*

mediolateral axis
imaginary line around which sagittal plane rotations occur

anteroposterior axis
imaginary line around which frontal plane rotations occur

longitudinal axis
imaginary line around which transverse plane rotations occur

All of these directional terms can be paired as antonyms—words having opposite meanings. Saying that the elbow is proximal to the wrist is as correct as saying that the wrist is distal to the elbow. Similarly, the nose is superior to the mouth and the mouth is inferior to the nose.

Anatomical Reference Planes

The three imaginary cardinal planes bisect the mass of the body in three dimensions. A *plane* is a two-dimensional surface with an orientation defined by the spatial coordinates of three discrete points not all contained in the same line. It may be thought of as an imaginary flat surface. The sagittal plane, also known as the anteroposterior (AP) plane, divides the body vertically into left and right halves, with each half containing the same mass. The frontal plane, also referred to as the coronal plane, splits the body vertically into front and back halves of equal mass. The horizontal or transverse plane separates the body into top and bottom halves of equal mass. For an individual standing in anatomical reference position, the three cardinal planes all intersect at a single point known as the body's center of mass or center of gravity (Figure 2-3). These imaginary reference planes exist only with respect to the human body. If a person turns at a angle to the right, the reference planes also turn at a angle to the right.

Although the entire body may move along or parallel to a cardinal plane, the movements of individual body segments may also be described as sagittal plane movements, frontal plane movements, and transverse plane movements. When this occurs, the movements being described are usually in a plane that is parallel to one of the cardinal planes. For example, movements that involve forward and backward motion are referred to as sagittal plane movements. When a forward roll is executed, the entire body moves parallel to the sagittal plane. During running in place, the motion of the arms and legs is generally forward and backward, although the planes of motion pass through the shoulder and hip joints rather than the center of the body. Marching, bowling, and cycling are all largely sagittal plane movements (Figure 2-4). Frontal plane movement is lateral (side-to-side) movement; an example of total-body frontal plane movement is the cartwheel. Jumping jacks, side stepping, and side kicks in soccer require frontal plane movement at certain body joints. Examples of total-body transverse plane movement include a twist executed by a diver, trampolinist, or airborne gymnast and a dancer's pirouette.

Although many of the movements conducted by the human body are not oriented sagittally, frontally, or transversely, or are not planar at all, the three major reference planes are still useful. Gross-body movements and specifically named movements that occur at joints are often described as primarily frontal, sagittal, or transverse plane movements.

Anatomical Reference Axes

When a segment of the human body moves, it rotates around an imaginary axis of rotation that passes through a joint to which it is attached. There are three reference axes for describing human motion, and each is oriented perpendicular to one of the three planes of motion. The mediolateral axis, also known as the frontal-horizontal axis, is perpendicular to the sagittal plane. Rotation in the frontal plane occurs around the anteroposterior axis, or sagittal-horizontal axis (Figure 2-5). Transverse plane rotation is around the longitudinal axis, or vertical axis. It is important to recognize that each of these three axes is always associated with the same single plane—the one to which the axis is perpendicular.

CHAPTER 2:KINEMATIC CONCEPTS FOR ANALYZING HUMAN MOTION   35

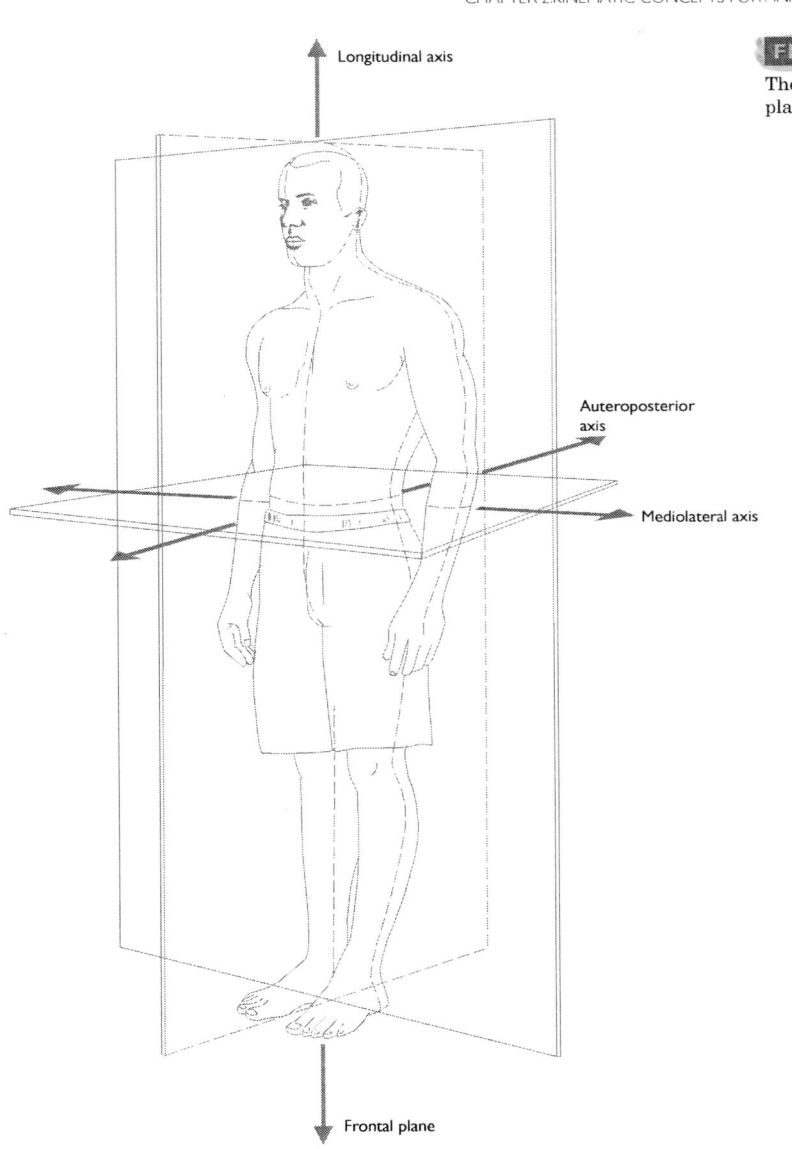

Longitudinal axis

Auteroposterior
axis

Mediolateral axis

Frontal plane

FIGURE 2-3

The three cardinal reference
planes.

36   BASIC BIOMECHANICS

FIGURE 2-4

Cycling requires sagittal plane movement of the legs.

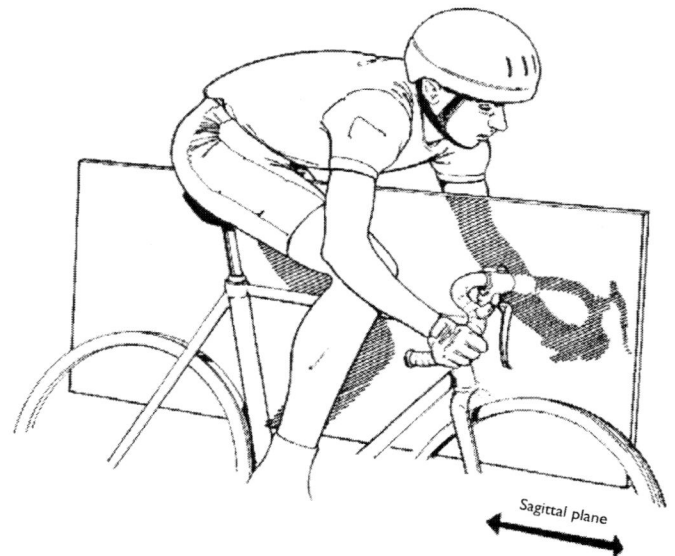

FIGURE 2-5

For a jumping jack, the major axes of rotation are anteroposterior axes passing through the shoulders and hips.

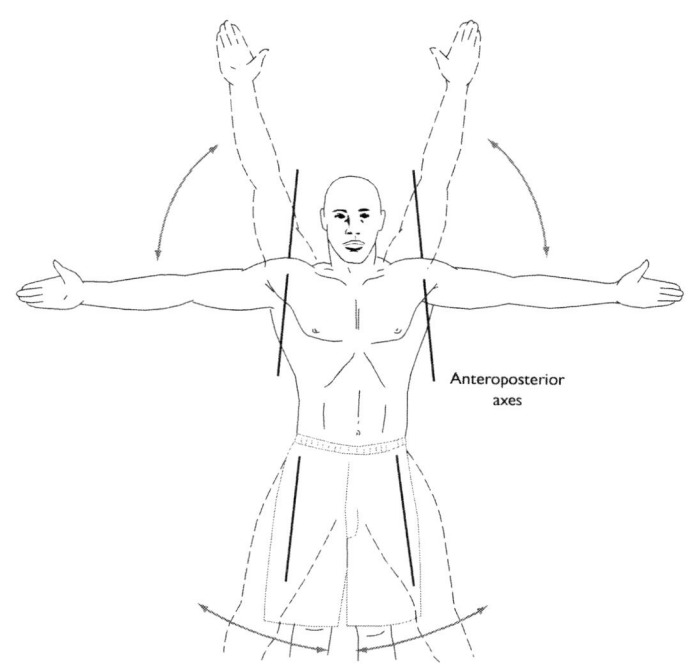

JOINT MOVEMENT TERMINOLOGY

When the human body is in anatomical reference position, all body segments are considered to be positioned at zero degrees. Rotation of a body segment away from anatomical position is named according to the direction of motion and is measured as the angle between the body segment's position and anatomical position.

Sagittal Plane Movements

From anatomical position, the three primary movements occurring in the sagittal plane are *flexion, extension,* and *hyperextension* (Figure 2-6). Flexion includes anteriorly directed sagittal plane rotations of the head, trunk, upper arm, forearm, hand, and hip, and posteriorly directed sagittal plane rotation of the lower leg. Extension is defined as the movement that returns a body segment to anatomical position from a position of flexion, and hyperextension is the rotation beyond anatomical position in the direction opposite the direction of flexion. If the arms or legs are internally or externally rotated from anatomical position, flexion, extension, and hyperextension at the knee and elbow may occur in a plane other than the sagittal.

Sagittal plane rotation at the ankle occurs both when the foot is moved relative to the lower leg and when the lower leg is moved relative to the foot. Motion bringing the top of the foot toward the lower leg is known as *dorsiflexion,* and the opposite motion, which can be visualized as "planting" the ball of the foot, is termed *plantar flexion* (Figure 2-7).

• *Sagittal plane movements include flexion, extension, and hyperextension, as well as dorsiflexion and plantar flexion.*

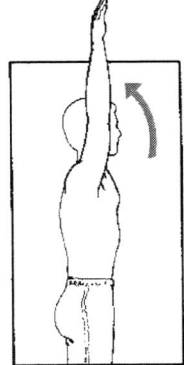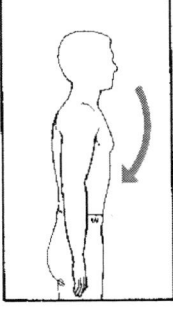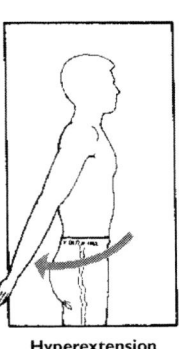

Flexion   Extension   Hyperextension

FIGURE 2-6

Sagittal plane movements at the shoulder.

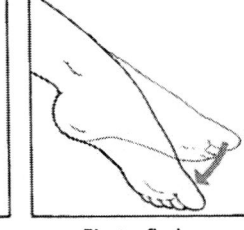

Dorsiflexion   Plantar flexion

FIGURE 2-7

Sagittal plane movements of the foot.

38   BASIC BIOMECHANICS

•*Frontal plane movements include abduction and adduction, lateral flexion, elevation and depression, inversion and eversion, and radial and ulnar deviation.*

Frontal Plane Movements

The major frontal plane rotational movements are *abduction* and *adduction*. Abduction (*abduct* meaning "to take away") moves a body segment away from the midline of the body; adduction (*add* meaning "to bring back") moves a body segment closer to the midline of the body (Figure 2-8).

Other frontal plane movements include sideways rotation of the trunk, which is termed right or left *lateral flexion* (Figure 2-9). *Elevation* and *depression* of the shoulder girdle refer to movement of the shoulder girdle in superior and inferior directions, respectively (Figure 2-10). Rotation of the hand at the wrist in the frontal plane toward the radius (thumb side) is referred to as *radial deviation,* and *ulnar deviation* is hand rotation toward the ulna (little finger side) (Figure 2-11).

Movements of the foot that occur largely in the frontal plane are eversion and inversion. Outward rotation of the sole of the foot is termed *eversion,* and inward rotation of the sole of the foot is called *inversion* (Figure 2-12). Abduction and adduction are also used to describe outward and inward rotation of the entire foot. *Pronation* and *supination* are often used to describe motion occurring at the subtalar joint. Pronation at the subtalar joint consists of a combination of eversion, abduction, and dorsiflexion, and supination involves inversion, adduction, and plantar flexion.

FIGURE 2-8

Frontal plane movements at the hip.

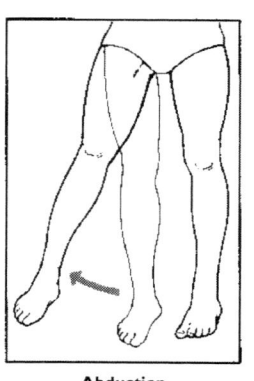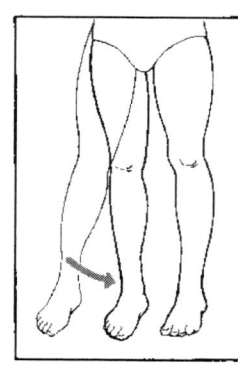

Abduction   Adduction

FIGURE 2-9

Frontal plane movements of the spinal column.

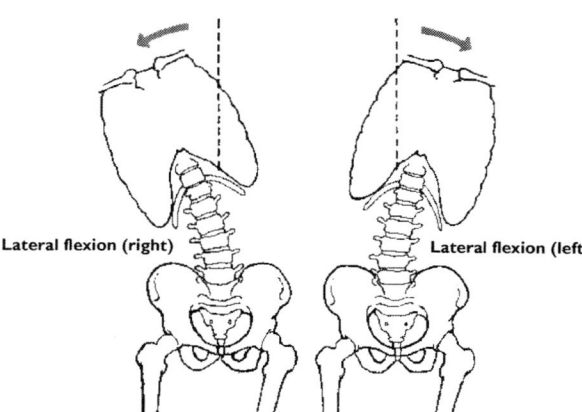

Lateral flexion (right)   Lateral flexion (left)

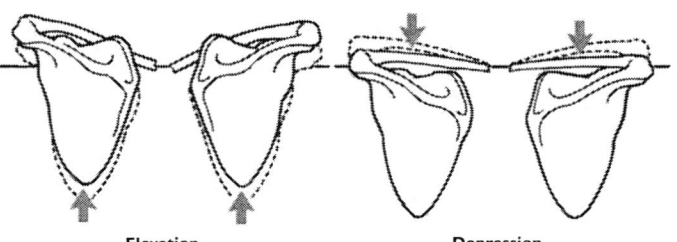

Elevation   Depression

FIGURE 2-10

Frontal plane movements of the shoulder girdle.

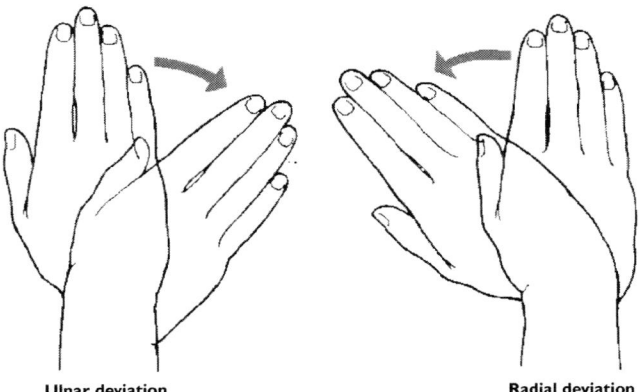

Ulnar deviation   Radial deviation

FIGURE 2-11

Frontal plane movements of the hand.

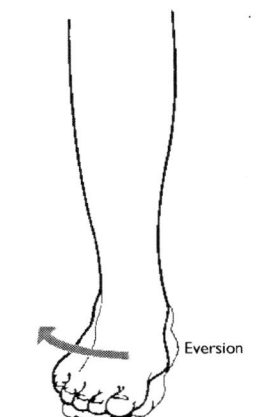
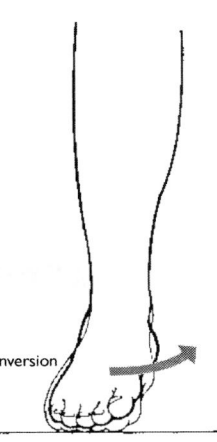

Eversion   Inversion

FIGURE 2-12

Frontal plane movements of the foot.

40   BASIC BIOMECHANICS

FIGURE 2-13

Transverse plane movements of the leg.

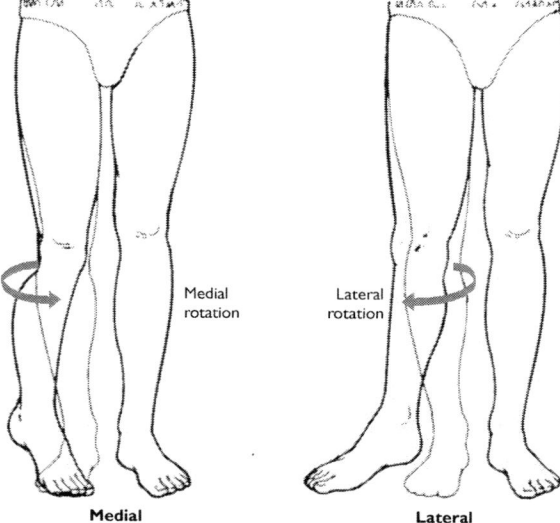

Medial rotation

Lateral rotation

Medial   **Lateral**

Transverse Plane Movements

●*Transverse plane movements include left and right rotation, medial and lateral rotation, supination and pronation, and horizontal abduction and adduction.*

Body movements in the transverse plane are rotational movements about a longitudinal axis. *Left rotation* and *right rotation* are used to describe transverse plane movements of the head, neck, and trunk. Rotation of an arm or leg as a unit in the transverse plane is called *medial rotation*, or internal rotation, when rotation is toward the midline of the body, and *lateral rotation*, or external rotation, when the rotation is away from the midline of the body (Figure 2-13).

Specific terms are used for rotational movements of the forearm. Outward and inward rotations of the forearm are respectively known as *supination* and *pronation* (Figure 2-14). In anatomical position the forearm is in a supinated position.

Although abduction and adduction are frontal plane movements, when the arm or thigh is flexed to a position, movement of these segments in the transverse plane from an anterior position to a lateral position is termed *horizontal abduction*, or horizontal extension (Figure 2-15). Movement in the transverse plane from a lateral to an anterior position is called *horizontal adduction*, or horizontal flexion.

Other Movements

Many movements of the body limbs take place in planes that are oriented diagonally to the three traditionally recognized cardinal planes. Because human movements are so complex, however, nominal identification of every plane of human movement is impractical.

One special case of general motion involving circular movement of a body segment is designated as *circumduction*. Tracing an imaginary circle in the air with a fingertip while the rest of the hand is stationary requires circumduction at the metacarpophalangeal joint (Figure 2-16). Circumduction combines flexion, extension, abduction, and adduction, resulting in a conical trajectory of the moving body segment.

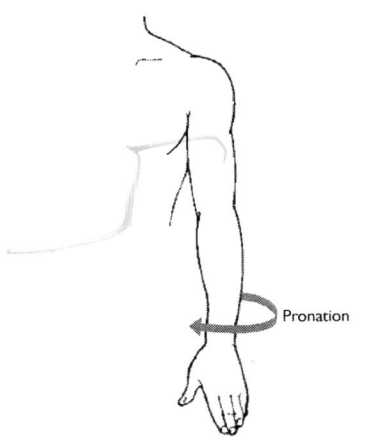
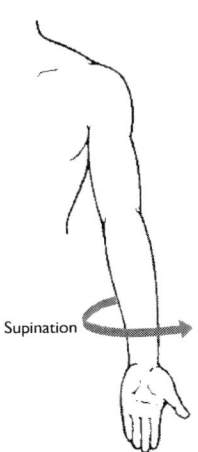

FIGURE 2-14

Transverse plane movements of the forearm.

Pronation

Supination

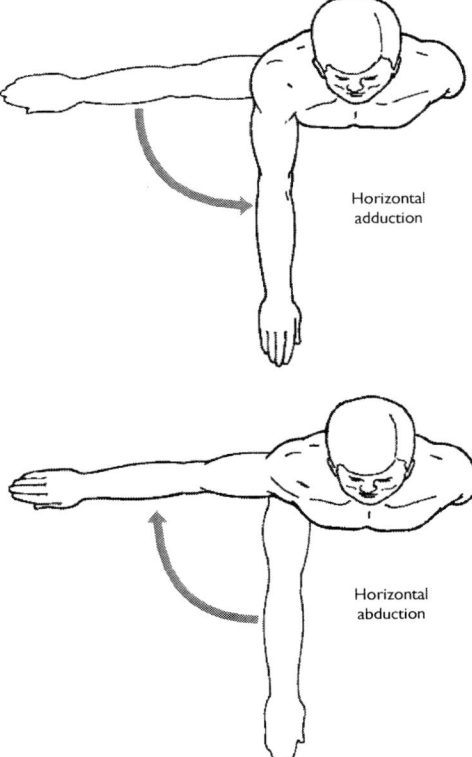

FIGURE 2-15

Transverse plane movements at the shoulder.

Horizontal adduction

Horizontal abduction

42   BASIC BIOMECHANICS

FIGURE 2-16

Circumduction of the index finger at the metacarpophalangeal joint.

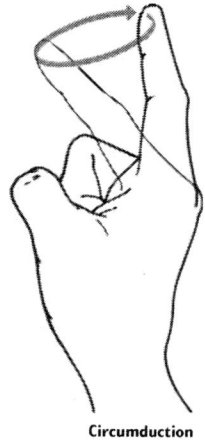

Circumduction

A tennis serve requires arm movement in a diagonal plane.

● *Qualitative analysis requires knowledge of the specific biomechanical purpose of the movement and the ability to detect the causes of errors.*

SPATIAL REFERENCE SYSTEMS

Whereas the three cardinal planes and their associated axes of rotation move along with the body, it is also often useful to make use of a fixed system of reference. When biomechanists quantitatively describe the movement of living organisms, they use a spatial reference system to standardize the measurements taken. The system most commonly used is a Cartesian coordinate system, in which units are measured in the directions of either two or three primary axes.

Movements that are primarily in a single direction, or planar, such as running, cycling, or jumping, can be analyzed using a two-dimensional Cartesian coordinate system (Figure 2-17). In two-dimensional Cartesian coordinate systems, points of interest are measured in units in the x, or horizontal, direction and in the y, or vertical, direction. When a biomechanist is analyzing the motion of the human body, the points of interest are usually the body's joints, which constitute the end points of the body segments. The location of each joint center can be measured with respect to the two axes and described as (x,y), where x is the number of horizontal units away from the y-axis and y is the number of vertical units away from the x-axis. These units can be measured in both positive and negative directions (Figure 2-18). When a movement of interest is three-dimensional, the analysis can be extended to the third dimension by adding a z-axis perpendicular to the x- and y-axes and measuring units away from the x,y plane in the z direction. With a two-dimensional coordinate system, the y-axis is normally vertical, and the x-axis horizontal. In the case of a three-dimensional coordinate system, it is usually the z-axis that is vertical, with the x- and y-axes representing the two horizontal directions.

QUALITATIVE ANALYSIS OF HUMAN MOVEMENT

A good command of the language associated with forms of motion, standard reference terminology, and joint movement terminology is essential for being able to describe a qualitative analysis of human movement. The ability to qualitatively assess human movement also requires both knowledge of

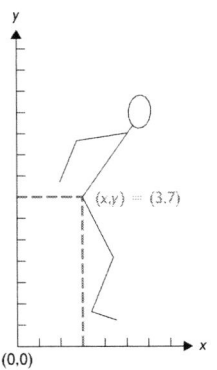

FIGURE 2-17

A Cartesian coordinate system showing the *x* and *y* coordinates of the hip.

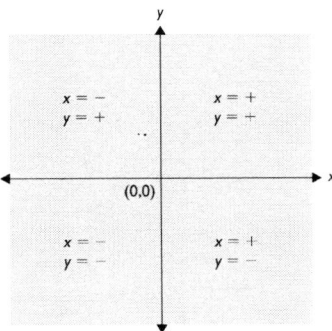

FIGURE 2-18

Coordinates can be both positive and negative in a Cartesian coordinate system.

the movement characteristics desired and the ability to observe and analyze whether a given performance incorporates these characteristics (6). As introduced in Chapter 1, the word *qualitative* refers to a description of quality without the use of numbers. Visual observation is the most commonly used approach for qualitatively analyzing the mechanics of human movement. Based on information gained from watching an athlete perform a skill, a patient walk down a ramp, or a student attempt a novel task, coaches, clinicians, and teachers make judgments and recommendations on a daily basis. To be effective, however, a qualitative analysis cannot be conducted haphazardly, but must be carefully planned and conducted by an analyst with knowledge of the biomechanics of the movement.

Prerequisite Knowledge for a Qualitative Analysis

There are two main sources of information for the analyst diagnosing a motor skill. The first is the kinematics or technique exhibited by the performer, and the second is the performance outcome (12). Evaluating performance outcome is of limited value, since the root of optimal performance outcome is appropriate biomechanics.

To effectively analyze a motor skill, it is very helpful for the analyst to understand the specific purpose of the skill from a biomechanical perspective. The general goal of a volleyball player serving a ball is to legally project the ball over the net and into the opposite court. Specifically, this

44 BASIC BIOMECHANICS

Many jobs require conducting qualitative analyses of human movement daily.

•*Analysts should be able to distinguish the cause of a problem from symptoms of the problem or an unrelated movement idiosyncrasy.*

•*Experience in performing a motor skill does not necessarily translate to proficiency in analyzing the skill.*

requires a coordinated summation of forces produced by trunk rotation, shoulder extension, elbow extension, and forward translation of the total-body center of gravity, as well as contacting the ball at an appropriate height and angle. Whereas the ultimate purpose of a competitive sprint cyclist is to maximize speed while maintaining balance in order to cross the finish line first, biomechanically this requires factors such as maximizing perpendicular force production against the pedals and maintaining a low body profile to minimize air resistance.

Without knowledge of relevant biomechanical principles, analysts may have difficulty in identifying the factors that contribute to (or hinder) performance and may misinterpret the observations they make. More specifically, to effectively analyze a motor skill, the analyst must be able to identify the *cause* of a technique error, as opposed to a symptom of the error, or a performance idiosyncrasy. Inexperienced coaches of tennis or golf may focus on getting the performer to display an appropriate follow-through after hitting the ball. Inadequate follow-through, however, is merely a symptom of the underlying performance error, which may be failure to begin the stroke or swing with sufficient trunk rotation and backswing, or failure to swing the racquet or club with sufficient velocity. The ability to identify the cause of a performance error is dependent on an understanding of the biomechanics of the motor skill.

One potential source of knowledge about the biomechanics of a motor skill is experience in performing the skill. A person who performs a skill proficiently usually is better equipped to qualitatively analyze that skill than is a person less familiar with the skill. For example, research shows that experienced tennis players evaluate arm and racquet motion during the serve, whereas novices focus on the ball (5). Likewise, advanced batters demonstrate greater perceptual decision making during a pitch than do intermediate batters, particularly when the pitch is a curve ball (12). Research on physical education student teachers also shows that when they analyze a movement, the focus of attention differs with personal background experiences (1). In most cases, a high level of familiarity with the skill or movement being performed improves the analyst's ability to focus attention on the critical aspects of the event.

Direct experience in performing a motor skill, however, is not the only or necessarily the best way to acquire expertise in analyzing the skill. Skilled athletes often achieve success not because of the form or technique they display, but in spite of it! Furthermore, highly accomplished athletes do not always become the best coaches, and highly successful coaches may have had little or no participatory experience in the sports they coach.

The conscientious coach, teacher, or clinician typically uses several avenues to develop a knowledge base from which to evaluate a motor skill. One is to read available materials from textbooks, scientific journals, and lay (coaching) journals, despite the facts that not all movement patterns and skills have been researched and that some biomechanics literature is so esoteric that advanced training in biomechanics is required to understand it. However, when selecting reading material, it is important to distinguish between articles supported by research and those based primarily on opinion, as "commonsense" approaches to skill analyses may be flawed. There are also opportunities to interact directly with individuals who have expert knowledge of particular skills at conferences and workshops.

Planning a Qualitative Analysis

Even the simplest qualitative analysis may yield inadequate or faulty information if approached haphazardly. As the complexity of the skill

Hall: Basic Biomechanics, | 2. Kinematic Concepts for | Text | © The McGraw–Hill
Fifth Edition | Analyzing Human Motion | | Companies, 2007

and/or the level of desired analytical detail increases, so does the level of required planning.

The first step in any analysis is to identify the major question or questions of interest. Often, these questions have already been formulated by the analyst, or they serve as the original purpose for the observation. For example, has a post–knee surgery patient's gait returned to normal? Why is a volleyball player having difficulty hitting cross-court? What might be causing a secretary's wrist pain? Or simply, is a given skill being performed as effectively as possible? Having one or more particular questions or problems in mind helps to focus the analysis. Preparing a criteria sheet or a checklist prior to performing an analysis is a useful way to help focus attention on the critical elements of the movement being evaluated (11). Of course, the ability to identify appropriate analysis questions and formulate a checklist is dependent on the analyst's knowledge of the biomechanics of the movement. When an analyst is observing a skill that is less than familiar, it can be helpful to recall that many motor skills have commonalties. For example, serves in tennis and volleyball and the badminton overhead clear might all be considered part of the "overarm throw family" (15).

A tennis player's eyes should follow the oncoming ball long enough to enable the player to contact the ball with the racket.

The analyst should next determine the optimal perspective(s) from which to view the movement. If the major movements are primarily planar, as with the legs during cycling or the pitching arm during a softball pitch, a single viewing perspective such as a side view or a rear view may be sufficient. If the movement occurs in more than one plane, as with the motions of the arms and legs during the breaststroke or the arm motion during a baseball batter's swing, the observer may need to view the movement from more than one perspective to see all critical aspects of interest. For example, a rear view, a side view, and a top view of a martial artist's kick all yield different information about the movement (Figure 2-19).

Even when a movement is primarily planar, using more than a single viewing perspective may be useful. Sometimes, for example, observing the performer's eye movements yields valuable information. A common error among beginning tennis players is looking across the net to where they expect to hit the ball rather than visually tracking enough of the oncoming ball's trajectory to establish racket contact with it. In fencing, focusing the eyes on the rapidly moving tip of an opponent's blade can be a drastic performance error, facilitating the effectiveness of the opponent's feints (16).

The analyst's viewing distance from the performer should also be selected thoughtfully (Figure 2-20). If the analyst wishes to observe subtalar pronation and supination in a patient walking on a treadmill, a close-up rear view of the lower legs and feet is necessary. Analyzing where a particular volleyball player moves on the court during a series of plays under rapidly changing game conditions is best accomplished from a reasonably distant, elevated position.

Another consideration is the number of trials or executions of the movement that should be observed in the course of formulating an analysis. A skilled athlete may display movement kinematics that deviate only slightly across performances, but a child learning to run may take no two steps alike. Basing an analysis on observation of a single performance is usually unwise. The greater the inconsistency in the performer's kinematics, the larger the number of observations that should be made.

Other factors that potentially influence the quality of observations of human movement are the performer's attire and the nature of the surrounding environment. When biomechanic researchers study the kinematics of a particular movement, the subjects typically wear minimal attire so that movements of body segments will not be obscured. Although

●*Repeated observation of a motor skill is useful in helping the analyst to distinguish consistent performance errors from random errors.*

●*Use of a video camera provides both advantages and disadvantages to the movement analyst.*

46   BASIC BIOMECHANICS

FIGURE 2-19

Whereas skills that are primarily planar may require only one viewing perspective, the movement analyst should view multiplanar skills from more than one direction.

FIGURE 2-20

The observation distance between analyst and performer should be selected based on the specific questions of interest.

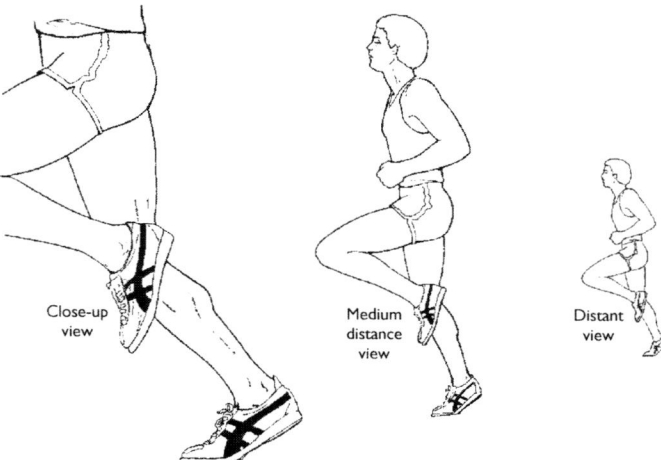
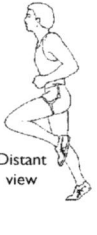

there are many situations, such as instructional classes, competitive events, and team practices, for which this may not be practical, analysts should be aware that loose clothing can obscure subtle motions. Adequate lighting and a nondistracting background of contrasting color also improve the visibility of the observed movement.

A final consideration is whether to rely on visual observation alone or to use a video camera. As the speed of the movement of interest increases, it becomes progressively less practical to rely on visual observation. The human eye cannot resolve events that occur in less than approximately one-fifth of a second (5). Consequently, even the most careful observer may miss important aspects of a rapidly executed movement. Video also enables the performer to view the movement, as well as allowing repeated viewing of the movement by analyst and performer, enabling performance feedback that can enhance the learning of a motor skill (4). Better-quality playback units also enable slow-motion viewing and single-picture advance that facilitate isolation of the critical aspects of a movement.

The analyst should be aware, however, that there is a potential drawback to the use of video. The subject's awareness of the presence of a camera sometimes results in changes in performance. Movement analysts should be aware that subjects may be distracted or unconsciously modify their techniques when a recording device is used.

Conducting a Qualitative Analysis

Despite careful planning of a qualitative analysis, new questions occasionally emerge during the course of collecting observations. Movement modifications may be taking place with each performance as learning occurs, especially when the performer is unskilled. Even when this is not the case, the observations made may suggest new questions of interest. For example, what is causing the inconsistencies in a golfer's swing? What technique changes are occurring over the 30–40 m range in a 100 m sprint? A careful analysis is not strictly preprogrammed, but often involves identifying new questions to answer or problems to solve. The teacher, clinician, or coach often is involved in a continuous process of formulating an analysis, collecting additional observations, and formulating an updated analysis (Figure 2-21).

Answering questions that have been identified requires that the analyst be able to focus on the critical aspects of the movement. Once a biomechanical error has been generally identified, it is often useful for the analyst to watch the performer over several trials and to progressively zero in on the specific problem. Evaluating a softball pitcher's technique might begin with observation of insufficient ball speed, progress to an evaluation of upper-extremity kinematics, and end with an identification of insufficient wrist snap at ball release.

The analyst should also be aware that every performance of a motor skill is affected by the characteristics of the performer. These include the performer's age, gender, and anthropometry; the developmental and skill levels at which the performer is operating; and any special physical or personality traits that may impact performance. Providing a novice, preschool-aged performer with cues for a skilled, mature performance may be counterproductive, since young children do not have the same motor capabilities as adults. Likewise, although training can ameliorate loss of muscular strength and joint range of motion once thought to be inevitably associated with aging, human movement analysts need increased knowledge of and sensitivity to the special needs of older adults who wish to develop new motor skills. Analysts should also be aware that although

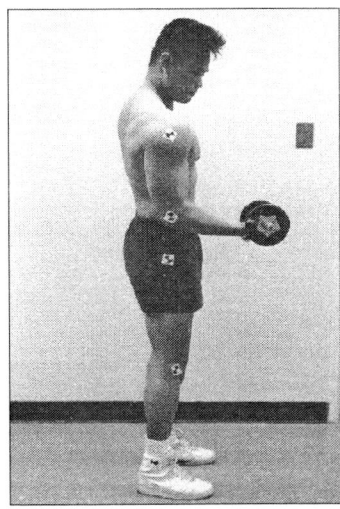

When performers are minimally attired, analysts are better able to observe the joint motions taking place.

A video camera can be a useful tool for human movement analysts.

48   BASIC BIOMECHANICS

FIGURE 2-21

The qualitative analysis process is often cyclical, with observations leading to refinement of the original question.

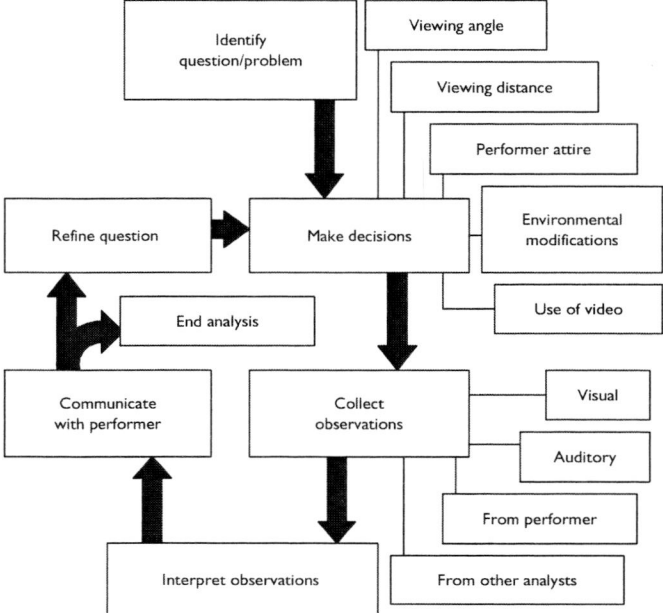

Auditory information is often a valuable source in the analysis of human motor skills.

gender has traditionally been regarded as a basis for performance differences, research has shown that before puberty most gender-associated performance differences are probably culturally derived rather than biologically determined (13). Young girls are usually not expected to be as skilled or even as active as young boys. Unfortunately, in many settings, these expectations extend beyond childhood into adolescence and adulthood. The belief that an activity is not gender appropriate has been shown to negatively affect college-aged women's ability to learn a new motor skill (2). Analysts of female performers should not reinforce this cultural misunderstanding by lowering their expectations of girls or women based on gender. Analysts should also be sensitive to other factors that can influence performance. Has the performer experienced a recent emotional upset? Is the sun in his eyes? Is she tired? Being an effective observer requires full awareness of the surrounding environment (3).

To supplement visual observation, the analyst should be aware that nonvisual forms of information can also sometimes be useful during a movement analysis. For example, auditory information can provide clues about the way in which a movement was executed. Proper contact of a golf club with a ball sounds distinctly different from when a golfer "tops" the ball. Similarly, the crack of a baseball bat hitting a ball indicates that the contact was direct rather than glancing. The sound of a double contact of a volleyball player's arms with the ball may identify an illegal hit. The sound of a patient's gait usually reveals whether an asymmetry is present.

Another potential source of information is feedback from the performer (Sample Application 2.1). A performer who is experienced enough to recognize the way a particular movement feels as compared to the way a slight modification of the same movement feels is a useful source of information. However, not all performers are sufficiently kinesthetically attuned

SAMPLE APPLICATION 2.1

Problem: Sally, a powerful outside hitter on a high school volleyball team, has been out for two weeks with mild shoulder bursitis, but has recently received her physician's clearance to return to practice. Joan, Sally's coach, notices that Sally's spikes are traveling at a slow speed and are being easily handled by the defensive players.

Planning the Analysis
1. What specific problems need to be solved or questions need to be answered regarding the movement? Joan first questions Sally to make sure that the shoulder is not painful. She then reasons that a technique error is present.
2. From what angle(s) and distance(s) can problematic aspects of the movement best be observed? Is more than one view needed? Although a volleyball spike involves transverse plane rotation of the trunk, the arm movement is primarily in the sagittal plane. Joan therefore decides to begin by observing a sagittal view from the side of Sally's hitting arm.
3. How many movement performances should be observed? Since Sally is a skilled player and her spikes are consistently being executed at reduced velocity, Joan reasons that only a few observations may be needed.
4. Is special subject attire, lighting, or background environment needed to facilitate observation? The gym where the team works out is well lit and the players wear sleeveless tops. Therefore, no special accommodations for the analysis seem necessary.
5. Will a video recording of the movement be necessary or useful? A volleyball spike is a relatively fast movement, but there are definite checkpoints that the knowledgeable observer can watch in real time. Is the jump primarily vertical, and is it high enough for the player to contact the ball above the net? Is the hitting arm positioned with the upper arm in maximal horizontal abduction prior to arm swing to allow a full range of arm motion? Is the hitting movement initiated by trunk rotation followed by shoulder flexion, then elbow extension, then snaplike wrist flexion? Is the movement being executed in a coordinated fashion to enable imparting a large force to the ball?

Conducting the Analysis
1. Review, and sometimes reformulate, specific questions of focus. After watching Sally execute two spikes, Joan observes that her arm range of motion appears to be relatively small.
2. Repeatedly view movements to gradually zero in on causes of performance errors. After watching Sally spike three more times, Joan suspects that Sally is not positioning her upper arm in maximal horizontal abduction in preparation for the hit.
3. Be aware of the influence of performer characteristics. Joan talks to Sally on the sideline and asks her to put her arm in the preparatory position for a hit. She asks Sally if this position is painful, and Sally responds that it is not.
4. Pay attention to nonvisual cues. (None are apparent in this situation.)
5. When appropriate, ask the performer to self-analyze. Joan tells Sally that she suspects Sally has been protecting the shoulder by not rotating her arm back far enough in preparation for spikes. She can correct the problem. Sally's next few spikes are executed at much faster velocity.
6. Consider involving other analysts to assist. Joan asks her assistant coach to watch Sally for the remainder of practice to determine whether the problem has been corrected.

to provide meaningful subjective feedback of this nature. The performer being analyzed may also assist in other ways. As Hoffman (6) has pointed out, performance deficiencies may result from errors in technique, perception, or decision making. Identification of perceptual and decision-making errors by the performer often requires more than visual observation of the performance. In these cases, asking meaningful questions of the performer may be useful. However, the analyst should consider subjective input from the performer in conjunction with more objective observations.

Another potential way to enhance the thoroughness of an analysis is to involve more than one analyst. This reduces the likelihood of oversight. Students in the process of learning a new motor skill may also benefit from teaming up to analyze each other's performances under appropriate teacher direction.

● *The ability to effectively analyze human movement improves with practice.*

Finally, analysts must remember that observation skills improve with practice. Research indicates that training in both general analysis protocol and visual discrimination of critical features of a specific motor skill can dramatically improve an analyst's ability (9, 14). As analysts gain experience, the analysis process becomes more natural, and the analyses conducted are likely to become more effective and informative. The expert analyst is better able to both identify and diagnose errors than the novice (10). Novice analysts should take every opportunity to practice movement analysis in carefully planned and structured settings, as such practice has been shown to improve the ability to focus attention on the critical aspects of performance (7).

TOOLS FOR MEASURING KINEMATIC QUANTITIES

Biomechanics researchers have available a wide array of equipment for studying human movement kinematics. Knowledge gained through the use of this apparatus is often published in professional journals for teachers, clinicians, coaches, and others interested in human movement.

Video and Film

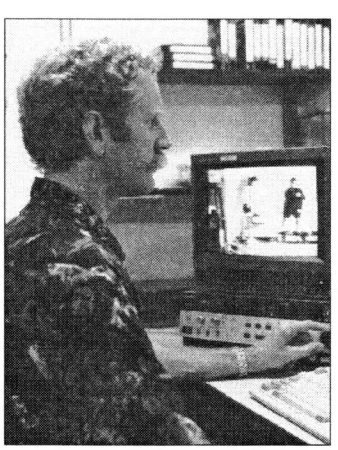

A digitizer is an instrument that identifies x- and y-position coordinates for joint centers and other points.

Photographers began employing cameras in the study of human and animal movement during the late nineteenth century. One famous early photographer was Eadweard Muybridge, a British landscape photographer and a rather colorful character who frequently published essays praising his own work (8). Muybridge used electronically controlled still cameras aligned in sequence with an electromagnetic tripping device to capture serial shots of trotting and galloping horses, thereby resolving the controversy about whether all four hooves are ever airborne simultaneously (they are). More importantly, however, he amassed three volumes of photographic work on human and animal motions that provided scientific documentation of some of the subtle differences between normal and pathological gait.

Movement analysts today have quite an array of camera types from which to choose. The type of movement and the requirements of the analysis largely determine the camera and analysis system of choice. Those most commonly used for documenting human movement sequences are video cameras and 8- and 16-mm movie cameras.

Because of the widespread availability, durability, and ease of use of modern video cameras and playback units, video is the most common motion picture medium for qualitative analysis of human movement today.

Standard video provides 60 resolvable pictures per second, which is perfectly adequate for many human movement applications. Scientists and clinicians performing detailed quantitative study of the kinematics of human motion typically require a more sophisticated video camera and playback unit, with higher rates of picture capture. Digital video capture systems designed for human movement analysis are commercially available with frame rates of up to 2000 Hz. For both qualitative and quantitative analysis, however, a consideration often of greater importance than camera speed is the clarity of the captured images. It is the camera's shutter speed that allows user control of the exposure time, or length of time that the shutter is open when each picture in the video record is taken. The faster the movement being analyzed, the shorter the duration of the exposure time required to prevent blurring of the image captured.

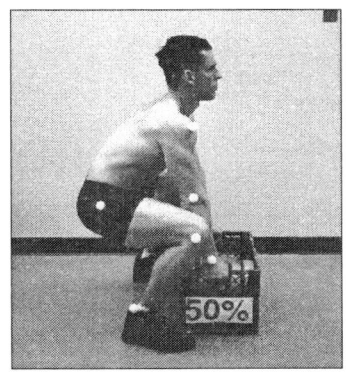

Reflective joint markers can be tracked by a camera for automatic digitizing of the movement.

Another important consideration when analyzing human movement with video is the number of cameras required to adequately capture the aspects of interest. Because most human movement is not constrained to a single plane, it is typically necessary to use multiple cameras to ensure that all of the movements can be viewed and recorded accurately for a detailed analysis. Quantitative biomechanical analyses typically involve six to eight cameras strategically positioned around the staging area. When practicality dictates that a single camera be used, thoughtful consideration should be given to camera positioning relative to the movement of interest. Only when human motion is occurring perpendicular to the optical axis of a camera are the angles present at joints viewed without distortion.

Biomechanists usually perform a quantitative video analysis with computer-linked equipment that enables the calculation of kinematic as well as kinetic quantities of interest for each picture. The traditional procedure for analyzing each picture from a film or video involves a process called *digitizing*. Oringally, this was a tedious and time-consuming process that involved the activation of a hand-held pen, cursor, or mouse over the image of the individual's joint centers or other points of interest, with the position coordinates of each point stored in a computer data file. Today, however, automated systems that track reflective markers on joint centers and store their 3-D locations in data files are common. These files are subsequently accessed by software that calculates kinematic and kinetic quantities of interest. Some more advanced video-based systems enable automated tracking and digitizing of high-contrast markers on the film or video by computer software.

Other Movement-Monitoring Systems

Other technologies for scientific and clinical applications involving kinematic analysis of human movement are also available today. These systems provide real-time tracking of electromagnetic markers, which are attached to the skin over joint centers or other points of interest. This approach eliminates the necessity of keeping a camera's line of sight free from obstructions, but enables only about a tenth the capture rate of digital video.

Other Assessment Tools

Other tools used by biomechanic researchers are available in commercial and homemade versions. The hand-operated goniometer used for assessing the angle present at a joint is also available in an electronic version

52   BASIC BIOMECHANICS

An electrogoniometer is a device that can be interfaced to a recorder to provide a graphical record of the angle present at a joint.

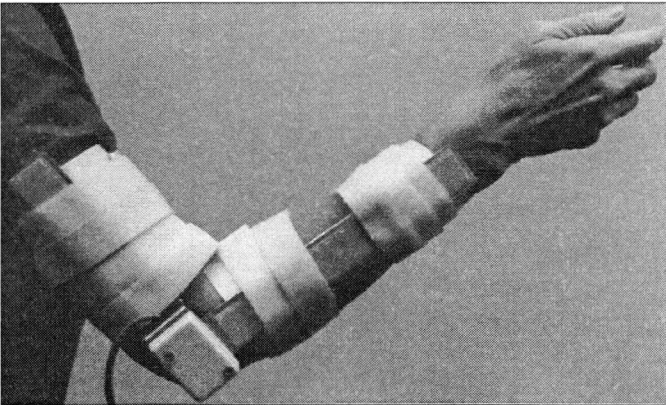

known as an *electrogoniometer,* or elgon (see Chapter 5). The center of the elgon is positioned over the center of rotation of the joint to be monitored, with the arms of the elgon aligned and firmly attached over the longitudinal axes of the adjacent body segments. When motion occurs at the joint, the electrical output from the potentiometer in the center of rotation provides a continuous record of the angle present at the joint.

Systems combining photocells, light beams, and timers can be used to directly measure movement velocity. The system is usually configured so that light beams intercept photocells at two or more carefully measured positions (Figure 2-22). The photocells are electrically connected to a timer so that the time interval between interruption of the light beams by a moving body segment or an object such as a thrown ball can be precisely recorded. The velocity of the moving body is calculated as the measured distance between the photocells divided by the recorded time.

An *accelerometer* is a transducer used for the direct measurement of acceleration. The accelerometer is attached as rigidly as possible to the body segment or other object of interest, with electrical output channeled to a recording device. Three-dimensional accelerometers that incorporate multiple linear accelerometers are commercially available for monitoring acceleration during nonlinear movements.

FIGURE 2-22

Lights, photocells, and a timer, set up for measuring movement velocity. As a ball travels through the apparatus zone, the light beams focused on the photocells are interrupted, sending a signal to the timer. The ball's velocity is calculated as the measured distance between photocells divided by the measured time interval.

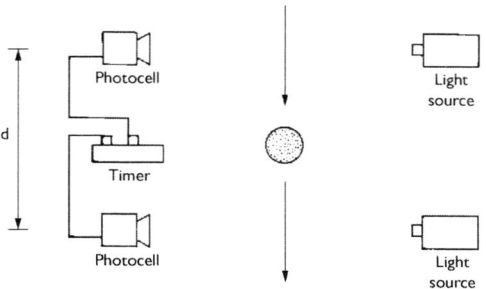

SUMMARY

Movements of the human body are referenced to the sagittal, frontal, and transverse planes, with their respectively associated mediolateral, anteroposterior, and longitudinal axes. Most human motion is general, with both linear and angular components. A set of specialized terminology is used to describe segment motions and joint actions of the human body.

Teachers of physical activities, clinicians, and coaches all routinely perform qualitative analyses to assess, correct, or improve human movements. Both knowledge of the specific biomechanical purpose of the movement and careful preplanning are necessary for an effective qualitative analysis. A number of special tools are available to assist researchers in collecting kinematic observations of human movement.

INTRODUCTORY PROBLEMS

1. Using appropriate movement terminology, write a qualitative description of the performance of a maximal vertical jump. Your description should be sufficiently detailed that the reader can completely and accurately visualize the movement.
2. Select a movement that occurs primarily in one of the three major reference planes. Qualitatively describe this movement in enough detail that the reader of your description can visualize the movement.
3. List five movements that occur primarily in each of the three cardinal planes. The movements may be either sport skills or activities of daily living.
4. Select a familiar animal. Does the animal move in the same major reference planes in which humans move? What are the major differences in the movement patterns of this animal and the movement patterns of humans?
5. Select a familiar movement, and list the factors that contribute to skilled versus unskilled performance of that movement.
6. Test your observation skills by carefully observing the two photos shown on the next page. List the differences that you are able to identify between these two photos.
7. Choose a familiar movement, and list aspects of that movement that are best observed from close up, from 2 to 3 m away, and from reasonably far away. Write a brief explanation of your choices.
8. Choose a familiar movement, and list aspects of that movement that are best observed from the side view, front view, rear view, and top view. Write a brief explanation of your choices.
9. Choose one of the instrumentation systems described, and write a short paragraph explaining the way in which it might be used to study a question related to analysis of a human movement of interest to you.

FOR USERS OF THE *DYNAMIC HUMAN* CD

1. Use the *Dynamic Human* software to review the chapter content on planes, axes, and directional terminology. Beginning at the main menu, select Human Body, Explorations, Anatomical Orientation, then Planes and Directional Terminology.

ADDITIONAL PROBLEMS

1. Select a familiar movement, and identify the ways in which performance of that movement is affected by strength, flexibility, and coordination.
2. List three human movement patterns or skills that are best observed from a side view, from a front or rear view, and from a top view.
3. Select a movement that is nonplanar, and write a qualitative description of that movement sufficiently detailed to enable the reader of your description to picture the movement.
4. Select a nonplanar movement of interest, and list the protocol you would employ in analyzing that movement.
5. What special expectations, if any, should the analyst have of movement performances if the performer is an older adult? An elementary school–aged girl? A novice? An obese high school–aged boy?
6. What are the advantages and disadvantages of collecting observational data on a sport skill during a competitive event as opposed to a practice session?
7. Select a movement with which you are familiar, and list at least five questions that you, as a movement analyst, might ask the performer of the movement to gain additional knowledge about a performance.
8. List the auditory characteristics of five movements, and explain in each case how these characteristics provide information about the nature of the movement performance.
9. List the advantages and disadvantages of using a video camera as compared to the human eye for collecting observational data.
10. Locate an article in a professional or research journal that involves kinematic description of a movement of interest to you. What instrumentation was used by the researchers? What viewing distances and perspectives were used? How might the analysis described have been improved?

NAME _____

DATE _____

LABORATORY EXPERIENCES

1. Observe and analyze a single performer executing two similar but different versions of a particular movement—for example, two pitching styles or two gait styles. Explain what viewing perspectives and distances you selected for collecting observational data on each movement. Write a paragraph comparing the kinematics of the two movements.

Movement selected: _____

Viewing perspectives: _____

Reasons for selection of viewing perspectives: _____

_____

Viewing distances: _____

Reasons for selection of viewing distances: _____

_____

Kinematic comparison: _____

_____

_____

_____

_____

_____

_____

_____

2. Observe a single sport skill as performed by a highly skilled individual, a moderately skilled individual, and an unskilled individual. Qualitatively describe the differences observed.

Sport skill selected: _____

Highly Skilled Performer	Moderately Skilled Performer	Unskilled Performer
_____	_____	_____
_____	_____	_____
_____	_____	_____
_____	_____	_____
_____	_____	_____
_____	_____	_____
_____	_____	_____
_____	_____	_____
_____	_____	_____

56   BASIC BIOMECHANICS

_____   _____   _____
_____   _____   _____
_____   _____   _____
_____   _____   _____
_____   _____   _____
_____   _____   _____
_____   _____   _____

3. Select a movement at which you are reasonably skilled. Plan and carry out observations of a less-skilled individual performing the movement, and provide verbal learning cues for that individual, if appropriate. Write a short description of the cues provided, with a rationale for each cue.

Movement selected: _____

Cues Provided   **Rationale**

_____   _____
_____   _____
_____   _____
_____   _____
_____   _____
_____   _____
_____   _____
_____   _____
_____   _____
_____   _____
_____   _____
_____   _____
_____   _____
_____   _____
_____   _____

4. Select a partner, and plan and carry out an observational analysis of a movement of interest. Write a composite summary analysis of the movement performance. Write a paragraph identifying in what ways the analysis process was changed by the inclusion of a partner.

Movement selected: _____

Analysis of Performance

_____

_____

_____

_____

_____

_____

_____

_____

_____

_____

How the analysis process was different when working with a partner: _____

_____

_____

_____

_____

_____

5. Plan and carry out a video session of a slow movement of interest as performed by two different subjects. Write a comparative analysis of the subjects' performances.

Subject 1 Performance   **Subject 2 Performance**

_____   _____

_____   _____

_____   _____

_____   _____

_____   _____

_____   _____

_____   _____

_____   _____

_____   _____

_____   _____

_____   _____

_____   _____

58   BASIC BIOMECHANICS

_____   _____
_____   _____
_____   _____
_____   _____
_____   _____
_____   _____
_____   _____
_____   _____

REFERENCES

1. Allison PC: What and how preservice physical education teachers observe during an early field experience, Res Q Exerc Sport 58:242, 1987.
2. Belcher D, Lee AM, Solmon MA, and Harrison L Jr: The influence of gender-related beliefs and conceptions of ability on women learning the hockey wrist shot, Res Q Exerc Sport 74:183, 2005.
3. Clark D: Developing observation strategies to enhance teaching effectiveness in the dance class, JOPERD 74:33, 2003.
4. Darden GF: Videotape feedback for student learning and performance: a learning stages approach, JOPERD 70:40, 1999.
5. Goulet C, Bard C, and Fleury: Expertise differences in preparing to return a tennis serve: a visual information processing approach, J Sport Exerc Psych 11:382, 1989.
6. Hoffman SJ: The contributions of biomechanics to clinical competence: a view from the gymnasium. In Shapiro R and Marett JR, eds: *Proceedings of the Second National Symposium on Teaching Kinesiology and Biomechanics in Sports,* Colorado Springs, CO, 1984, US Olympic Committee.
7. Jenkins JM, Garn A, and Jenkins P: Preservice teacher observations in peer coaching, J Teach Phys Educ 24:2, 2005.
8. Mozley AM: Introduction to the Dover edition. In *Muybridge's complete human and animal locomotion,* New York, 1979, Dover Publications.
9. Nielsen AB and Beauchamp L: The effect of training in conceptual kinesiology on feedback provision patterns, J Teach Phys Educ 11:126, 1992.
10. Pinheiro VED: Qualitative analysis for the elementary grades, JOPERD 71:18, 2000.
11. Pinheiro VED and Simon HA: An operational model of motor skill diagnosis, J Teach Phys Educ 11:288, 1992.
12. Radlo SJ, Janelle CM, Barba DA, and Frehlich SG: Perceptual decision making for baseball pitch recognition: using P300 letency and amplitude to index attentional processing, Res Q Exerc Sport 72:22, 2001.
13. Thomas JR and Thomas KT: Development of gender differences in physical activity, Quest 40:219, 1988.
14. Wilkinson S: A training program for improving undergraduates' analytic skill in volleyball, J Teach Phys Educ 11:177, 1991.
15. Wilkinson S: Transfer of qualitative skill analysis ability to similar sport-specific skills, JOPERD 71:16, 2000.
16. Williams D and Bradford B: Fighting eyes, Strategies 2:21, 1989.

ANNOTATED READINGS

Allard P, Stokes IAF, and Blanchi J-P: *Three-dimensional analysis of human movement,* Champaign, IL, 1995, Human Kinetics.
   Serves as an advanced text for theory and procedures for three-dimensional movement analysis.
Hudson JL: Core concepts of kinesiology, JOPERD 66:54, 1995.
   Describes 10 biomechanical concepts related to skillful movement using the analogy of a volume knob for music.
Muybridge E: *Muybridge's complete human and animal locomotion,* New York, 1979, Dover Publications.
   Includes a collection of photographic plates done by early cinematographer Eadweard Muybridge during the late 1800s, including the running stills used by Muybridge to prove the then-controversial claim that all four hooves of a horse are simultaneously elevated from the ground during part of the gallop stride.
Zatsiorsky VM: *Kinematics of human motion,* Champaign, IL, 1998, Human Kinetics.
   Serves as an advanced textbook for the student of human kinematics.

RELATED WEB SITES

Innovative Sports Training, Inc.
www.innsport.com
Provides information on virtual reality–based systems for use in biomechanics research and clinical applications.

Mikromak
www.mikromak.com
Advertises video hardware and software for sports, medicine, and product research.

Motion Analysis Corporation
www.motionanalysis.com
Offers an optical motion capture system utilizing reflective markers for entertainment, biomechanics, character animation, and motion analysis.

Northern Digital, Inc.
www.ndigital.com
Presents optoelectronic 3-D motion measurement systems that track light-emitting diodes for real-time analysis.

Qualisys, Inc.
www.qualisys.com
Presents a system in which infrared cameras track reflective markers, enabling real-time calculations; describes applications for research, clinical settings, industry, and animation.

Redlake Imaging
www.redlake.com/imaging
Advertises high-speed video products for scientific and clinical applications.

SIMI Reality Motion Systems
www.simi.com
Describes computer-based video analysis for the human body and cellular applications; includes a demo of gait analysis, among others.

Skill Technologies, Inc.
www.skilltechnologies.com
Advertises a motion capture-and-analysis system that provides 3-D graphical models and parameter graphs in real time, based on 120 Hz tracking of 16 electromagnetic markers; download of a free 3-D sports viewer available.

KEY TERMS

anatomical reference position	erect standing position with all body parts, including the palms of the hands, facing forward; considered the starting position for body segment movements
angular	involving rotation around a central line or point
anteroposterior axis	imaginary line around which frontal plane rotations occur
axis of rotation	imaginary line perpendicular to the plane of rotation and passing through the center of rotation
cardinal planes	three imaginary perpendicular reference planes that divide the body in half by mass
curvilinear	along a curved line
frontal plane	plane in which lateral movements of the body and body segments occur
general motion	motion involving translation and rotation simultaneously
linear	along a line that may be straight or curved, with all parts of the body moving in the same direction at the same speed
longitudinal axis	imaginary line around which transverse plane rotations occur
mediolateral axis	imaginary line around which sagittal plane rotations occur
rectilinear	along a straight line
sagittal plane	plane in which forward and backward movements of the body and body segments occur
system	mechanical system chosen by the analyst for study
translation	linear motion
transverse plane	plane in which horizontal body and body segment movements occur when the body is in an erect standing position

Kinetic Concepts for Analyzing Human Motion

After completing this chapter, you will be able to:

Define and identify common units of measurement for mass, force, weight, pressure, volume, density, specific weight, torque, and impulse.

Identify and describe the different types of mechanical loads that act on the human body.

Identify and describe the uses of available instrumentation for measuring kinetic quantities.

Distinguish between vector and scalar quantities.

Solve quantitative problems involving vector quantities using both graphic and trigonometric procedures.

Visit the Online Learning Center at www.mhhe.com/hall5e to access the Online Lab Manual and many additional resources.

62   BASIC BIOMECHANICS

A skater has a tendency to continue gliding with constant speed and direction due to inertia.

When muscles on opposite sides of a joint develop tension, what determines the direction of joint motion? In which direction will a swimmer swimming perpendicular to a river current actually travel? What determines whether a push can move a heavy piece of furniture? The answers to these questions are rooted in kinetics, the study of forces.

The human body both generates and resists forces during the course of daily activities. The forces of gravity and friction enable walking and manipulation of objects in predictable ways when internal forces are produced by muscles. Sport participation involves application of forces to balls, bats, racquets, and clubs, and absorption of forces from impacts with balls, the ground or floor, and opponents in contact sports. This chapter introduces basic kinetic concepts that form the basis for understanding these activities.

BASIC CONCEPTS RELATED TO KINETICS

Understanding the concepts of inertia, mass, weight, pressure, volume, density, specific weight, torque, and impulse provides a useful foundation for understanding the effects of forces.

Inertia

inertia
tendency of a body to resist a change in its state of motion

In common usage, inertia means resistance to action or to change (Figure 3-1). Similarly, the mechanical definition is resistance to acceleration. Inertia is the tendency of a body to maintain its current state of motion, whether motionless or moving with a constant velocity. For example, a 150 kg weight bar lying motionless on the floor has a tendency to remain motionless. A skater gliding on a smooth surface of ice has a tendency to continue gliding in a straight line with a constant speed.

Although inertia has no units of measurement, the amount of inertia a body possesses is directly proportional to its mass. The more massive an object is, the more it tends to maintain its current state of motion and the more difficult it is to disrupt that state.

FIGURE 3-1

A static object tends to maintain its motionless state because of inertia.

Mass

Mass (m) is the quantity of matter composing a body. The common unit of mass in the metric system is the kilogram (kg), with the English unit of mass being the *slug,* which is much larger than a kg.

mass
quantity of matter contained in an object

Force

A force (F) can be thought of as a push or a pull acting on a body. Each force is characterized by its magnitude, direction, and point of application to a given body. Body weight, friction, and air or water resistance are all forces that commonly act on the human body. The action of a force causes a body's mass to accelerate:

force
push or pull; the product of mass and acceleration

$$F = ma$$

Units of force are units of mass multiplied by units of acceleration (a). In the metric system, the most common unit of force is the Newton (N), which is the amount of force required to accelerate 1 kg of mass at 1 m/s^2:

$$1 \text{ N} = (1 \text{ kg})(1 \text{ m/s}^2)$$

In the English system, the most common unit of force is the pound (lb). A pound of force is the amount of force necessary to accelerate a mass of 1 slug at 1 ft/s^2, and 1 lb is equal to 4.45 N:

$$1 \text{ lb} = (1 \text{ slug})(1 \text{ ft/s}^2)$$

Because a number of forces act simultaneously in most situations, constructing a free body diagram is usually the first step when analyzing the effects of forces on a body or system of interest. A *free body* is any object, body, or body part that is being focused upon for analysis. A free body diagram consists of a sketch of the system being analyzed and vector representations of the acting forces (Figure 3-2). Even though a hand must be applying force to a tennis racket in order for the racket to forcefully contact a ball, if the racket is the free body of interest, the hand is

free body diagram
sketch that shows a defined system in isolation with all of the force vectors acting on the system

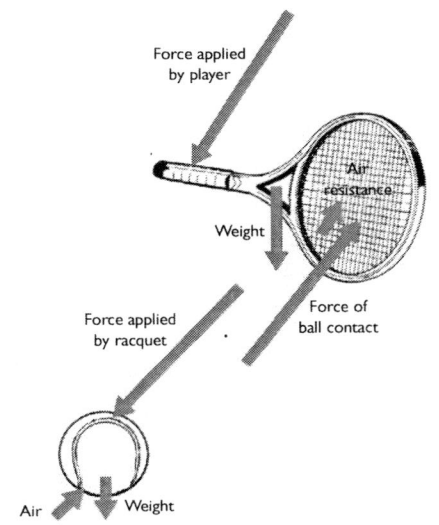

FIGURE 3-2

Two free body diagrams showing the acting forces.

represented in the free body diagram of the racket only as a force vector. Similarly, if the tennis ball constitutes the free body being studied, the force of the racket acting on the ball is displayed as a vector.

Since a force rarely acts in isolation, it is important to recognize that the overall effect of many forces acting on a system or free body is a function of the net force, which is the vector sum of all of the acting forces. When all acting forces are balanced, or cancel each other out, the net force is zero, and the body remains in its original state of motion, either motionless or moving with a constant velocity. When a net force is present, the body moves in the direction of the net force and with an acceleration that is proportional to the magnitude of the net force.

net force
resultant force derived from the composition of two or more forces

Center of Gravity

A body's center of gravity, or center of mass, is the point around which the body's weight is equally balanced, no matter how the body is positioned, (see Chapter 13). In motion analyses, the motion of the center of gravity serves as an index of total body motion. From a kinetic perspective, the location of the center of mass determines the way in which the body responds to external forces.

center of gravity
point around which a body's weight is equally balanced, no matter how the body is positioned

Weight

Weight is defined as the amount of gravitational force exerted on a body. Algebraically, its definition is a modification of the general definition of a force, with weight (wt) being equal to mass (m) multiplied by the acceleration of gravity (a_g):

weight
attractive force that the earth exerts on a body

$$wt = ma_g$$

Since weight is a force, units of weight are units of force—either N or lb.

As the mass of a body increases, its weight increases proportionally. The factor of proportionality is the acceleration of gravity, which is -9.81 m/s^2.

Although a body's mass remains unchanged on the moon, its weight is less due to smaller gravitational acceleration. Photo courtesy of NASA.

Hall: Basic Biomechanics, Fifth Edition | 3. Kinetic Concepts for Analyzing Human Motion | Text | © The McGraw–Hill Companies, 2007

The negative sign indicates that the acceleration of gravity is directed downward, or toward the center of the earth. On the moon or another planet with a different gravitational acceleration, a body's weight would be different, although its mass would remain the same.

Because weight is a force, it is also characterized by magnitude, direction, and point of application. The direction in which weight acts is always toward the center of the earth. Because the point at which weight is assumed to act on a body is the body's center of gravity, the center of gravity is the point where the weight vector is shown to act in free body diagrams.

Although body weights are often reported in kilograms, the kilogram is actually a unit of mass. To be technically correct, weights should be identified in Newtons and masses reported in kilograms. Sample Problem 3.1 illustrates the relationship between mass and weight.

SAMPLE PROBLEM 3.1

1. If a scale shows that an individual has a mass of 68 kg, what is that individual's weight?

Known

$$m = 68 \text{ kg}$$

Solution
Wanted: weight
Formulas: $wt = ma_g$
          $1 \text{ kg} = 2.2 \text{ lb}$ (English/metric conversion factor)

(Mass may be multiplied by the acceleration of gravity to convert to weight within either the English or the metric system.)

$$wt = ma_g$$
$$wt = (68 \text{ kg})(9.81) \text{ m/s}^2$$

$$wt = 667 \text{ N}$$

Mass in kg may be multiplied by the conversion factor 2.2 lb/kg to convert to weight in pounds:

$$(68 \text{ kg})(2.2 \text{ lb/kg}) = 150 \text{ lb}$$

2. What is the mass of an object weighing 1200 N?

Known

$$wt = 1200 \text{ N}$$

Solution
Wanted: mass
Formula: $wt = ma_g$

(Weight may be divided by the acceleration of gravity within a given system of measurement to convert to mass.)

$$wt = ma_g$$
$$1200 \text{ N} = m(9.81 \text{ m/s}^2)$$
$$\frac{1200 \text{ N}}{9.81 \text{ m/s}^2} = m$$

$$m = 122.32 \text{ kg}$$

66   BASIC BIOMECHANICS

Pressure

pressure
force per unit of area over which force acts

Pressure (p) is defined as force (F) distributed over a given area (A):

$$p = \frac{F}{A}$$

Units of pressure are units of force divided by units of area. Common units of pressure in the metric system are N per square centimeter (N/cm²) and Pascals (Pa). One Pascal represents one Newton per square meter (Pa = N/m²). In the English system, the most common unit of pressure is pounds per square inch (psi or lb/in²).

The pressure exerted by the sole of a shoe on the floor beneath it is the body weight resting on the shoe divided by the surface area between the sole of the shoe and the floor. As illustrated in Sample Problem 3.2, the smaller amount of surface area on the bottom of a spike heel as compared to a flat sole results in a much larger amount of pressure being exerted.

Volume

volume
space occupied by a body

A body's volume is the amount of space that it occupies. Because space is considered to have three dimensions (width, height, depth), a unit of volume is a unit of length multiplied by a unit of length multiplied by a unit of length. In mathematical shorthand, this is a unit of length raised to the exponential power of three, or a unit of length *cubed*. In the metric

Pairs of balls that are similar in volume but markedly different in weight.

SAMPLE PROBLEM 3.2

Is it better to be stepped on by a woman wearing a spike heel or by the same woman wearing a smooth-soled court shoe? If a woman's weight is 556 N, the surface area of the spike heel is 4 cm^2, and the surface area of the court shoe is 175 cm^2, how much pressure is exerted by each shoe?

Known

$$wt = 556 \text{ N}$$
$$A_s = 4 \text{ cm}^2$$
$$A_c = 175 \text{ cm}^2$$

Solution

Wanted: pressure exerted by the spike heel
         pressure exerted by the court shoe

Formula: $p = F/A$

Deduction: It is necessary to recall that weight is a force.

For the spike heel:

$$p = \frac{556 \text{ N}}{4 \text{ cm}^2}$$

$$p = 139 \text{ N/cm}^2$$

For the court shoe:

$$p = \frac{556}{175 \text{ cm}^2}$$

$$p = 3.18 \text{ N/cm}^2$$

Comparison of the amounts of pressure exerted by the two shoes:

$$\frac{p_{\text{spike heel}}}{p_{\text{court shoe}}} = \frac{139}{3.18} = 43.75$$

Therefore, 43.75 times more pressure is exerted by the spike heel than by the court shoe worn by the same woman.

system, common units of volume are cubic centimeters (cm^3), cubic meters (m^3), and liters (l):

$$1\ l\ =\ 1000\ cm^3$$

In the English system of measurement, common units of volume are cubic inches (in^3) and cubic feet (ft^3). Another unit of volume in the English system is the quart (qt):

$$1\ qt\ =\ 57.75\ in^3$$

Volume should not be confused with weight or mass. An 8 kg shot and a softball occupy approximately the same volume of space, but the weight of the shot is much greater than that of the softball.

Density

The concept of density combines the mass of a body with the body volume. Density is defined as **mass per unit of volume**. The conventional symbol for density is the Greek letter rho (ρ).

$$density\ (\rho)\ =\ mass/volume$$

Units of density are units of mass divided by units of volume. In the metric system, a common unit of density is the kilogram per cubic meter (**kg/m^3**). In the English system of measurement, units of density are not commonly used. Instead, units of specific weight (weight density) are employed.

Specific weight is defined as weight per unit of volume. Because weight is proportional to mass, specific weight is proportional to density. Units of specific weight are units of weight divided by units of volume. The metric unit for specific weight is Newtons per cubic meter (N/m^3), and the English system uses pounds per cubic foot (lb/ft^3).

Although a golf ball and a ping-pong ball occupy approximately the same volume, the golf ball has a greater density and specific weight than the ping-pong ball because the golf ball has more mass and more weight. Similarly, a lean person with the same body volume as an obese person has a higher total body density because muscle is denser than fat. Thus, percent body fat is inversely related to body density.

Torque

When a force is applied to an object such as a pencil lying on a desk, either translation or general motion may result. If the applied force is directed parallel to the desktop and through the center of the pencil (a *centric force*), the pencil will be translated in the direction of the applied force. If the force is applied parallel to the desktop but directed through a point other than the center of the pencil (an *eccentric force*), the pencil will undergo both translation and rotation (Figure 3-3).

The rotary effect created by an eccentric force is known as torque (T), or moment of force. Torque, which may be thought of as *rotary force,* is the angular equivalent of linear force. Algebraically, torque is the product of force (F) and the perpendicular distance ($d_\perp$) from the force's line of action to the axis of rotation:

$$T\ =\ Fd_\perp$$

The greater the amount of torque acting at the axis of rotation, the greater the tendency for rotation to occur. Units of torque in both the metric and the English systems follow the algebraic definition. They are units of force multiplied by units of distance: Newton-meters (N-m) or foot-pounds (ft-lb).

density
mass per unit of volume

specific weight
weight per unit of volume

torque
rotary effect of a force

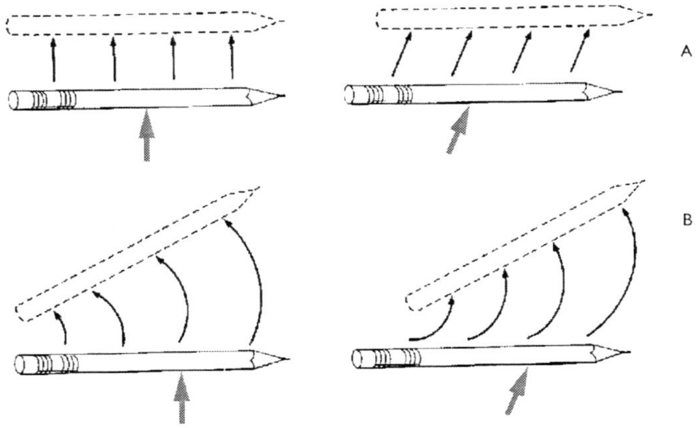

FIGURE 3-3

A. Centric forces produce translation. **B.** Eccentric forces produce translation and rotation.

Impulse

When a force is applied to a body, the resulting motion of the body is dependent not only on the magnitude of the applied force but also on the duration of force application. The product of force (F) and time (t) is known as impulse:

$$impulse = Ft$$

A large change in an object's state of motion may result from a small force acting for a relatively long time or from a large force acting for a relatively short time. A golf ball rolling across a green gradually loses speed because of the small force of rolling friction. The speed of a baseball struck vigorously by a bat changes because of the large force exerted by the bat during the fraction of a second it is in contact with the ball. When a vertical jump is executed, the larger the impulse generated against the floor, the greater the jumper's takeoff velocity and the higher the resulting jump.

Units of physical quantities commonly used in biomechanics are shown in Table 3-1.

impulse
product of force and the time over which the force acts

QUANTITY	SYMBOL	METRIC UNIT	ENGLISH UNIT
Mass	m	kg	slug
Force	F	N	lb
Pressure	p	Pa	psi
Volume (solids) (liquids)	V	m^3 liter	ft^3 gallon
Density	ρ	kg/m^3	
Specific weight	γ	N/m^3	lb/ft^3
Torque	T	N-m	ft-lb
Impulse		$N \cdot s$	$lb \cdot s$

TABLE 3-1

Common Units for Kinetic Quantities

70   BASIC BIOMECHANICS

MECHANICAL LOADS ON THE HUMAN BODY

Muscle forces, gravitational force, and bone-breaking force such as that encountered in a skiing accident all affect the human body differently. The effect of a given force depends on its direction and duration as well as its magnitude, as described in the following section.

Compression, Tension, and Shear

compression
pressing or squeezing force directed axially through a body

Compressive force, or compression, can be thought of as a squeezing force (Figure 3-4). An effective way to press wildflowers is to place them inside the pages of a book and to stack other books on top of that book. The weight of the books creates a compressive force on the flowers. Similarly, the weight of the body acts as a compressive force on the bones that support it. When the trunk is erect, each vertebra in the spinal column must support the weight of that portion of the body above it.

tension
pulling or stretching force directed axially through a body

The opposite of compressive force is tensile force, or tension (Figure 3-4). Tensile force is a pulling force that creates tension in the object to which it is applied. When a child sits in a playground swing, the child's weight creates tension in the chains supporting the swing. A heavier child creates even more tension in the supports of the swing. Muscles produce tensile force that pulls on the attached bones.

shear
force directed parallel to a surface

A third category of force is termed shear. Whereas compressive and tensile forces act along the longitudinal axis of a bone or other structure to which they are applied, shear force acts parallel or tangent to a surface. Shear force tends to cause one portion of the object to slide, displace, or shear with respect to another portion of the object (Figure 3-4). For example, a force acting at the knee joint in a direction parallel to the tibial plateau is a shearing force at the knee (1). During the performance of a squat exercise, joint shear at the knee is greatest at the full squat position (1). This position places a large amount of stress on the ligaments and muscle tendons that prevent the femur from sliding off the tibial plateau (Figure 3-5).

FIGURE 3-4

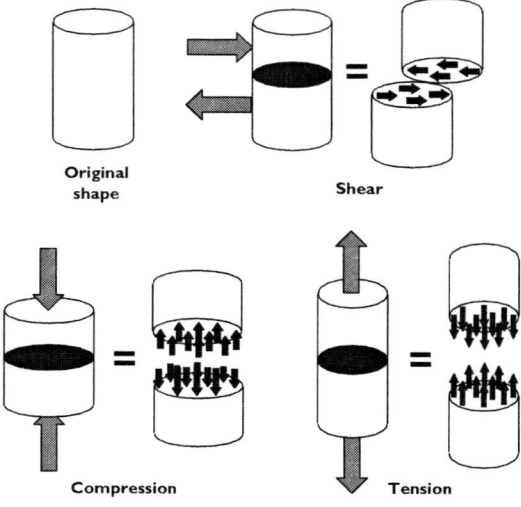

Original shape

Shear

Compression

Tension

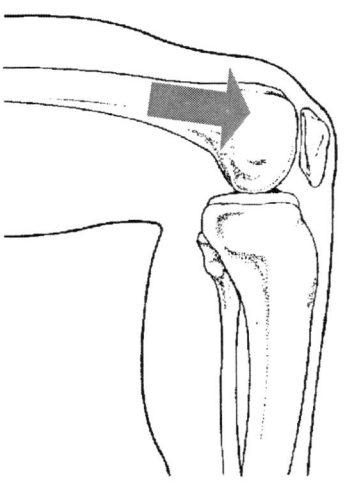

FIGURE 3-5

During performance of squat or knee bend exercises, shear force acting at the knee is maximal when flexion at the knee is maximal. The shear at the joint is produced by the axial force in the femur.

Mechanical Stress

Another factor affecting the outcome of the action of forces on the human body is the way in which the force is distributed. Whereas pressure represents the distribution of force external to a solid body, stress represents the resulting force distribution inside a solid body when an external force acts. Stress is quantified in the same way as pressure: force per unit of area over which the force acts. As shown in Figure 3-6, a given force acting on a small surface produces greater stress than the same force acting over a larger surface. When a blow is sustained by the human body, the likelihood of injury to body tissue is related to the magnitude and direction of the stress created by the blow. Compressive stress, tensile stress, and shear stress are terms that indicate the direction of the acting stress.

Because the lumbar vertebrae bear more of the weight of the body than the thoracic vertebrae when a person is in an upright position, the compressive stress in the lumbar region should logically be greater. However, the amount of stress present is not directly proportional to the amount of weight borne, because the load-bearing surface areas of the lumbar vertebrae are greater than those of the vertebrae higher in the spinal column (Figure 3-7). This increased surface area reduces the amount of compressive stress present.

stress
distribution of force within a body, quantified as force divided by the area over which the force acts

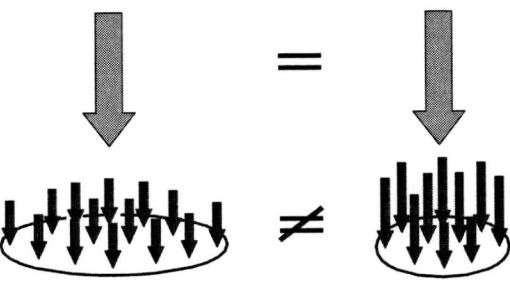

FIGURE 3-6

The amount of mechanical stress created by a force is inversely related to the size of the area over which the force is spread.

72   BASIC BIOMECHANICS

The surfaces of the vertebral bodies increase in surface area as more weight is supported.

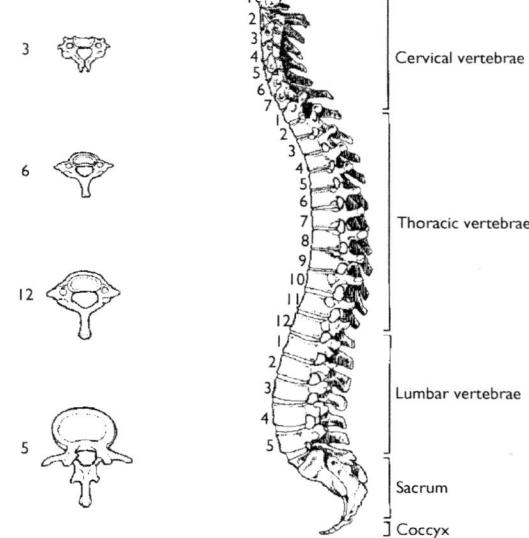

Nevertheless, the L5-S1 intervertebral disc (at the bottom of the lumbar spine) is the most common site of disc herniations, although other factors also play a role (see Chapter 9). Quantification of mechanical stress is demonstrated in Sample Problem 3.3.

Torsion, Bending, and Combined Loads

bending
asymmetric loading that produces tension on one side of a body's longitudinal axis and compression on the other side

axial
directed along the longitudinal axis of a body

torsion
load-producing twisting of a body around its longitudinal axis

combined loading
simultaneous action of more than one of the pure forms of loading

A somewhat more complicated type of loading is called bending. Pure compression and tension are both axial forces—that is, they are directed along the longitudinal axis of the affected structure. When an eccentric (or nonaxial) force is applied to a structure, the structure bends, creating compressive stress on one side and tensile stress on the opposite side (Figure 3-8).

Torsion occurs when a structure is caused to twist about its longitudinal axis, typically when one end of the structure is fixed. Torsional fractures of the tibia are not uncommon in football injuries and skiing accidents in which the foot is held in a fixed position while the rest of the body undergoes a twist.

The presence of more than one form of loading is known as combined loading. Because the human body is subjected to a myriad of simultaneously acting forces during daily activities, this is the most common type of loading on the body.

THE EFFECTS OF LOADING

deformation
change in shape

When a force acts on an object, there are two potential effects. The first is acceleration and the second is deformation, or change in shape. When a diver applies force to the end of a springboard, the board both accelerates and deforms. The amount of deformation that occurs in response to a given force depends on the stiffness of the object acted upon.

When an external force is applied to the human body, several factors influence whether an injury occurs. Among these are the magnitude and

SAMPLE PROBLEM 3.3

How much compressive stress is present on the L1, L2 vertebral disc of a 625 N woman, given that approximately 45% of body weight is supported by the disc (a) when she stands in anatomical position and (b) when she stands erect holding a 222 N suitcase? (Assume that the disc is oriented horizontally and that its surface area is 20 cm^2)

Solution

1. Given:
$$F = (625 \text{ N})(0.45)$$
$$A = 20 \text{ cm}^2$$

Formula:
$$\text{stress} = F/A$$
$$\text{stress} = \frac{(625 \text{ N})(0.45)}{20 \text{ cm}^2}$$
$$\text{stress} = 14 \text{ N/cm}^2$$

2. Given:
$$F = (625 \text{ N})(0.45) + 222 \text{ N}$$

Formula:
$$\text{stress} = F/A$$
$$\text{stress} = \frac{(625 \text{ N})(0.45) + 222 \text{ N}}{20 \text{ cm}^2}$$
$$\text{stress} = 25.2 \text{ N/cm}^2$$

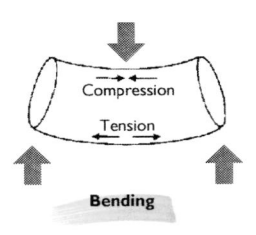

Bending

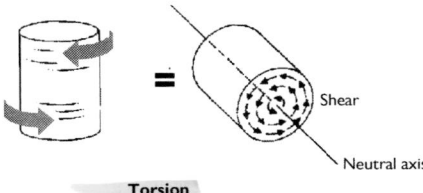

Torsion

FIGURE 3-8

Objects loaded in bending are subject to compression on one side and tension on the other. Objects loaded in torsion develop internal shear stress, with maximal stress at the periphery and no stress at the neutral axis.

direction of the force, and the area over which the force is distributed. Also important, however, are the material properties of the loaded body tissues.

The relationship between the amount of force applied to a structure and the structure's response is illustrated by a load deformation curve (Figure 3-9). With relatively small loads, deformation occurs, but the response is elastic, meaning that when the force is removed the structure returns to its original size and shape. Since stiffer materials display less deformation in response to a given load, greater stiffness translates to a steeper

74   BASIC BIOMECHANICS

FIGURE 3-9

When a structure is loaded, it deforms, or changes shape. The deformation is temporary within the elastic region and permanent in the plastic region. Structural integrity is lost at the ultimate failure point.

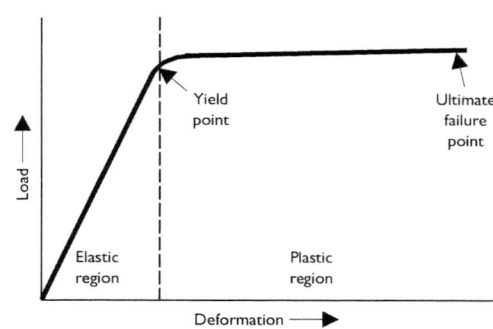

yield point (elastic limit)
point on the load deformation curve past which deformation is permanent

failure
loss of mechanical continuity

repetitive loading
repeated application of a subacute load that is usually of relatively low magnitude

acute loading
application of a single force of sufficient magnitude to cause injury to a biological tissue

slope of the load deformation curve in the elastic region. If the force applied causes the deformation to exceed the structure's yield point or elastic limit, however, the response is plastic, meaning that some amount of deformation is permanent. Deformations exceeding the ultimate failure point produce mechanical failure of the structure, which in the human body means fracturing of bone or rupturing of soft tissues.

Repetitive versus Acute Loads

The distinction between repetitive and acute loading is also important. When a single force large enough to cause injury acts on biological tissues, the injury is termed *acute* and the causative force is termed *macrotrauma*. The force produced by a fall, a rugby tackle, or an automobile accident may be sufficient to fracture a bone.

Injury can also result from the repeated sustenance of relatively small forces. For example, each time a foot hits the pavement during running, a force of approximately two to three times body weight is sustained. Although a single force of this magnitude is not likely to result in a fracture of healthy bone, numerous repetitions of such a force may cause a fracture of an otherwise healthy bone somewhere in the lower extremity. When repeated or chronic loading over a period produces an injury, the injury is called a *chronic injury* or a *stress injury,* and the causative mechanism is termed *microtrauma*. The relationship between the magnitude of the load sustained, the frequency of loading, and the likelihood of injury is shown in Figure 3-10.

FIGURE 3-10

The general pattern of injury likelihood as a function of load magnitude and repetition. Injury can be sustained, but is less likely, with a single large load and with a repeated small load.

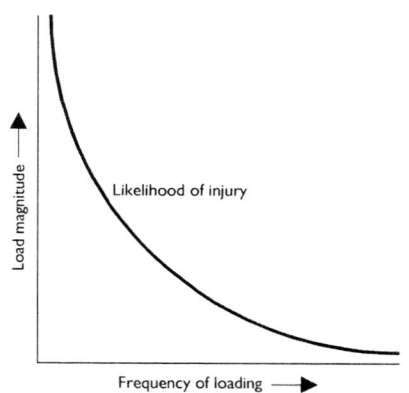

TOOLS FOR MEASURING KINETIC QUANTITIES

Biomechanics researchers use equipment for studying both muscle forces and forces generated by the feet against the ground during gait and other activities. Knowledge gained through the use of these apparatus is often published in professional journals for teachers, clinicians, coaches, and others interested in human movement.

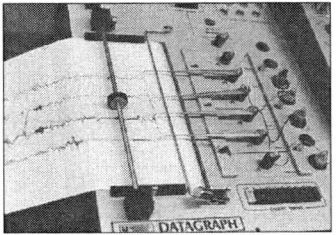

An electromyography system.

Electromyography

Eighteenth-century Italian scientist Galvani made two interesting discoveries about skeletal muscle: (a) It develops tension when electrically stimulated, and (b) it produces a detectable current or voltage when developing tension, even when the stimulus is a nerve impulse. The latter discovery was of little practical value until the twentieth century, when technology became available for the detection and recording of extremely small electrical charges. The technique of recording electrical activity produced by muscle, or myoelectric activity, is known today as *electromyography* (EMG).

myoelectric activity
electric current or voltage produced by a muscle developing tension

Electromyography is used to study neuromuscular function, including identification of which muscles develop tension throughout a movement and which movements elicit more or less tension from a particular muscle or muscle group. It is also used clinically to assess nerve conduction velocities and muscle response in conjunction with the diagnosis and tracking of pathological conditions of the neuromuscular system. Scientists also employ electromyographic techniques to study the ways in which individual motor units respond to central nervous system commands.

The process of electromyography involves the use of transducers known as *electrodes* that sense the level of myoelectric activity present at a particular site over time. Depending on the questions of interest, either surface electrodes or fine wire electrodes are used. Surface electrodes, consisting of small discs of conductive material, are positioned on the surface of the skin over a muscle or muscle group to pick up global myoelectric activity. When more localized pickup is desired, indwelling, fine-wire electrodes are injected directly into a muscle. Output from the electrodes is amplified and graphically displayed or mathematically processed and stored by a computer.

transducers
devices that detect signals

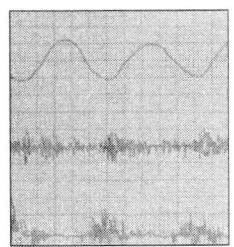

A graphic printout showing changes in joint range of motion (top trace) and myoelectric activity recorded from two muscle groups.

Dynamography

Scientists have devised several types of platforms and portable systems for the measurement of forces and pressure on the plantar surface of the foot. These systems have been employed primarily in gait research, but have also been used to study phenomena such as starts, takeoffs, landings, baseball and golf swings, and balance. Those systems that provide a graphical time-history of recorded force also allow the calculation of impulse as the area under the force–time curve.

Both commercially available and homemade *force platforms* and *pressure platforms* are typically built rigidly into a floor flush with the surface and are interfaced to a computer that calculates kinetic quantities of interest. Force platforms are usually designed to transduce ground reaction forces in vertical, lateral, and anteroposterior directions with respect to the platform itself; pressure platforms provide graphical or digital maps of pressures across the plantar surfaces of the feet. The force platform is a relatively sophisticated instrument, but its limitations include the restrictions of a laboratory setting and

76   BASIC BIOMECHANICS

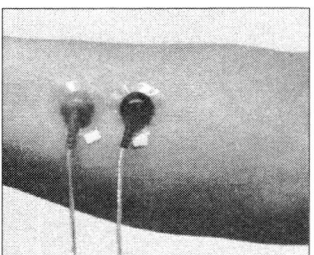

Surface EMG electrodes are small discs that attach directly to the skin over a muscle or muscle group of interest to transduce electrical activity in the underlying tissue.

vector
physical quantity that possesses both magnitude and direction

scalar
physical quantity that is completely described by its magnitude

vector composition
process of determining a single vector from two or more vectors by vector addition

resultant
single vector that results from vector composition

potential difficulties associated with the subject's consciously targeting the platform.

Portable systems for measuring plantar forces and pressures are also available in commercial and homemade models as instrumented shoes, shoe inserts, and thin transducers that adhere to the plantar surfaces of the feet. These systems provide the advantage of data collection outside the laboratory but lack the precision of the built-in platforms.

VECTOR ALGEBRA

A vector is a quantity that has both magnitude and direction. Vectors are represented by arrow-shaped symbols. The magnitude of a vector is its size; for example, the number 12 is of greater magnitude than the number 10. A vector symbol's orientation on paper represents direction, and its length represents magnitude. Force, weight, pressure, specific weight, and torque are kinetic vector quantities; displacement, velocity, and acceleration (see Chapter 10) are kinematic vector quantities. No vector is fully defined without the identification of both its magnitude and its direction. Scalar quantities possess magnitude but have no particular direction associated with them. Mass, volume, length, and speed are examples of scalar quantities.

Vector Composition

When vectors are added together, the operation is called vector composition. The composition of two or more vectors that have exactly the same direction results in a single vector that has a magnitude equal to the sum of the magnitudes of the vectors being added (Figure 3-11). The single vector resulting from a composition of two or more vectors is known as the resultant vector, or the resultant. If two vectors that are oriented in exactly opposite directions are composed, the resultant has the direction of the longer vector and a magnitude equal to the difference in the magnitudes of the two original vectors (Figure 3-12).

It is also possible to add vectors that are not oriented in the same or opposite directions. When the vectors are coplanar, that is, contained in the same plane, a procedure that may be used is the *"tip-to-tail"* method, in which the tail of the second vector is placed on the tip of the first vector, and the resultant is then drawn with its tail on the tail of the first vector and its tip on the tip of the second vector. This procedure may be used for

FIGURE 3-11

The composition of vectors with the same direction requires adding their magnitudes.

→ + → = ⟶

↑ + ↑ = ↑

↗ + ↗ = ↗

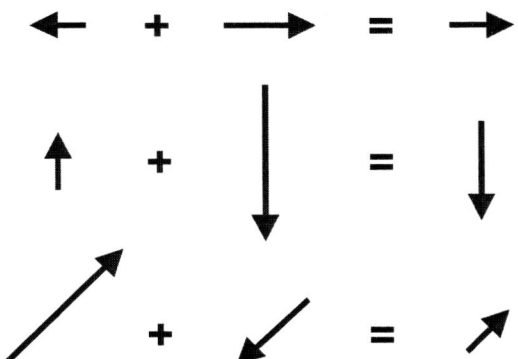

FIGURE 3-12

Composition of vectors with opposite directions requires subtracting their magnitudes.

combining any number of vectors if each successive vector is positioned with its tail on the tip of the immediately preceding vector and the resultant connects the tail of the first vector to the tip of the previous vector (Figure 3-13).

Through the laws of vector combination, we often can calculate or better visualize the resultant effect of combined vector quantities. For example, a canoe floating down a river is subject to both the force of the current and the force of the wind. If the magnitudes and directions of these two forces are known, the single resultant or *net force* can be derived through the process of vector composition (Figure 3-14). The canoe travels in the direction of the net force.

Vector Resolution

Determining the perpendicular components of a vector quantity relative to a particular plane or structure is often useful. For example, when a ball is thrown into the air, the horizontal component of its velocity determines the distance it travels, and the vertical component of its velocity determines the height it reaches (see Chapter 10). When a vector is resolved into perpendicular components—a process known as vector resolution—

vector resolution
operation that replaces a single vector with two perpendicular vectors such that the vector composition of the two perpendicular vectors yields the original vector

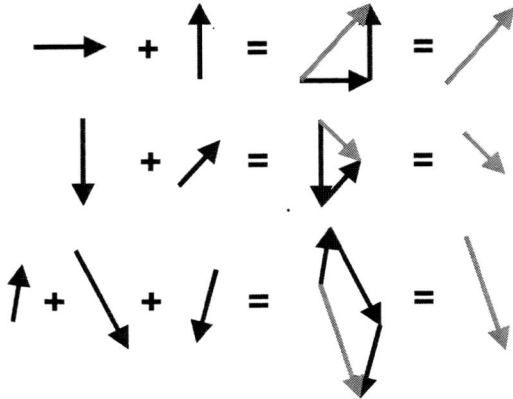

FIGURE 3-13

The "tip-to-tail" method of vector composition.

78   BASIC BIOMECHANICS

The net force is the resultant of all acting forces.

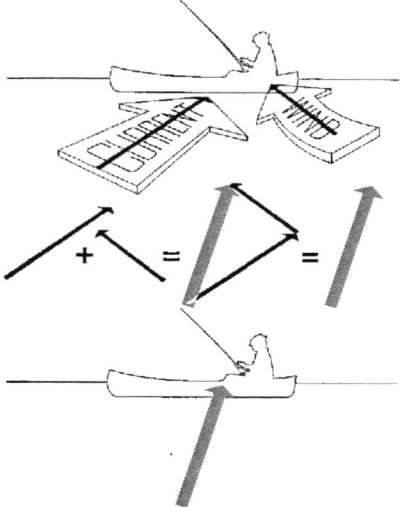

the vector sum of the components always yields a resultant that is equal to the original vector (Figure 3-15). The two perpendicular components, therefore, are a different but equal representation of the original vector.

Graphic Solution of Vector Problems

When vector quantities are uniplanar (contained in a single plane), vector manipulations may be done graphically to yield approximate results. Graphic solution of vector problems requires the careful measurement of vector orientations and lengths to minimize error. Vector lengths, which represent the magnitudes of vector quantities, must be drawn to scale. For example, 1 cm of vector length could represent 10 N of force. A force of 30 N would then be represented by a vector 3 cm in length, and a force of 45 N would be represented by a vector of 4.5 cm length.

Trigonometric Solution of Vector Problems

A more accurate procedure for quantitatively dealing with vector problems involves the application of trigonometric principles. Through the use of trigonometric relationships, the tedious process of measuring and drawing vectors to scale can be eliminated (see Appendix B). Sample Problem 3.4 provides an example of the processes of both graphic and trigonometric solutions using vector quantities.

Vectors may be resolved into perpendicular components. The vector composition of each perpendicular pair of components yields the original vector.

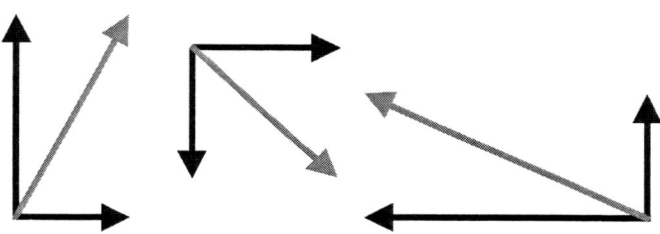

SAMPLE PROBLEM 3.4

Terry and Charlie must move a refrigerator to a new location. They both push parallel to the floor, Terry with a force of 350 N and Charlie with a force of 400 N, as shown in the diagram below. (a) What is the magnitude of the resultant of the forces produced by Terry and Charlie? (b) If the amount of friction force that directly opposes the direction of motion of the refrigerator is 700 N, will they be able to move the refrigerator?

Graphic Solution
1. Use the scale 1 cm = 100 N to measure the length of the resultant.

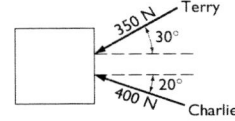

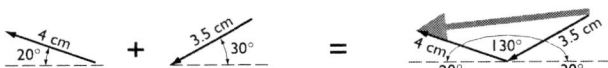

The length of the resultant is approximately 6.75 cm, or 675 N.

2. Since 675 N < 700 N, they will not be able to move the refrigerator.

Trigonometric Solution
Given: F_T = 350 N
                                     F_C = 400 N

Wanted: magnitude of the resultant force
Horizontal plane free body diagram:

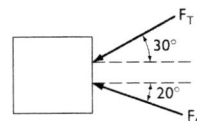

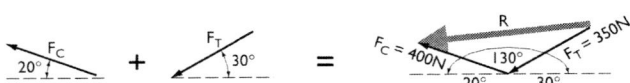

Formula:
$$C^2 = A^2 + B^2 - 2(A)(B)\cos \gamma \text{ (the law of cosines)}$$
$$R^2 = 400^2 + 350^2 - 2(400)(350) \cos 130$$

$$R = 680 \text{ N}$$

3. Since 680 N < 700 N, they will not be able to move the refrigerator unless they exert more collective force while pushing at these particular angles. (If both Terry and Charlie pushed at a 90° angle to the refrigerator, their combined force would be sufficient to move it.)

SUMMARY

Basic concepts related to kinetics include mass, the quantity of matter composing an object; inertia, the tendency of a body to maintain its current state of motion; force, a push or pull that alters or tends to alter a body's state of motion; center of gravity, the point around which a body's weight is balanced; weight, the gravitational force exerted on a body; pressure, the amount of force distributed over a given area; volume, the space occupied by a body; density, the mass or weight per unit of body volume; and torque, the rotational effect of a force.

Several types of mechanical loads act on the human body. These include compression, tension, shear, bending, and torsion. Generally, some combination of these loading modes is present. The distribution of force within a body structure is known as mechanical stress. The nature and magnitude of stress determine the likelihood of injury to biological tissues.

Vector quantities have magnitude and direction; scalar quantities possess magnitude only. Problems with vector quantities can be solved using either a graphic or a trigonometric approach. Of the two procedures, the use of trigonometric relationships is more accurate and less tedious.

INTRODUCTORY PROBLEMS

1. William Perry, defensive tackle and part-time running back better known as "The Refrigerator," weighed in at 1352 N during his 1985 rookie season with the Chicago Bears. What was Perry's mass? (Answer: 138 kg)
2. How much force must be applied to a 0.5 kg hockey puck to give it an acceleration of 30 m/s^2? (Answer: 15 N)
3. A rugby player is contacted simultaneously by three opponents who exert forces of the magnitudes and directions shown in the diagram at right. Using a graphic solution, show the magnitude and direction of the resultant force.

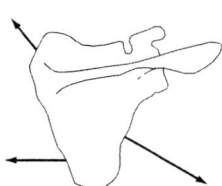

4. Using a graphic solution, compose the muscle force vectors to find the net force acting on the scapula shown below.

5. Draw the horizontal and vertical components of the vectors shown below.

6. A gymnastics floor mat weighing 220 N has dimensions of 3 m × 4 m × 0.04 m. How much pressure is exerted by the mat against the floor? (Answer: 18.33 Pa)
7. What is the volume of a milk crate with sides of 25 cm, 40 cm, and 30 cm? (Answer: 30,000 cm^3 or 30 l)
8. Choose three objects that are within your field of view, and estimate the volume of each. List the approximate dimensions you used in formulating your estimates.
9. If the contents of the crate described in Problem 7 weigh 120 N, what are the average density and specific weight of the box and contents? (Answer: 0.0004 kg/cm^3; 0.004 N/cm^3)
10. Two children sit on opposite sides of a playground seesaw. Joey, who weighs 220 N, sits 1.5 m from the axis of the seesaw, and Suzy, who weighs 200 N, sits 1.7 m from the axis of the seesaw. How much torque is created at the axis by each child? In which direction will the seesaw tip? (Answer: Joey, 330 N-m; Suzy, 340 N-m; Suzy's end)

ADDITIONAL PROBLEMS

1. What is your own body mass in kg?
2. Gravitational force on planet X is 40% of that found on the earth. If a person weighs 667.5 N on earth, what is the person's weight on planet X? What is the person's mass on the earth and on planet X? (Answer: weight on planet X = 267 N; mass = 68 kg on either planet)
3. A football player is contacted by two tacklers simultaneously. Tackler A exerts a force of 400 N, and tackler B exerts a force of 375 N. If the forces are coplanar and directed perpendicular to each other, what is the magnitude and direction of the resultant force acting on the player? (Answer: 548 N at an angle of 43° to the line of action of tackler A)
4. A 75 kg skydiver in free fall is subjected to a crosswind exerting a force of 60 N and to a vertical air resistance force of 100 N. Describe the resultant force acting on the skydiver. (Answer: 638.6 N at an angle of 5.4° to vertical)
5. Use a trigonometric solution to find the magnitude of the resultant of the following coplanar forces: 60 N at 90°, 80 N at 120°, and 100 N at 270°. (Answer: 49.57 N)
6. If 37% of body weight is distributed above the superior surface of the L5 intervertebral disc and the area of the superior surface of the disc is 25 cm^2, how much pressure exerted on the disc is attributable to body weight for a 930 N man? (Answer: 13.8 N/cm^2)
7. In the nucleus pulposus of an intervertebral disc, the compressive load is 1.5 times the externally applied load. In the annulus fibrosus, the compressive force is 0.5 times the external load. What are the compressive loads on the nucleus pulposus and annulus fibrosus of the L5-S1 intervertebral disc of a 930 N man holding a 445 N weight bar across his shoulders, given that 37% of body weight is distributed above the disc? (Answer: 1183.7 N acts on the nucleus pulposus; 394.5 N acts on the annulus fibrosus.)
8. Estimate the volume of your own body. Construct a table that shows the approximate body dimensions you used in formulating your estimate.

9. Given the mass or weight and the volume of each of the following objects, rank them in the order of their densities.

OBJECT	WEIGHT OR MASS	VOLUME
A	50 kg	15.00 in^3
B	90 lb	12.00 cm^3
C	3 slugs	1.50 ft^3
D	450 N	0.14 m^3
E	45 kg	30.00 cm^3

10. Two muscles develop tension simultaneously on opposite sides of a joint. Muscle A, attaching 3 cm from the axis of rotation at the joint, exerts 250 N of force. Muscle B, attaching 2.5 cm from the joint axis, exerts 260 N of force. How much torque is created at the joint by each muscle? What is the net torque created at the joint? In which direction will motion at the joint occur? (Answer: A, 7.5 N-m; B, 6.5 N-m; net torque equals 1 N-m in the direction of A)

NAME _____

DATE _____

LABORATORY EXPERIENCES

1. Use a ruler to measure the dimensions of the sole of one of your shoes in centimeters. Being as accurate as possible, calculate an estimate of the surface area of the sole. (If a planimeter is available, use it to more accurately assess surface area by tracing around the perimeter of the sole.) Knowing your own body weight, calculate the amount of pressure exerted over the sole of one shoe. How much change in pressure would result if your body weight changed by 22 N (5 lb)?

Surface area calculation:

Surface area: _____

Body weight: _____

Pressure calculation:

Pressure: _____

Pressure calculation with 22 N (5 lb) change in body weight:

Pressure: _____

2. Place a large container filled three-quarters full of water on a scale, and record its weight. To assess the volume of an object of interest, completely submerge the object in the container, holding it just below the surface of the water. Record the *change* in weight on the scale. Remove the object from the container. Carefully pour water from the container into a measuring cup until the container weighs its original weight less the change in weight recorded. The volume of water in the measuring cup is the volume of the submerged object. (Be sure to use correct units when recording your measured values.)

Weight of container of water: _____

Change in weight with object submerged: _____

Volume of object: _____

84   BASIC BIOMECHANICS

3. Secure one end of a pencil by firmly clamping it in a vise. Grip the other end of the pencil with an adjustable wrench, and slowly apply a bending load to the pencil until it begins to break. Observe the nature of the break.

On which side of the pencil did the break begin? _____

Is the pencil stronger in resisting compression or tension? _____

Repeat the exercise using another pencil and applying a torsional (twisting) load. What does the nature of the initial break indicate about the distribution of shear stress within the pencil?

4. Experiment with pushing open a door by applying force with one finger. Apply force at distances of 10 cm, 20 cm, 30 cm, and 40 cm from the hinges. Write a brief paragraph explaining at which force application distance it is easiest/hardest to open the door.

5. Stand on a bathroom scale, and perform a vertical jump as a partner carefully observes the pattern of change in weight registered on the scale. Repeat the jump several times, as needed for your partner to determine the pattern. Trade positions, and observe the pattern of weight change as your partner performs a jump. In consultation with your partner, sketch a graph of the change in exerted force (vertical axis) across time (horizontal axis) during the performance of a vertical jump.

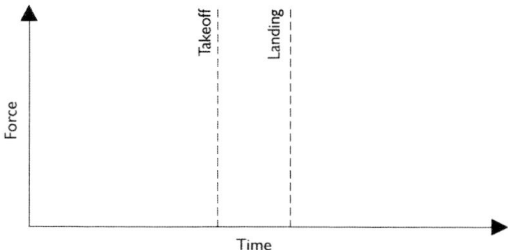

What does the area under the curve represent? _____

REFERENCES

1. Escamilla RF: Knee biomechanics of the dynamic squat exercise, Med Sci Sports Exerc 33:127, 2001.

ANNOTATED READINGS

Caldwell GE, Hamill J, Kamen G, Whittlesey SN, and Robertson DGE: *Research methods in biomechanics*, Champaign, IL, 2004, Human Kinetics.
   Includes chapters on kinetics, forces and their measurement, inverse dynamics, and electromyography, among others.

Leis AA and Trapani VC: *Atlas of electromyography*, Oxford, 2000, Oxford University Press.
   Includes high-quality anatomical illustrations of skeletal muscles that include nerve, plexus, and root supply; photographs of each muscle in healthy subjects to enable the practitioner to identify the optimum site of EMG needle or electrode positioning; and clinical features of the major conditions affecting peripheral nerves.

Panjabi MM and White AA: *Biomechanics in the musculoskeletal system*, New York, 2001, Churchill Livingstone.
   Provides more advanced coverage of the basic kinetic concepts discussed in the chapter.

Zatsiorski V: *Kinetics of human motion*, Champaign, IL, 2002, Human Kinetics.
   Includes chapters on external contact forces, statics of multilink chains, inertial properties of the human body, basic mechanics, and joint torques and forces, among others.

RELATED WEB SITES

Advanced Medical Technology, Inc.
www.amti.biz
   Provides information on the AMTI force platforms, with reference to force and torque sensors, gait analysis, balance and posture, and other topics.
B & L Engineering
www.bleng.com
   Describes electromyography systems and footswitches for gait analysis.
Biokinetics and Associates, Ltd.
www.biokinetics.com
   Markets products designed to prevent injury.
Bortec Biomedical Ltd.
www.bortec.ca
   Describes a multichannel telemetered electromyography system.
Delsys, Inc.
www.delsys.com/
   Provides a description of surface electromyography equipment.
Kistler
www.kistler.com
   Describes a series of force platforms.
RSscan
www.isbweb.org/~byp/rsscan.html
   Describes a within-shoe pressure measurement system.

KEY TERMS

acute loading	application of a single force of sufficient magnitude to cause injury to a biological tissue
axial	directed along the longitudinal axis of a body
bending	asymmetric loading that produces tension on one side of a body's longitudinal axis and compression on the other side

center of gravity	point around which a body's weight is equally balanced, no matter how the body is positioned
combined loading	simultaneous action of more than one of the pure forms of loading
compression	pressing or squeezing force directed axially through a body
deformation	change in shape
density	mass per unit of volume
failure	loss of mechanical continuity
force	push or pull; the product of mass and acceleration
free body diagram	sketch that shows a defined system in isolation with all of the force vectors acting on the system
impulse	product of force and the time over which the force acts
inertia	tendency of a body to resist a change in its state of motion
mass	quantity of matter contained in an object
myoelectric activity	electric current or voltage produced by a muscle developing tension
net force	resultant force derived from the composition of two or more forces
pressure	force per unit of area over which a force acts
repetitive loading	repeated application of a subacute load that is usually of relatively low magnitude
resultant	single vector that results from vector composition
scalar	physical quantity that is completely described by its magnitude
shear	force directed parallel to a surface
specific weight	weight per unit of volume
stress	distribution of force within a body, quantified as force divided by the area over which the force acts
tension	pulling or stretching force directed axially through a body
torque	rotary effect of a force
torsion	load-producing twisting of a body around its longitudinal axis
transducers	devices that detect signals
vector	physical quantity that possesses both magnitude and direction
vector composition	process of determining a single vector from two or more vectors by vector addition
vector resolution	operation that replaces a single vector with two perpendicular vectors such that the vector composition of the two perpendicular vectors yields the original vector
volume	space occupied by a body
weight	attractive force that the earth exerts on a body
yield point (elastic limit)	point on the load deformation curve past which deformation is permanent

Linear Kinematics of Human Movement

After completing this chapter, you will be able to:

Discuss the interrelationships among kinematic variables.

Correctly associate linear kinematic quantities with their units of measure.

Identify and describe the effects of factors governing projectile trajectory.

Explain why the horizontal and vertical components of projectile motion are analyzed separately.

Distinguish between average and instantaneous quantities, and identify the circumstances under which each is a quantity of interest.

Select and use appropriate equations to solve problems related to linear kinematics.

**Visit the Online Learning Center at www.mhhe.com/hall5e
to access the Online Lab Manual and many additional resources.**

W hy is a sprinter's acceleration close to zero in the middle of a race? How does the size of a dancer's foot affect the performance time that a choreographer must allocate for jumps? At what angle should a discus or a javelin be thrown to achieve maximum distance? Why does a ball thrown horizontally hit the ground at the same time as a ball dropped from the same height? These questions all relate to the kinematic characteristics of a pure form of movement: linear motion. This chapter introduces the study of human movement mechanics with a discussion of linear kinematic quantities and projectile motion.

LINEAR KINEMATIC QUANTITIES

kinematics
the form, pattern, or sequencing of movement with respect to time

Kinematics is the geometry, pattern, or form of motion with respect to time. Kinematics, which describes the appearance of motion, is distinguished from kinetics, the forces associated with motion. Linear kinematics involves the shape, form, pattern, and sequencing of linear movement through time, without particular reference to the forces that cause or result from the motion.

Careful kinematic analyses of performance are invaluable for clinicians, physical activity teachers, and coaches. When people learn a new motor skill, a progressive modification of movement kinematics reflects the learning process. This is particularly true for young children, whose movement kinematics changes with the normal changes in anthropometry and neuromuscular coordination that accompany growth. Likewise, when a patient rehabilitates an injured joint, the therapist or clinician looks for the gradual return of normal joint kinematics.

Kinematics spans both qualitative and quantitative forms of analysis. For example, qualitatively describing the kinematics of a soccer kick entails identifying the major joint actions, including hip flexion, knee extension, and possibly plantar flexion at the ankle. A more detailed qualitative kinematic analysis might also describe the precise sequencing and timing of body segment movements, which translates to the degree of skill evident on the part of the kicker. Although most assessments of hu-

Movement kinematics is also referred to as form *or* technique.

man movement are carried out qualitatively through visual observation, quantitative analysis is also sometimes appropriate. Physical therapists, for example, often measure the range of motion of an injured joint to help determine the extent to which range of motion exercises may be needed. When a coach measures an athlete's performance in the shot put or long jump, this too is a quantitative assessment.

Sport biomechanists often quantitatively study the kinematic factors that characterize an elite performance or the biomechanical factors that may limit the performance of a particular athlete. Sometimes this type of analysis involves construction of a model that details the kinematic characteristics of sound performance for practical use by coaches and athletes. Kinematic analysis can also help to identify injury potential during sport skill execution. For example, a study comparing the kinematics of American and Korean professional baseball pitchers identified a variety of specific differences that contribute to 10% greater ball velocity for the American pitchers but that also likely contribute to increased incidence of injury to the elbow and shoulder (10).

Most biomechanical studies of human kinematics, however, are performed on non-elite subjects. Kinematic research has shown that infants begin to use stable patterns of coordination in reaching for objects at age 12–15 months, with adultlike reaching movements occurring by about 2 years (18). Scientists have also studied the kinematic characteristics of progressive gait development and throwing ability in young children (15). In collaboration with adapted physical education specialists, biomechanists have documented the characteristic kinematic patterns associated with relatively common disabling conditions such as cerebral palsy, Down syndrome, and stroke. Quantitative kinematic screening tests are used to evaluate treatment and progression of a wide variety of motor disorders (30). Kinematic analysis indicates that walking on a treadmill with a grade just greater than 12% may be optimal for minimizing patellofemoral discomfort and potential strain on the anterior cruciate ligament (ACL) in post–ACL reconstruction patients (20).

Biomechanists commonly use high-speed cinematography or videography to perform quantitative kinematic analyses. The process involves taking a carefully planned film or video of a performance, with subsequent computerized or computer-assisted analysis of the performance on a picture-by-picture basis, as described in Chapter 2.

Distance and Displacement

Units of distance and displacement are units of length. In the metric system, the most commonly used unit of distance and displacement is the meter (m). A kilometer (km) is 1000 m, a centimeter (cm) is $\frac{1}{100}$ m, and a millimeter (mm) is $\frac{1}{1000}$ m. In the English system, common units of length are the inch, the foot (0.30 m), the yard (0.91 m), and the mile (1.61 km).

Distance and displacement are assessed differently. Distance is measured along the path of motion. When a runner completes 1½ laps around a 400 m track, the distance that the runner has covered is equal to 600 (400 + 200) m. Linear displacement is measured in a straight line from position 1 to position 2, or from initial position to final position. At the end of 1½ laps around the track, the runner's displacement is the length of the straight imaginary line that transverses the field, connecting the runner's initial position to the runner's final position halfway around the track (see Introductory Problem 1). At the completion of 2 laps around the track, the distance run is 800 m. Because initial and final positions are the same, however, the runner's displacement is zero. When a skater moves around

meter
the most common international unit of length, on which the metric system is based

linear displacement
change in location, or the directed distance from initial to final location

● *The metric system is the predominant standard of measurement in every major country in the world except the United States.*

FIGURE 10-1

The distance a skater travels may be measured from the track on the ice. The skater's displacement is measured in a straight line from initial position to final position.

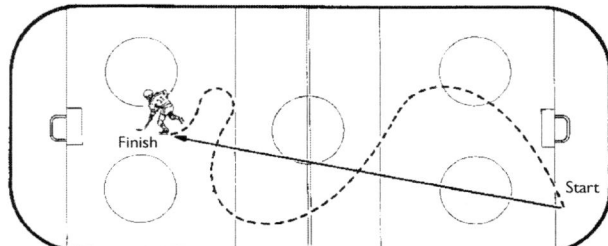

a rink, the distance the skater travels may be measured along the tracks left by the skates. The skater's displacement is measured along a straight line from initial to final positions on the ice (Figure 10-1).

Another difference is that distance is a scalar quantity while displacement is a vector quantity. Consequently, the displacement includes more than just the length of the line between two positions. Of equal importance is the *direction* in which the displacement occurs. The direction of a displacement relates the final position to the initial position. For example, the displacement of a yacht that has sailed 900 m on a tack due south would be identified as 900 m to the south.

The direction of a displacement may be indicated in several different, equally acceptable ways. Compass directions such as south and northwest and the terms *left / right, up / down,* and *positive / negative* are all appropriate labels. The positive direction is typically defined as upwards and/or to the right, with negative regarded as downwards and/or to the left. This enables indication of direction using plus and minus signs. The most important thing is to be consistent in using the system or convention adopted for indicating direction in a given context. It would be confusing to describe a displacement as 500 m north followed by 300 m to the right.

Either distance or displacement may be the more important quantity of interest depending on the situation. Many 5 km and 10 km racecourses are set up so that the finish line is only a block or two from the starting line. Participants in these races are usually interested in the number of kilometers of distance covered or the number of kilometers left to cover as they progress along the racecourse. Knowledge of displacement is not particularly valuable during this type of event. In other situations, however, displacement is more important. For example, triathlon competitions may involve a swim across a lake. Because swimming in a perfectly straight line across a lake is virtually impossible, the actual distance a swimmer covers is always somewhat greater than the width of the lake (see Sample Problem 10.1). However, the course is set up so that the identified length of the swim course is the length of the displacement between the entry and exit points on the lake.

•*Distance covered and displacement may be equal for a given movement. Or, distance may be greater than displacement, but the reverse is never true.*

Displacement magnitude and distance covered can be identical. When a cross-country skier travels down a straight path through the woods, both distance covered and displacement are equal. However, any time the path of motion is not rectilinear, the distance traveled and the size of the displacement will differ.

Speed and Velocity

linear velocity
the rate of change in location

Two quantities that parallel distance and linear displacement are speed and linear velocity. These terms are often used synonymously in general

SAMPLE PROBLEM 10.1

A swimmer crosses a lake that is 0.9 km wide in 30 minutes. What was his average velocity? Can his average speed be calculated?

Known

After reading the problem carefully, the next step is to sketch the problem situation, showing all quantities that are known or may be deduced from the problem statement:

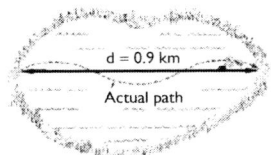

t = 30 min (0.5 hr)

d = 0.9 km

Actual path

Solution

In this situation, we know that the swimmer's displacement is 0.9 km. However, we know nothing about the exact path that he may have followed. The next step is to identify the appropriate formula to use to find the unknown quantity, which is velocity:

$$v = \frac{d}{t}$$

The known quantities can now be filled in to solve for velocity:

$$v = \frac{0.9 \text{ km}}{0.5 \text{ hr}}$$

$$= 1.8 \text{ km/hr}$$

Speed is calculated as distance divided by time. Although we know the time taken to cross the lake, we do not know, nor can we surmise from the information given, the exact distance covered by the swimmer. Therefore, his speed cannot be calculated.

conversation, but in mechanics, they have precise and different meanings. *Speed,* a scalar quantity, is defined as the distance covered divided by the time taken to cover it:

$$\text{speed} = \frac{\text{length (or distance)}}{\text{change in time}}$$

Velocity (v) is the change in position, or displacement, that occurs during a given period of time:

$$v = \frac{\text{change in position (or displacement)}}{\text{change in time}}$$

Because the Greek capital letter delta (Δ) is commonly used in mathematical expressions to mean "change in," a shorthand version of the relationship expressed follows, with t representing the amount of time elapsed during the velocity assessment:

$$v = \frac{\Delta \text{ position}}{\Delta \text{ time}} = \frac{d}{\Delta t}$$

●*Displacement and velocity are vector equivalents of the scalar quantities distance and speed.*

Another way to express change in position is position$_2$ − position$_1$, in which position$_1$ represents the body's position at one point in time and position$_2$ represents the body's position at a later point:

$$\text{velocity} = \frac{\text{position}_2 - \text{position}_1}{\text{time}_2 - \text{time}_1}$$

Because velocity is based on displacement, it is also a vector quantity. Consequently, description of velocity must include an indication of both the direction and the magnitude of the motion. If the direction of the motion is positive, velocity is positive; if the direction is negative, velocity is negative. A change in a body's velocity may represent a change in its speed, movement direction, or both.

Whenever two or more velocities act, the laws of vector algebra govern the ultimate speed and direction of the resultant motion. For example, the path actually taken by a swimmer crossing a river is determined by the vector sum of the swimmer's speed in the intended direction and the velocity of the river's current (Figure 10-2). Sample Problem 10.2 provides an illustration of this situation.

Units of speed and velocity are units of length divided by units of time. In the metric system, common units for speed and velocity are meters per second (m/s) and kilometers per hour (km/hr). However, any unit of length divided by any unit of time yields an acceptable unit of speed or velocity. For example, a speed of 5 m/s can also be expressed as 5000 mm/s or 18,000 m/hr. It is usually most practical to select units that will result in expression of the quantity in the smallest, most manageable form.

For human gait, speed is the product of stride length and stride frequency. Adults in a hurry tend to walk with both longer stride lengths and faster stride frequency than they use under more leisurely circumstances. However, for toddlers, women wearing high-heeled shoes, and elderly individuals, it is often difficult to significantly increase stride length without losing balance. Stride lengths during normal walking gait among

•*Units of speed and velocity are always units of length divided by units of time.*

FIGURE 10-2

The velocity of a swimmer in a river is the vector sum of the swimmer's velocity and the velocity of the current.

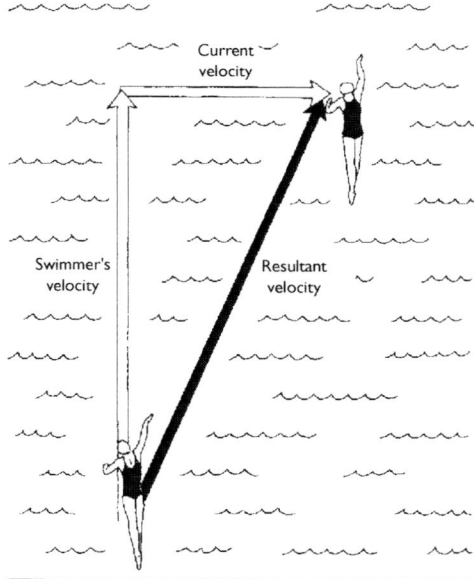

SAMPLE PROBLEM 10.2

A swimmer orients herself perpendicular to the parallel banks of a river. If the swimmer's velocity is 2 m/s and the velocity of the current is 0.5 m/s, what will be her resultant velocity? How far will she actually have to swim to get to the other side if the banks of the river are 50 m apart?

Solution
A diagram showing vector representations of the velocities of the swimmer and the current is drawn:

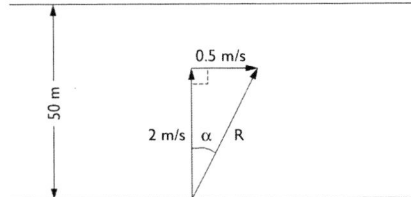

The resultant velocity can be found graphically by measuring the length and the orientation of the vector resultant of the two given velocities:

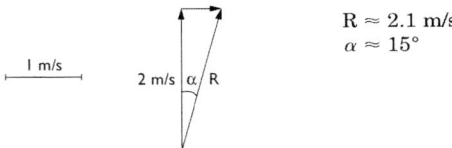

$R \approx 2.1$ m/s
$\alpha \approx 15°$

The resultant velocity can also be found using trigonometric relationships. The magnitude of the resultant velocity may be calculated using the Pythagorean theorem:

$$R^2 = (2 \text{ m/s})^2 + (0.5 \text{ m/s})^2$$
$$R^2 = \sqrt{(2 \text{ m/s})^2} + \sqrt{(0.5 \text{ m/s})^2}$$
$$= 2.06 \text{ m/s}$$

The direction of the resultant velocity may be calculated using the cosine relationship:

$$R \cos \alpha = 2 \text{ m/s}$$
$$(2.06 \text{ m/s}) \cos \alpha = 2 \text{ m/s}$$
$$\alpha = \arccos\left(\frac{2 \text{ m/s}}{2.06 \text{ m/s}}\right)$$
$$= 14°$$

If the swimmer travels in a straight line in the direction of her resultant velocity, the cosine relationship may be used to calculate her resultant displacement:

$$D \cos \alpha = 50 \text{ m}$$
$$D \cos 14 = 50 \text{ m}$$
$$\boxed{D = 51.5 \text{ m}}$$

328 BASIC BIOMECHANICS

Running speed is the product of stride length and stride frequency.

young children are characterized by large variability, with stride consistency gradually increasing through the early teenage years (13).

Increased variability of walking kinematics has also been associated with elevated risk of falls in older adults. Assessing kinematic variability is not an easy task, however. According to one research study, accurate determination of the kinematic variation in human gait requires analysis of at least 400 steps (28)! A large degree of variability in gait kinematics is apparently present in other species as well. Researchers examining the trotting gait of 10 Labrador retrievers on a treadmill found that the dogs' gait was not repeatable either for individual dogs at different points in the data collection or between different dogs at the same point in the data collection (6).

During running, a kinematic variable such as stride length is not simply a function of the runner's body height, but is also influenced by muscle fiber composition, footwear, level of fatigue, injury history, and the inclination (grade) and stiffness of the running surface (2, 12). Runners traveling at a slow pace tend to increase velocity primarily by increasing stride length. At faster running speeds, recreational runners rely more on increasing stride frequency to increase velocity (Figure 10-3). In cross-country skiing, as speed increases, stride rate increases and stride length tends to decrease (27). Overstriding, or using an overly long stride length, should be avoided in both running and skiing, since it is a risk factor for hamstring strains.

Those who run regularly for exercise usually prefer a given stride frequency over a range of slow-to-moderate running speeds. One reason for this may be related to running economy—the oxygen consumption required for performing a given task (1). Most runners tend to choose a combination of stride length and stride frequency that minimizes the physiological cost of running (3). As discussed in Chapter 1, many species of animals do the same thing. Running on downhill and uphill surfaces tends to respectively increase and decrease running speed, with these differences primarily a function of increased and decreased stride length (29). The presence of fatigue, as would be expected near the end of a marathon event, tends to result in increased stride frequency and decreased stride length (19).

FIGURE 10-3

Changes in stride length and stride rate with running velocity. From Luhtanen P and Komi PV: Mechanical factors influencing running speed. In Asmussen E and Jorgensen K, eds: *Biomechanics VI-B*, Baltimore, 1978, University Park Press.

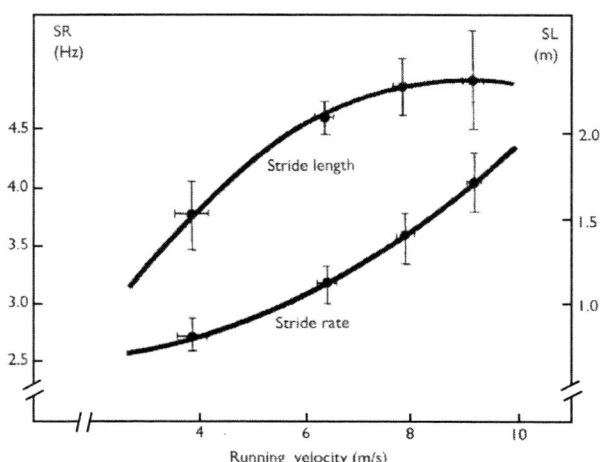

Since maximizing speed is the objective of all racing events, sport biomechanists have focused on the kinematic features that appear to accompany fast performances in running, skiing, skating, cycling, swimming, and rowing events. Research has shown that the best male and female sprinters are distinguished from their less-skilled counterparts by extremely high stride frequencies and short ground contact times, although their stride lengths are usually only average or slightly greater than average (9). In contrast, the fastest cross-country skiers have longer-than-average cycle lengths, with cycle rates that are only average (32). Research on skating kinematics has shown that better ice skaters appear to excel because of higher stride rates (23), whereas elite roller skaters are distinguished by longer strides (37). Interestingly, analysis of elite swimmers in the 100 m and 200 m breaststroke events has demonstrated that the optimum ratio of stroke rate to stroke length is unique to each individual swimmer (34).

When racing performances are analyzed, comparisons are usually based on pace rather than speed or velocity. *Pace* is the inverse of speed. Rather than units of distance divided by units of time, pace is presented as units of time divided by units of distance. Pace is the time taken to cover a given distance and is commonly quantified as minutes per km or minutes per mile.

ACCELERATION

We are well aware that the consequence of pressing down or letting up on the accelerator (gas) pedal of an automobile is usually a change in the automobile's speed (and velocity). Linear acceleration (a) is defined as the rate of change in velocity, or the change in velocity occurring over a given time interval (t):

linear acceleration
the rate of change in linear velocity

$$a = \frac{\text{change in velocity}}{\text{change in time}} = \frac{\Delta v}{\Delta t}$$

Another way to express change in velocity is $v_2 - v_1$, where v_1 represents velocity at one point in time and v_2 represents velocity at a later point:

$$a = \frac{v_2 - v_1}{\Delta t}$$

Units of acceleration are units of velocity divided by units of time. If a car increases its velocity by 1 km/hr each second, its acceleration is 1 km/hr/s. If a skier increases velocity by 1 m/s each second, the acceleration is 1 m/s/s. In mathematical terms, it is simpler to express the skier's acceleration as 1 m/s squared (1 m/s^2). A common unit of acceleration in the metric system is m/s^2.

Acceleration is the rate of change in velocity, or the degree with which velocity is changing with respect to time. For example, a body accelerating in a positive direction at a constant rate of 2 m/s^2 is increasing its velocity by 2 m/s each second. If the body's initial velocity was zero, a second later its velocity would be 2 m/s, a second after that its velocity would be 4 m/s, and a second after that its velocity would be 6 m/s.

In general usage, the term *accelerating* means speeding up, or increasing in velocity. If v_2 is greater than v_1, acceleration is a positive number, and the body in motion may have speeded up during the period in question. However, because it is sometimes appropriate to label the direction of motion as positive or negative, a positive value of acceleration may not mean that the body is speeding up.

330 BASIC BIOMECHANICS

Sliding into a base involves negative acceleration of the base runner.

If the direction of motion is described in terms other than positive or negative, a positive value of acceleration does indicate that the body being analyzed has speeded up. For example, if a sprinter's velocity is 3 m/s on leaving the blocks and is 5 m/s a second later, calculation of the acceleration that has occurred will yield a positive number. Because $v_1 = 3$ m/s, $v_2 = 5$ m/s, and $t = 1$ s:

$$a = \frac{v_2 - v_1}{\Delta t}$$
$$= \frac{5 \text{ m/s} - 3 \text{ m/s}}{1 \text{ s}}$$
$$= 2 \text{ m/s}^2$$

Whenever the direction of motion is described in terms other than positive or negative, and v_2 is greater than v_1, the value of acceleration will be a positive number, and the object in question is speeding up.

Acceleration can also assume a negative value. As long as the direction of motion is described in terms other than positive or negative, negative acceleration indicates that the body in motion is slowing down, or that its velocity is decreasing. For example, when a base runner slides to a stop over home plate, acceleration is negative. If a base runner's velocity is 4 m/s when going into a 0.5 s slide that stops the motion, $v_1 = 4$ m/s, $v_2 = 0$, and $t = 0.5$ s. Acceleration may be calculated as the following:

$$a = \frac{v_2 - v_1}{t}$$
$$= \frac{0 - 4 \text{ m/s}}{0.5 \text{ s}}$$
$$= -8 \text{ m/s}^2$$

Whenever v_1 is greater than v_2 in this type of situation, acceleration will be negative. Sample Problem 10.3 provides another example of a situation involving negative acceleration.

Understanding acceleration is more complicated when one direction is designated as positive and the opposite direction is designated as negative. In this situation, a positive value of acceleration can indicate either that the object is speeding up in a positive direction or that it is slowing down in a negative direction (Figure 10-4).

Consider the case of a ball being dropped from a hand. As the ball falls faster and faster because of the influence of gravity, it is gaining speed—for example, 0.3 m/s to 0.5 m/s to 0.8 m/s. Because the downward direction is considered as the negative direction, the ball's velocity is actu-

SAMPLE PROBLEM 10.3

A soccer ball is rolling down a field. At t = 0, the ball has an instantaneous velocity of 4 m/s. If the acceleration of the ball is constant at -0.3 m/s^2, how long will it take the ball to come to a complete stop?

Known

After reading the problem carefully, the next step is to sketch the problem situation, showing all quantities that are known or given in the problem statement.

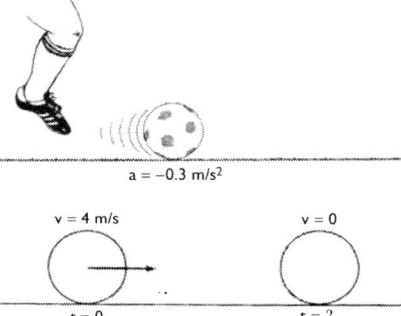

a = -0.3 m/s^2

v = 4 m/s   v = 0

t = 0   t = ?

Solution

The next step is to identify the appropriate formula to use to find the unknown quantity:

$$a = \frac{v_2 - v_1}{t}$$

The known quantities can now be filled in to solve for the unknown variable (time):

$$-0.3 \text{ m/s}^2 = \frac{0 - 4 \text{ m/s}}{t}$$

Rearranging the equation, we have the following:

$$t = \frac{0 - 4 \text{ m/s}}{-0.3 \text{ m/s}^2}$$

Simplifying the expression on the right side of the equation, we have the solution:

$$t = 13.3 \text{ s}$$

---

ally -0.3m/s to -0.5 m/s to -0.8 m/s. If $\dot{v}_1 = -0.3$ m/s, $v_2 = -0.5$ m/s, and t = 0.02 s, acceleration is calculated as follows:

$$a = \frac{v_2 - v_1}{t}$$

$$= \frac{-0.5 \text{ m/s} - (-0.3 \text{ m/s})}{0.02 \text{ s}}$$

$$= -10 \text{ m/s}^2$$

332   BASIC BIOMECHANICS

FIGURE 10-4

Right is regarded as the positive direction, and *left* as the negative direction. Acceleration may be positive, negative, or equal to zero, based on the direction of the motion and the direction of the change in velocity.

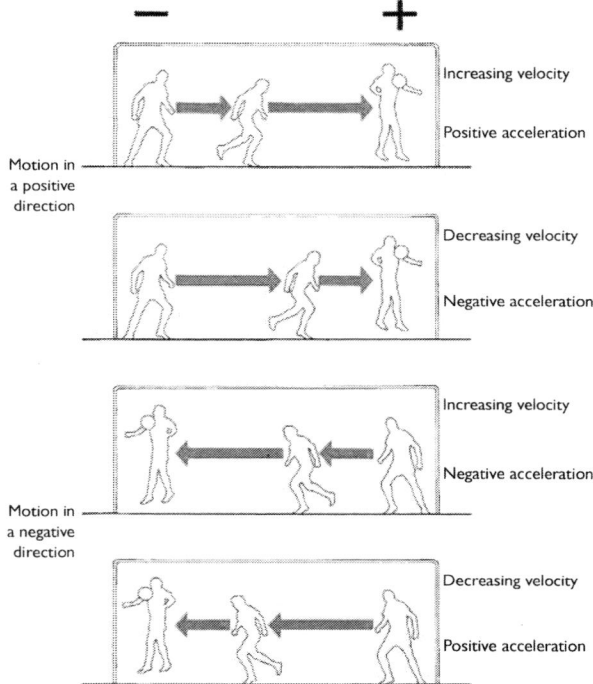

In this situation, the ball is speeding up, yet its acceleration is negative because it is speeding up in a negative direction. If acceleration is negative, velocity may be either increasing in a negative direction or decreasing in a positive direction. Alternatively, if acceleration is positive, velocity may be either increasing in a positive direction or decreasing in a negative direction.

The third alternative is for acceleration to be equal to zero. Acceleration is zero whenever velocity is constant, that is, when v_1 and v_2 are the same. In the middle of a 100 m sprint, a sprinter's acceleration should be close to zero, because at that point the runner should be running at a constant, near-maximum velocity.

● *When acceleration is zero, velocity is constant.*

Acceleration and deceleration (the lay term for negative acceleration) have implications for injury of the human body, since changing velocity results from the application of force (see Chapter 12). The anterior cruciate ligament, which restricts the forward sliding of the femur on the tibial plateaus during knee flexion, is often injured when an athlete who is running decelerates rapidly or changes directions quickly.

It is important to remember that since acceleration is a vector quantity, changing directions, even while maintaining a constant speed, represents a change in acceleration. The concept of angular acceleration, with direction constantly changing, is discussed in Chapter 11. The forces associated with change in acceleration based on change in direction must be compensated for by skiers and velodrome cyclists, in particular. That topic is discussed in Chapter 14.

Average and Instantaneous Quantities

It is often of interest to determine the velocity of acceleration of an object or body segment at a particular time. For example, the instantaneous velocity of a shot or a discus at the moment the athlete releases it greatly affects the distance that the implement will travel. It is sometimes sufficient to quantify the average speed or velocity of the entire performance.

When speed and velocity are calculated, the procedures depend on whether the average or the instantaneous value is the quantity of interest. Average velocity is calculated as the final displacement divided by the total time. Average acceleration is calculated as the difference in the final and initial velocities divided by the entire time interval. Calculation of instantaneous values can be approximated by dividing differences in velocities over an extremely small time interval. With calculus, velocity can be calculated as the derivative of displacement, and acceleration as the derivative of velocity.

Selection of the time interval over which speed or velocity is quantified is important when analyzing the performance of athletes in racing events. Many athletes can maintain world record paces for the first one-half or three-fourths of the event, but slow during the last leg because of fatigue. In a study involving female high school sprinters performing the 100 m dash, it was found that maximum running speeds of 8.0–8.4 m/s were reached 23–37 m from the start, and that an average of 7.3% of maximum speed was lost when the runners entered the final 10 m (4). Alternatively, some athletes may intentionally perform at a controlled pace during earlier segments of a race and then achieve maximum speed at the end. The longer the event is, the more information is potentially lost or concealed when only the final time or average speed is reported.

instantaneous
occurring during a small interval of time

average
occurring over a designated time interval

The instantaneous velocity of the shot at the moment of release primarily determines the ultimate horizontal displacement of the shot.

KINEMATICS OF PROJECTILE MOTION

Bodies projected into the air are projectiles. A basketball, a discus, a high jumper, and a sky diver are all projectiles as long as they are moving through the air unassisted. Depending on the projectile, different kinematic quantities are of interest. The resultant horizontal displacement of the projectile determines the winner of the contest in field events such as the shot put, discus throw, and javelin throw. High jumpers and pole-vaulters maximize ultimate vertical displacement to win events. Sky divers manipulate both horizontal and vertical components of velocity to land as close as possible to targets on the ground.

However, not all objects that fly through the air are projectiles. A projectile is a body in free fall that is subject only to the forces of gravity and air resistance. Therefore, objects such as airplanes and rockets do not qualify as projectiles, because they are also influenced by the forces generated by their engines.

projectile
body in free fall that is subject only to the forces of gravity and air resistance

Horizontal and Vertical Components

Just as it is more convenient to analyze general motion in terms of its linear and angular components, it is usually more meaningful to analyze the horizontal and vertical components of projectile motion separately. This is true for two reasons. First, the vertical component is influenced by gravity, whereas no force (neglecting air resistance) affects the horizontal component. Second, the horizontal component of motion relates to the distance the projectile travels, and the vertical component relates to the maximum height achieved by the projectile. Once a body has been projected into the

334 BASIC BIOMECHANICS

The vertical and horizontal components of projectile motion are independent. A ball hit horizontally has the same vertical component as a ball dropped with no horizontal velocity.

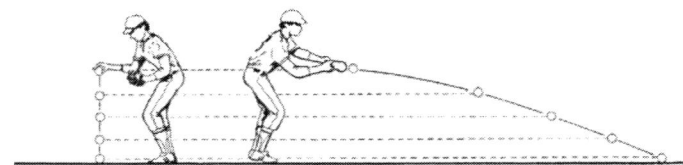

The human body becomes a projectile during the airborne phase of a jump.

● *The force of gravity produces a constant acceleration on bodies near the surface of the earth equal to approximately −9.81 m/s².*

apex
the highest point in the trajectory of a projectile

Projectile trajectories without (A) and with (B) gravitational influence.

air, its overall (resultant) velocity is constantly changing because of the forces acting on it. When examined separately, however, the horizontal and vertical components of projectile velocity change predictably.

Horizontal and vertical components of projectile motion are independent of each other. In the example shown in Figure 10-5, a baseball is dropped from a height of 1 m at the same instant that a second ball is horizontally struck by a bat at a height of 1 m, resulting in a line drive. Both balls land on the level field simultaneously, because the vertical components of their motions are identical. However, because the line drive also has a horizontal component of motion, it undergoes some horizontal displacement as well.

Influence of Gravity

A major factor that influences the vertical but not the horizontal component of projectile motion is the force of gravity, which accelerates bodies in a vertical direction toward the surface of the earth (Figure 10-6). Unlike aerodynamic factors that may vary with the velocity of the wind, gravitational force is a constant, unchanging force that produces a constant downward vertical acceleration. Using the convention that upward is positive and downward is negative, the acceleration of gravity is treated as a negative quantity (-9.81 m/s²). This acceleration remains constant regardless of the size, shape, or weight of the projectile. The vertical component of the initial projection velocity determines the maximum vertical displacement achieved by a body projected from a given relative projection height.

Figure 10-7 illustrates the influence of gravity on projectile flight in the case of a ball tossed into the air by a juggler. The ball leaves the juggler's hand with a certain vertical velocity. As the ball travels higher and higher, the magnitude of its velocity decreases because it is undergoing a negative acceleration (the acceleration of gravity in a downward direction). At the peak or apex of the flight, which is that instant between going up and coming down, vertical velocity is zero. As the ball falls downward, its speed progressively increases, again because of gravitational acceleration. Since the direction of motion is downward, the ball's velocity is

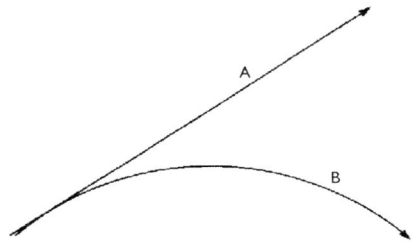

FIGURE 10-7

The pattern of change in the vertical velocity of a projectile is symmetrical about the apex of the trajectory.

becoming progressively more negative. If the ball is caught at the same height from which it was tossed, the ball's speed is exactly the same as its initial speed, although its direction is now reversed. Graphs of the vertical displacement, velocity, and acceleration of a tossed ball are shown in Figure 10-8.

Influence of Air Resistance

If an object were projected in a vacuum (with no air resistance), the horizontal component of its velocity would remain exactly the same throughout the flight. However, in most real-life situations, air resistance affects the horizontal component of projectile velocity. A ball thrown with a given initial velocity in an outdoor area will travel much farther if it is thrown with a tailwind rather than into a headwind. Because the effects of air

● *Neglecting air resistance, the horizontal speed of a projectile remains constant throughout the trajectory.*

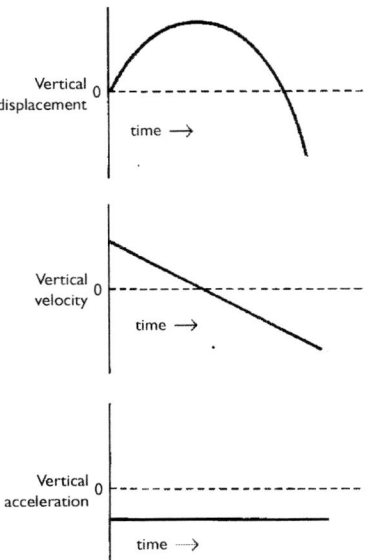

FIGURE 10-8

Vertical displacement, velocity, and acceleration graphs for a ball tossed into the air that falls to the ground.

FIGURE 10-9

Factors affecting the trajectory of a projectile include projection angle, projection speed, and relative height of projection.

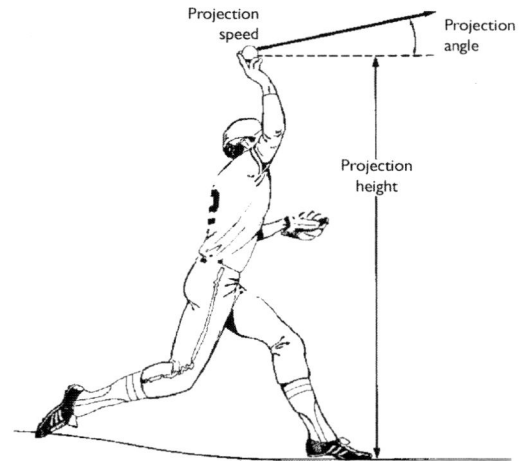

resistance are variable, however, for purposes of simplification, the horizontal component of a given projectile's velocity will be regarded as an unchanging (constant) quantity in this chapter.

When a projectile drops vertically through the air in a typical real-life situation, its velocity at any point is also related to air resistance. A sky diver's velocity, for example, is much smaller after the opening of the parachute than before its opening.

FACTORS INFLUENCING PROJECTILE TRAJECTORY

trajectory
the flight path of a projectile

● *The three mechanical factors that determine a projectile's motion are projection angle, projection speed, and relative height of projection.*

Three factors influence the trajectory (flight path) of a projectile: (a) the angle of projection, (b) the projection speed, and (c) the relative height of projection (Figure 10-9) (Table 10-1). Understanding how these factors interact is useful within the context of sport both for determining how to best project balls and other implements and for predicting how to best catch or strike projected balls.

TABLE 10-1

Factors Influencing Projectile Motion (Neglecting Air Resistance)

VARIABLE	FACTORS OF INFLUENCE
Flight time	Initial vertical velocity Relative projection height
Horizontal displacement	Horizontal velocity Relative projection height
Vertical displacement	Initial vertical velocity Relative projection height
Trajectory	Initial speed Projection angle Relative projection height

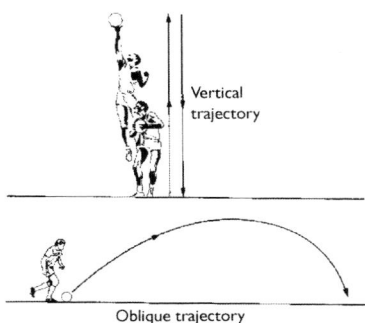

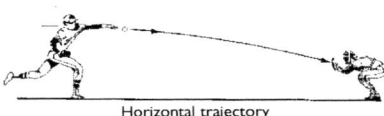

FIGURE 10-10

The effect of projection angle on projectile trajectory.

angle of projection
the direction at which a body is projected with respect to the horizontal

Projection angle is particularly important in the sport of basketball. A common error among novice players is shooting the ball with too flat a trajectory.

Projection Angle

The angle of projection and the effects of air resistance govern the shape of a projectile's trajectory. Changes in projection speed influence the size of the trajectory, but trajectory shape is solely dependent on projection angle. In the absence of air resistance, the trajectory of a projectile assumes one of three general shapes, depending on the angle of projection. If the projection angle is perfectly vertical, the trajectory is also perfectly vertical, with the projectile following the same path straight up and then straight down again. If the projection angle is oblique (at some angle between 0° and 90°), the trajectory is *parabolic,* or shaped like a parabola. A parabola is symmetrical, so its right and left halves are mirror images of each other. A body projected perfectly horizontally (at an angle of 0°) will follow a trajectory resembling one-half of a parabola (Figure 10-10). Figure 10-11 displays scaled, theoretical trajectories for an object projected at different angles at a given speed. A ball thrown upward at a projection angle of 80° to the horizontal follows a relatively high and narrow trajectory, achieving more height than horizontal distance. A ball projected upward at a 10° angle to the horizontal follows a trajectory that is flat and long in shape.

Projection angle has direct implications for success in the sport of basketball, since a steep angle of entry into the basket allows a somewhat

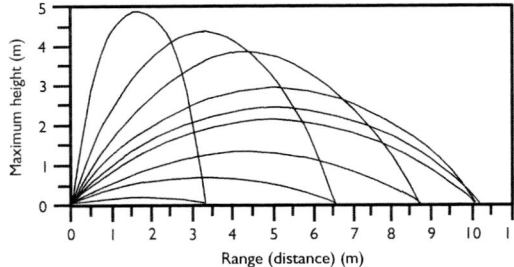

FIGURE 10-11

This scaled diagram shows the size and shape of trajectories for an object projected at 10 m/s.

FIGURE 10-12

In real-life situations, air resistance causes a projectile to deviate from its theoretical parabolic trajectory.

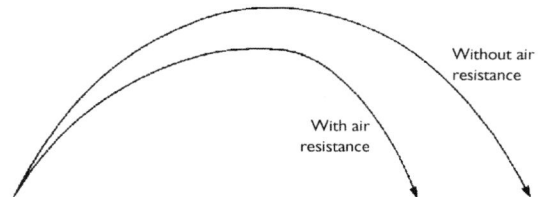

Without air resistance

With air resistance

larger margin of error than a shallow angle of entry. Within 4.57 m of the basket, jump shot release angles are about 52–55°, providing a relatively steep angle of entry, whereas shots taken from 6.40 m tend to be released at 48–50°, allowing for a minimum release speed, but a less steep angle of entry (25). When shooting in close proximity to a defender, players tend to release the ball at a greater release angle and from a greater height than is the case when a player is open (31). Although the strategy behind this is typically to keep the shot from being blocked, it may also result in more accurate shooting.

In projection situations on a field, air resistance may, in reality, create irregularities in the shape of a projectile's trajectory. A typical modification in trajectory caused by air resistance is displayed in Figure 10-12. For purposes of simplification, the effects of aerodynamic forces will be disregarded in the discussion of projectile motion.

Projection Speed

projection speed
the magnitude of projection velocity

●*A projectile's range is the product of its horizontal speed and flight time.*

range
the horizontal displacement of a projectile at landing

When projection angle and other factors are constant, the projection speed determines the length or size of a projectile's trajectory. For example, when a body is projected vertically upward, the projectile's initial speed determines the height of the trajectory's apex. For a body that is projected at an oblique angle, the speed of projection determines both the height and the horizontal length of the trajectory (Figure 10-13). The combined effects of projection speed and projection angle on the horizontal displacement, or range, of a projectile are shown in Table 10-2.

Performance in the execution of a vertical jump on a flat surface is entirely dependent on takeoff speed; that is, the greater the vertical velocity at takeoff, the higher the jump, and the higher the jump, the greater the amount of time the jumper is airborne (see margin). Elite beach volleyball players can jump higher and stay airborne longer when taking off from a

FIGURE 10-13

The effect of projection speed on projectile trajectory with projection angle held constant.

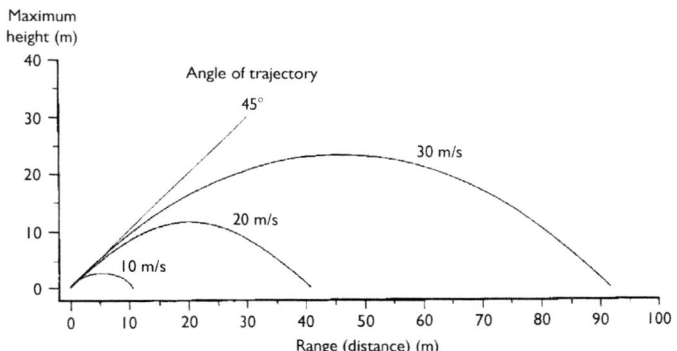

Maximum height (m)

Angle of trajectory

45°

30 m/s

20 m/s

10 m/s

Range (distance) (m)

PROJECTION SPEED (m/s)	PROJECTION ANGLE (°)	RANGE (m)
10	10	3.49
10	20	6.55
10	30	8.83
10	40	10.04
10	45	10.19
10	50	10.04
10	60	8.83
10	70	6.55
10	80	3.49
20	10	13.94
20	20	26.21
20	30	35.31
20	40	40.15
20	45	40.77
20	50	40.15
20	60	35.31
20	70	26.21
20	80	13.94
30	10	31.38
30	20	58.97
30	30	79.45
30	40	90.35
30	45	91.74
30	50	90.35
30	60	79.45
30	70	58.97
30	80	31.38

TABLE 10-2

The Effect of Projection Angle on Range (Relative Projection Height = 0)

solid surface than from sand because the instability of the sand produces a reduction in takeoff velocity (11).

The time required for the performance of a vertical jump can be an important issue for dance choreographers. The incorporation of vertical jumps into a performance must be planned carefully (21). If the tempo of the music necessitates that vertical jumps be executed within one-third of a second, the height of the jumps is restricted to approximately 12 cm. The choreographer must be aware that under these circumstances, most dancers do not have sufficient floor clearance to point their toes during jump execution.

340 BASIC BIOMECHANICS

relative projection height
the difference between projection height and landing height

●*A projectile's flight time is increased by increasing the vertical component of projection velocity or by increasing the relative projection height.*

VERTICAL JUMP HEIGHT (cm)	FLIGHT TIME (s)
5	0.2
11	0.3
20	0.4
31	0.5
44	0.6
60	0.7
78	0.8
99	0.9

Relative Projection Height

The third major factor influencing projectile trajectory is the relative projection height (Figure 10-14). This is the difference in the height from which the body is initially projected and the height at which it lands or stops. When a discus is released by a thrower from a height of 1½ m above the ground, the relative projection height is 1½ m, because the projection height is 1½ m greater than the height of the field on which the discus lands. If a driven golf ball becomes lodged in a tree, the relative projection height is negative, because the landing height is greater than the projection height. When projection velocity is constant, greater relative projection height translates to longer flight time and greater horizontal displacement of the projectile.

In the sport of diving, relative projection height is the height of the springboard or platform above the water. If a diver's center of gravity is elevated 1.5 m above the springboard at the apex of the trajectory, flight time is about 1.2 s from a 1 m board and 1.4 s from a 3 m board. This provides enough time for a skilled diver to complete 3 somersaults from a 1 m board and 3½-somersaults from a 3 m board (38). The implication is that a diver attempting to learn a 3½-somersault dive from the 3 m springboard should first be able to easily execute a 2½ somersault dive from the 1 m board.

Optimum Projection Conditions

In sporting events based on achieving maximum horizontal displacement or maximum vertical displacement of a projectile, the athlete's primary goal is to maximize the speed of projection (26). In the throwing events, another objective is to maximize release height, because greater relative

FIGURE 10-14

The relative projection height.

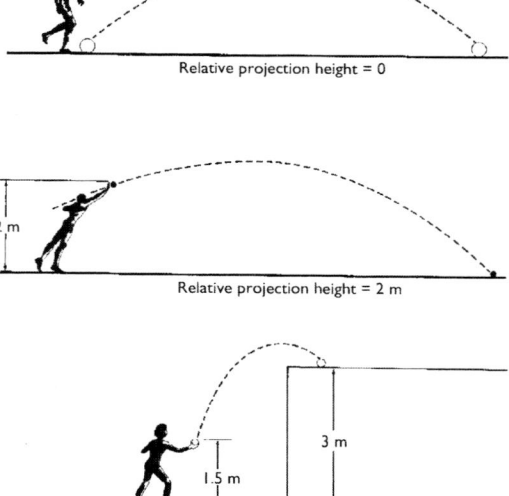

Relative projection height = 0

Relative projection height = 2 m

Relative projection height = −1.5 m

projection height produces longer flight time, and consequently greater horizontal displacement of the projectile. However, it is generally not prudent for a thrower to sacrifice release speed for added release height.

The factor that varies the most, with both the event and the performer, is the optimum angle of projection. When relative projection height is zero, the angle of projection that produces maximum horizontal displacement is 45°. As relative projection height increases, the optimum angle of projection decreases, and as relative projection height decreases, the optimum angle increases (Figure 10-15).

It is important to recognize that there are constraint relationships among projection speed, height, and angle, such that when one is shifted closer to what would theoretically be optimal, another moves farther away from optimum. This is because humans are not machines, and human anatomy dictates certain constraints. Research has shown, for example, that the constraint relationships among release speed, height, and angle for performance in the shot put are such that achievable release speed decreases with increasing release angle at 1.7 (m/s)/rad and decreases with increasing release height at 0.8 (m/s)/m (17).

Likewise, when the human body is the projectile during a jump, high takeoff speed serves to constrain the projection angle that can be achieved (33). In the performance of the long jump, for example, because takeoff and landing heights are the same, the theoretically optimum angle of takeoff is 45° with respect to the horizontal. However, it has been estimated by Hay (14) that to obtain this theoretically optimum takeoff angle, long jumpers would decrease the horizontal velocity they could otherwise obtain by approximately 50%. Research has shown that success in the long jump, high jump, and pole vault are all related to the athlete's ability to maximize horizontal velocity going into takeoff (5, 8, 35). The actual takeoff angles employed by elite long jumpers range from approximately 18° to 27° (14). Takeoff angles during all three phases of the triple jump are

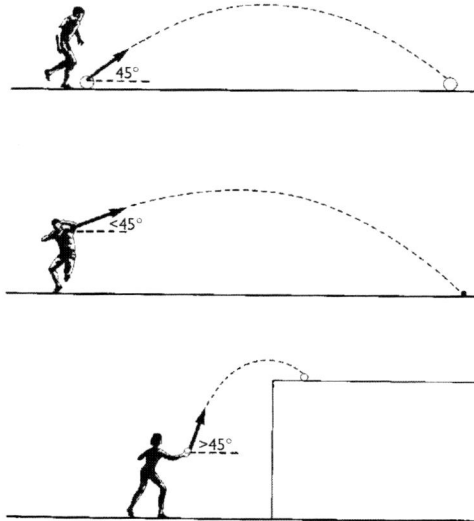

FIGURE 10-15

When projection speed is constant and aerodynamics are not considered, the optimum projection angle is based on the relative height of projection. When the relative projection height is zero, an angle of 45° is optimum. As the relative projection height increases, optimum projection angle decreases. As the relative projection height becomes increasingly negative, the optimum projection angle increases.

342 BASIC BIOMECHANICS

even smaller for elite performers than those used in the long jump (24). Performance in the triple jump is complicated by the fact that there is a direct trade-off between horizontal velocity and vertical velocity during the jumps (39). In the ski jump, where athletes have the advantage of a large relative height between takeoff and landing, takeoff angles are as small as 4.6–6.2° (36). In an event such as the high jump, in which the goal is to maximize vertical displacement, takeoff angles among skilled Fosbury Flop–style jumpers range from 40°–48° (7).

In the throwing events, the aerodynamic characteristics of the projected implements also influence the trajectory (see Chapter 15). In these events (shot, discus, javelin, and hammer), only the trajectory of the shot is not appreciably affected by aerodynamic forces. The concept that the optimum angle of release must not restrict release speed is still a paramount consideration for performance in the shot put. The release angles reported among elite shot-putters are approximately 36–37° (16). It has been shown, however, that optimum release angle for the shot put varies from athlete to athlete because of individual differences in the decrease of release speed with increasing release angle (22).

ANALYZING PROJECTILE MOTION

initial velocity
vector quantity incorporating both angle and speed of projection

Because velocity is a vector quantity, the initial velocity of a projectile incorporates both the initial speed (magnitude) and the angle of projection (direction) into a single quantity. When the initial velocity of a projectile is resolved into horizontal and vertical components, the horizontal component has a certain speed or magnitude in a horizontal direction, and the vertical component has a speed or magnitude in a vertical direction (Figure 10-16). The magnitudes of the horizontal and vertical components are always quantified so that if they were added together through the process of vector composition, the resultant velocity vector would be equal in magnitude and direction to the original initial velocity vector. The horizontal and vertical components of initial velocity may be quantified both graphically and trigonometrically (see Sample Problem 10.4).

• *The vertical speed of a projectile is constantly changing because of gravitational acceleration.*

• *The horizontal acceleration of a projectile is always zero.*

For purposes of analyzing the motion of projectiles, it will be assumed that the horizontal component of projectile velocity is constant throughout the trajectory and that the vertical component of projectile velocity is constantly changing because of the influence of gravity

FIGURE 10-16

The vertical and horizontal components of projection velocity.

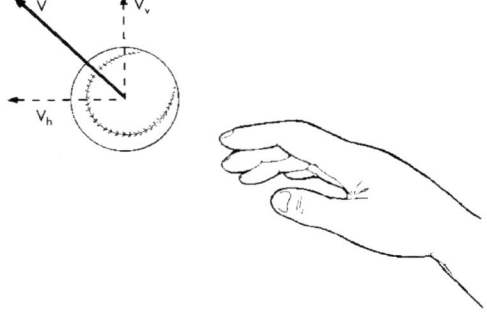

SAMPLE PROBLEM 10.4

A basketball is released with an initial speed of 8 m/s at an angle of 60°. Find the horizontal and vertical components of the ball's initial velocity, both graphically and trigonometrically.

Known

A diagram showing a vector representation of the initial velocity is drawn using a scale of 1 cm = 2 m/s:

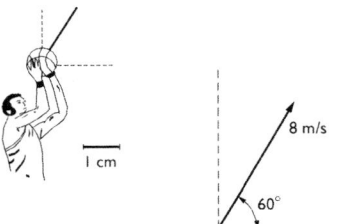

Solution

The horizontal component is drawn in along the horizontal line to a length that is equal to the length that the original velocity vector extends in the horizontal direction. The vertical component is then drawn in the same fashion in a direction perpendicular to the horizontal line:

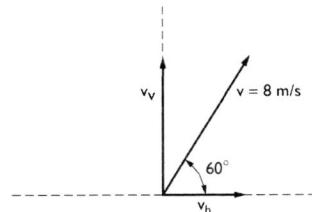

The lengths of the horizontal and vertical components are then measured:

length of horizontal component = 2 cm
length of vertical component = 3.5 cm

To calculate the magnitudes of the horizontal and vertical components, use the scale factor of 2 m/s/cm:

Magnitude of horizontal component:

$$v_h = 2 \text{ cm} \times 2 \text{ m/s/cm}$$

$$v_h = 4 \text{ m/s}$$

Magnitude of vertical component:

$$v_h = 3.5 \text{ cm} \times 2 \text{ m/s/cm}$$

$$v_h = 7 \text{ m/s}$$

To solve for v_h and v_v trigonometrically, construct a right triangle with the sides being the horizontal and vertical components of initial velocity and the initial velocity represented as the hypotenuse:

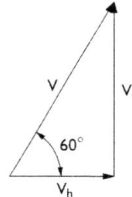

The sine and cosine relationships may be used to quantify the horizontal and vertical components:

$$v_h = (8 \text{ m/s}) (\cos 60)$$

$$v_h = 4 \text{ m/s}$$

$$v_v = (8 \text{ m/s})(\sin 60)$$

$$v_v = 6.9 \text{ m/s}$$

Note that the magnitude of the horizontal component is *always* equal to the magnitude of the initial velocity multiplied by the cosine of the projection angle. Similarly, the magnitude of the initial vertical component is *always* equal to the magnitude of the initial velocity multiplied by the sine of the projection angle.

(Figure 10-17). Since horizontal projectile velocity is constant, horizontal acceleration is equal to the constant of zero throughout the trajectory. The vertical acceleration of a projectile is equal to the constant 29.81 m/s^2.

Equations of Constant Acceleration

When a body is moving with a constant acceleration (positive, negative, or equal to zero), certain interrelationships are present among the kinematic quantities associated with the motion of the body. These interrelationships may be expressed using three mathematical equations originally derived by Galileo, which are known as the laws of constant acceleration, or the laws of uniformly accelerated motion. Using the variable symbols d, v, a, and t (representing displacement, velocity, acceleration, and time,

laws of constant acceleration
formulas relating displacement, velocity, acceleration, and time when acceleration is unchanging

FIGURE 10-17

The horizontal and vertical components of projectile velocity. Notice that the horizontal component is constant and the vertical component is constantly changing.

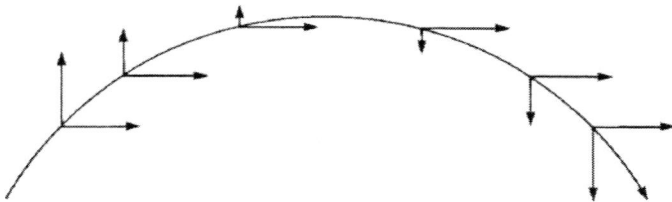

respectively) and with the subscripts $_1$ and $_2$ (representing first or initial and second or final points in time), the equations are the following:

$$v_2 = v_1 + at \qquad (1)$$

$$d = v_1 t + \tfrac{1}{2}at^2 \qquad (2)$$

$$v_2^2 = v_1^2 + 2ad \qquad (3)$$

Notice that each of the equations contains a unique combination of three of the four kinematic quantities: displacement, velocity, acceleration, and time. This provides considerable flexibility for solving problems in which two of the quantities are known and the objective is to solve for a third. The symbols used in these equations are listed in Table 10-3.

It is instructive to examine these relationships as applied to the horizontal component of projectile motion in which a = 0. In this case, each term containing acceleration may be removed from the equation. The equations then appear as the following:

$$v_2 = v_1 \qquad (1H)$$

$$d = v_1 t \qquad (2H)$$

$$v_2^2 = v_1^2 \qquad (3H)$$

Equations 1H and 3H reaffirm that the horizontal component of projectile velocity is a constant. Equation 2H indicates that horizontal displacement is equal to the product of horizontal velocity and time (see Sample Problem 10.5).

When the constant acceleration relationships are applied to the vertical component of projectile motion, acceleration is equal to -9.81 m/s^2, and the equations cannot be simplified by the deletion of the acceleration term. However, in analysis of the vertical component of projectile motion, the initial velocity (v_1) is equal to zero in certain cases. For example, when an object is dropped from a stationary position, the initial velocity of the object is zero. When this is the case, the equations of constant acceleration may be expressed as the following:

$$v_2 = at \qquad (1V)$$

$$d = \tfrac{1}{2}at^2 \qquad (2V)$$

$$v_2^2 = 2ad \qquad (3V)$$

When an object is dropped, equation 1V relates that the object's velocity at any instant is the product of gravitational acceleration and the amount of time the object has been in free fall. Equation 2V indicates that the vertical distance through which the object has fallen can be calculated from gravitational acceleration and the amount of time the object has been falling. Equation 3V expresses the relationship between the object's velocity and vertical displacement at a certain time and gravitational acceleration.

It is useful in analyzing projectile motion to remember that at the apex of a projectile's trajectory, the vertical component of velocity is zero. If the goal is to determine the maximum height achieved by a projectile, v_2 in equation 3 may be set equal to zero:

$$0 = v_1^2 + 2ad \qquad (3A)$$

An example of this use of equation 3A is shown in Sample Problem 10.6. If the problem is to determine the total flight time, one approach is to calculate the time it takes to reach the apex, which is one-half of the total

TABLE 10-3

Kinematic Variables

SYMBOL	MEANING	REPRESENTING IN EQUATIONS
d	Displacement	Change in position
v	Velocity	Rate of change in position
a	Acceleration	Rate of change in velocity
t	Time	Time interval
v_1	Initial or first velocity	Velocity at time 1
v_2	Later or final velocity	Velocity at time 2
v_v	Vertical velocity	Vertical component of total velocity
v_h	Horizontal velocity	Horizontal component of total velocity

SAMPLE PROBLEM 10.5

The score was tied 20–20 in the final 1987 AFC playoff game between the Denver Broncos and the Cleveland Browns. During the first overtime period, Denver had the opportunity to kick a field goal, with the ball placed at a distance of 29 m from the goalposts. If the ball was kicked with the horizontal component of initial velocity being 18 m/s and a flight time of 2 s, was the kick long enough to make the field goal?

Known

$$v_h = 18 \text{ m/s}$$
$$t = 2 \text{ s}$$

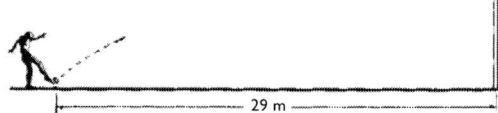

29 m

Solution

Equation 2H is selected to solve the problem, since two of the variables contained in the formula (v_h and t) are known quantities, and since the unknown variable (d) is the quantity we wish to find:

$$d_h = v_h t$$
$$d = (18 \text{ m/s}) \, (2 \text{ s})$$
$$d = 36 \text{ m}$$

The ball did travel a sufficient distance for the field goal to be good, and Denver won the game, advancing to Super Bowl XXI.

SAMPLE PROBLEM 10.6

A volleyball is deflected vertically by a player in a game housed in a high school gymnasium where the ceiling clearance is 10 m. If the initial velocity of the ball is 15 m/s, will the ball contact the ceiling?

Known

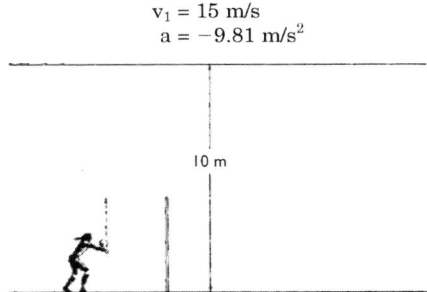

$$v_1 = 15 \text{ m/s}$$
$$a = -9.81 \text{ m/s}^2$$

10 m

Solution

The equation selected for use in solving this problem must contain the variable d for vertical displacement. Equation 2 contains d but also contains the variable t, which is an unknown quantity in this problem. Equation 3 contains the variable d, and, recalling that vertical velocity is zero at the apex of the trajectory, Equation 3A can be used to find d:

$$v_2^2 = v_1^2 + 2ad \tag{3}$$
$$0 = v_1^2 + 2ad \tag{3A}$$
$$0 = (15 \text{ m/s})^2 + (2)(-9.81 \text{ m/s}^2)d$$
$$(19.62 \text{ m/s}^2)d = 225 \text{ m}^2/\text{s}^2$$
$$d = 11.47 \text{ m}$$

Therefore, the ball has sufficient velocity to contact the 10 m ceiling.

---

flight time if the projection and landing heights are equal. In this case, v_2 in equation 1 for the vertical component of the motion may be set equal to zero because vertical velocity is zero at the apex:

$$0 = v_1 + at \tag{1A}$$

Sample Problem 10.7 illustrates this use of equation 1A.

When using the equations of constant acceleration, it is important to remember that they may be applied to the horizontal component of projectile motion or to the vertical component of projectile motion, but not to the resultant motion of the projectile. If the horizontal component of motion is being analyzed, a = 0, but if the vertical component is being analyzed, $a = -9.81 \text{ m/s}^2$. The equations of constant acceleration and their special variations are summarized in Table 10-4.

SAMPLE PROBLEM 10.7

A ball is kicked at a $35°$ angle, with an initial speed of 12 m/s. How high and how far does the ball go?

Solution

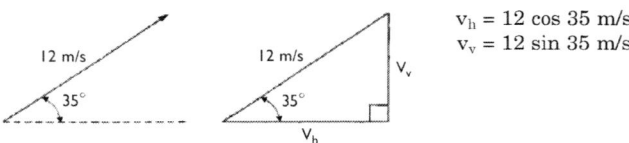

$v_h = 12 \cos 35$ m/s
$v_v = 12 \sin 35$ m/s

How high does the ball go?

Equation 1 cannot be used because it does not contain d. Equation 2 cannot be used unless t is known. Since vertical velocity is zero at the apex of the ball's trajectory, equation 3A is selected:

$$0 = v_1^2 + 2ad \qquad (3A)$$
$$0 = (12 \sin 35 \text{ m/s})^2 + (2)(-9.81 \text{ m/s}^2)d$$
$$(19.62 \text{ m/s}^2)d = 47.37 \text{ m}^2/\text{s}^2$$
$$d = 2.41 \text{ m}$$

How far does the ball go?

Equation 2H for horizontal motion cannot be used because t for which the ball was in the air is not known. Equation 1A can be used to solve for the time it took the ball to reach its apex:

$$0 = v_1 + at \qquad (1A)$$
$$0 = 12 \sin 35 \text{ m/s} + (-9.81 \text{ m/s}^2)t$$
$$t = \frac{6.88 \text{ m/s}}{9.81 \text{ m/s}^2}$$
$$t = 0.70 \text{ s}$$

Recalling that the time to reach the apex is one-half of the total flight time, total time is the following:

$$t = (0.70 \text{ s})(2)$$
$$t = 1.40 \text{ s}$$

Equation 2H can then be used to solve for the horizontal distance the ball traveled:

$$d_h = v_h t \qquad (2H)$$
$$d_h = (12 \cos 35 \text{ m/s})(1.40 \text{ s})$$
$$d_h = 13.76 \text{ m}$$

The Equations of Constant Acceleration
These equations may be used to relate linear kinematic quantities whenever acceleration (a) is a constant, unchanging value:

$$v_2 = v_1 + at \quad\quad\quad (1)$$
$$d = v_1 t + (\tfrac{1}{2})at^2 \quad\quad\quad (2)$$
$$v_2^2 = v_1^2 + 2ad \quad\quad\quad (3)$$

Special Case Applications of the Equations of Constant Acceleration
For the horizontal component of projectile motion, with a = 0:

$$d_h = v_h t \quad\quad\quad (2H)$$

For the vertical component of projectile motion, with $v_1 = 0$, as when the projectile is dropped from a static position:

$$v_2 = at \quad\quad\quad (1V)$$
$$d = (\tfrac{1}{2})at^2 \quad\quad\quad (2V)$$
$$v_2^2 = 2ad \quad\quad\quad (3V)$$

For the vertical component of projectile motion, with $v_2 = 0$, as when the projectile is at its apex:

$$0 = v_1 + at \quad\quad\quad (1A)$$
$$0 = v_1^2 + 2ad \quad\quad\quad (2A)$$

TABLE 10-4

Formulas Relating to Projectile Motion

SUMMARY

Linear kinematics is the study of the form or sequencing of linear motion with respect to time. Linear kinematic quantities include the scalar quantities of distance and speed, and the vector quantities of displacement, velocity, and acceleration. Depending on the motion being analyzed, either a vector quantity or its scalar equivalent and either an instantaneous or an average quantity may be of interest.

A projectile is a body in free fall that is affected only by gravity and air resistance. Projectile motion is analyzed in terms of its horizontal and vertical components. The two components are independent of each other, and only the vertical component is influenced by gravitational force. Factors that determine the height and distance the projectile achieves are projection angle, projection speed, and relative projection height. The equations of constant acceleration can be used to quantitatively analyze projectile motion, with vertical acceleration being 29.81 m/s^2 and horizontal acceleration being zero.

INTRODUCTORY PROBLEMS

Note: Some problems require vector algebra (see Chapter 3).

1. A runner completes 61/2 laps around a 400 m track during a 12 min (720 s) run test. Calculate the following quantities:
   a. The distance the runner covered
   b. The runner's displacement at the end of 12 min
   c. The runner's average speed
   d. The runner's average velocity
   e. The runner's average pace
   (Answers: a. 2.6 km; b. 160 m; c. 3.6 m/s; d. 0.22 m/s; e. 4.6 min/km)

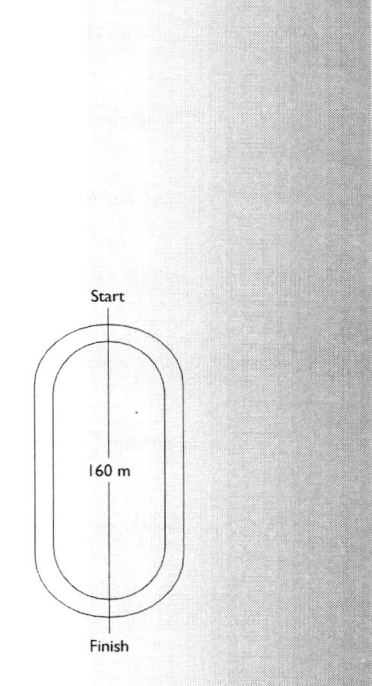

Start

160 m

Finish

2. A ball rolls with an acceleration of 20.5 m/s^2. If it stops after 7 s, what was its initial speed? (Answer: 3.5 m/s)

3. A wheelchair marathoner has a speed of 5 m/s after rolling down a small hill in 1.5 s. If the wheelchair underwent a constant acceleration of 3 m/s^2 during the descent, what was the marathoner's speed at the top of the hill? (Answer: 0.5 m/s)

4. An orienteer runs 400 m directly east and then 500 m to the northeast (at a 45° angle from due east and from due north). Provide a graphic solution to show final displacement with respect to the starting position.

5. An orienteer runs north at 5 m/s for 120 s, and then west at 4 m/s for 180 s. Provide a graphic solution to show the orienteer's resultant displacement.

6. Why are the horizontal and vertical components of projectile motion analyzed separately?

7. A soccer ball is kicked with an initial horizontal speed of 5 m/s and an initial vertical speed of 3 m/s. Assuming that projection and landing heights are the same and neglecting air resistance, identify the following quantities:
   a. The ball's horizontal speed 0.5 s into its flight
   b. The ball's horizontal speed midway through its flight
   c. The ball's horizontal speed immediately before contact with the ground
   d. The ball's vertical speed at the apex of the flight
   e. The ball's vertical speed midway through its flight
   f. The ball's vertical speed immediately before contact with the ground

8. If a baseball, a basketball, and a 71.2 N shot were dropped simultaneously from the top of the Empire State Building (and air resistance was not a factor), which would hit the ground first? Why?

9. A tennis ball leaves a racket during the execution of a perfectly horizontal ground stroke with a speed of 22 m/s. If the ball is in the air for 0.7 s, what horizontal distance does it travel? (Answer: 15.4m)

10. A trampolinist springs vertically upward with an initial speed of 9.2m/s. How high above the trampoline will the trampolinist go? (Answer: 4.31 m)

ADDITIONAL PROBLEMS

1. Answer the following questions pertaining to the split times (in seconds) presented below for Ben Johnson and Carl Lewis during the 100 m sprint in the 1988 Olympic Games.

	Johnson	Lewis
10 m	1.86	1.88
20 m	2.87	2.96
30 m	3.80	3.88
40 m	4.66	4.77
50 m	5.55	5.61
60 m	6.38	6.45
70 m	7.21	7.29
80 m	8.11	8.12
90 m	8.98	8.99
100 m	9.83	9.86

   a. Plot velocity and acceleration curves for both sprinters. In what ways are the curves similar and different?
   b. What general conclusions can you draw about performance in elite sprinters?

Hall: Basic Biomechanics, Fifth Edition | 10. Linear Kinematics of Human Movement | Text | © The McGraw–Hill Companies, 2007 | 121

2. Provide a trigonometric solution for Introductory Problem 4. (Answer: D = 832 m; ∠ = 25° north of due east)

3. Provide a trigonometric solution for Introductory Problem 5. (Answer: D = 937 m; ∠ = 50° west of due north)

4. A buoy marking the turn in the ocean swim leg of a triathlon becomes unanchored. If the current carries the buoy southward at 0.5 m/s, and the wind blows the buoy westward at 0.7 m/s, what is the resultant displacement of the buoy after 5 min? (Answer: 258m; ∠ = 54.5° west of due south)

5. A sailboat is being propelled westerly by the wind at a speed of 4 m/s. If the current is flowing at 2 m/s to the northeast, where will the boat be in 10 min with respect to its starting position? (Answer: D = 1.8 km; ∠ = 29° north of due west)

6. A Dallas Cowboy carrying the ball straight down the near sideline with a velocity of 8 m/s crosses the 50-yard line at the same time that the last Buffalo Bill who can possibly hope to catch him starts running from the 50-yard line at a point that is 13.7 m from the near sideline. What must the Bill's velocity be if he is to catch the Cowboy just short of the goal line? (Answer: 8.35 m/s)

7. A soccer ball is kicked from the playing field at a 45° angle. If the ball is in the air for 3 s, what is the maximum height achieved? (Answer: 11.0 m)

8. A ball is kicked a horizontal distance of 45.8 m. If it reaches a maximum height of 24.2 m with a flight time of 4.4 s, was the ball kicked at a projection angle less than, greater than, or equal to 458? Provide a rationale for your answer based on the appropriate calculations. (Answer: >45°)

9. A badminton shuttlecock is struck by a racket at a 35° angle, giving it an initial speed of 10 m/s. How high will it go? How far will it travel horizontally before being contacted by the opponent's racket at the same height from which it was projected? (Answer: d_v = 1.68 m; d_h = 9.58 m)

10. An archery arrow is shot with a speed of 45 m/s at an angle of 10°. How far horizontally can the arrow travel before hitting a target at the same height from which it was released? (Answer: 70.6 m)

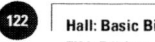

NAME _____

DATE _____

LABORATORY EXPERIENCES

1. At the *Basic Biomechanics* Online Learning Center (www.mhhe.com/hall5e), go to Student Center, Chapter 10, Lab Manual, Lab 1, and then click on the Instantaneous Speed simulation. After viewing this simulation several times, answer the following questions.

   a. What variables are represented on the horizontal and vertical axes of the graph?

      Horizontal axis: _____ vertical axis: _____

   b. What variable is represented by the slope of the graph? _____

   c. Explain what the car is doing when the slope of the graph is zero (the graph is

      horizontal). _____

      _____

2. At the *Basic Biomechanics* Online Learning Center (www.mhhe.com/hall5e), go to Student Center, Chapter 10, Lab Manual, Lab 2, and then click on the Vector Addition in Two Dimensions simulation. After experimenting with this simulation several times, answer the following questions.

   a. What are the numbers shown at the top of the graph for vector A? _____

      _____

      _____

   b. What are the numbers shown at the top of the graph for vector B? _____

      _____

      _____

   c. What are the numbers shown at the top of the graph for vector C? _____

      _____

      _____

   d. What is the name of the vector operation that is shown? _____

   e. Which vector is the resultant? _____

3. Calculate the horizontal and vertical components of velocity for a ball projected at 15 m/s at the following angles:

	V_h	V_v
30°	_____	_____
40°	_____	_____
50°	_____	_____
60°	_____	_____

   At the *Basic Biomechanics* Online Learning Center, click on the Vectors simulation and verify that your answers are correct.

354   BASIC BIOMECHANICS

4. At the *Basic Biomechanics* Online Learning Center (www.mhhe.com/hall5e), click on Student Center, Chapter 10, Lab Manual, Lab 4, and then click on the Projectile Motion (falling arrow) simulation. After viewing this simulation several times, write an explanation.

_____

_____

_____

_____

5. At the *Basic Biomechanics* Online Learning Center (www.mhhe.com/hall5e), click on Student Center, Chapter 10, Lab Manual, Lab 5, and then click on the Projectile Motion (baseball) simulation. Click on the player to activate a throw. Your target is first base, which is 80 m from the thrower. After experimenting with this simulation several times, answer the following questions.

   a. At what projection angle does a throw reach first base in the shortest time? _____

   b. At what projection angle can a ball be thrown and reach first base with the least projection speed?

   _____

   c. What are the answers to questions a and b if the player is on the moon?

      Angle for throw of shortest time: _____

      Angle for throw with least speed: _____

      Explain why these are different than on earth: _____

      _____

      _____

   d. What are the answers to questions a and b if the player is on Mars?

      Angle for throw of shortest time: _____

      Angle for throw with least speed: _____

      Explain why these are different than on earth: _____

      _____

      _____

REFERENCES

1. Cavanagh PR and Kram R: The efficiency of human movement—a statement of the problem, Med Sci Sports Exerc 17:304, 1985.

2. Cavanagh PR and Kram R: Stride length in distance running: Velocity, body dimensions, and added mass effects. In Cavanagh PR, ed: *Biomechanics of distance running,* Champaign, IL, 1990, Human Kinetics.

3. Cavanagh PR and Williams KR: The effect of stride length variation on oxygen uptake during distance running, Med Sci Sports Exerc 14:30, 1982.

4. Chow JW: Maximum speed of female high school runners, Int J Sport Biomech 3:110, 1987.

5. Chow JW and Hay JG: Computer simulation of the last support phase of the long jump, Med Sci Sports Exerc 37:115, 2005.

6. Clements DN, Owen MR, Carmichael S, and Reid SW: Kinematic analysis of the gait of 10 labrador retrievers during treadmill locomotion, Vet Rec 156:478, 2005.

7. Dapena J: Mechanics of translation in the Fosbury Flop, Med Sci Sports Exerc 12:37, 1980.

8. Dapena J and Chung CS: Vertical and radial motions of the body during the take-off phase of high jumping, Med Sci Sports Exerc 20:290, 1988.

9. Dillman CJ: Overview of the United States Olympic Committee sports medicine biomechanics program. In Butts NK, Gushiken TT, and Zarins BT, eds: *The elite athlete,* New York, 1985, Spectrum Publications.

10. Escamilla R, Fleisig G, Barrentine S, Andrews J, and Moorman C 3rd: Kinematic and kinetic comparisons between American and Korean professional baseball pitchers, Sports Biomech 1:213, 2002.

11. Giatsis G, Kollias I, Panoutsakopoulos V, and Papaiakovou G: Biomechanical differences in elite beach-volleyball players in vertical squat jump on rigid and sand surface, Sports Biomech 3:145, 2004.

12. Hardin EC, van den Bogert AJ, and Hamill J: Kinematic adaptations during running: effects of footwear, surface, and duration, Med Sci Sports Exerc 36:838, 2004.

13. Hausdorff JM, Zemany L, Peng C, and Goldberger AL: Maturation of gait dynamics: stride-to-stride variability and its temporal organization in children, J Appl Physiol 86:1040, 1999.

14. Hay JG: The biomechanics of the long jump, Exerc Sport Sci Rev 14:401, 1986.

15. Haywood KM and Getchell N: *Life span motor development* (3rd ed), Champaign, IL, 2001, Human Kinetics.

16. Hubbard M: The throwing events in track and field. In Vaughan CL, ed: *Biomechanics of sport,* Boca Raton, FL, 1989, CRC Press.

17. Hubbard M, de Mestre NJ, and Scott J: Dependence of release variables in the shot put, J Biomech 34:449, 2001.

18. Konczak J and Dichgans J: The development toward stereotypic arm kinematics during reaching in the first 3 years of life, Exp Brain Res 117:346, 1997.

19. Kyrolainen H et al: Effects of marathon running on running economy and kinematics, Eur J Appl Physiol 82:297, 2000.

20. Lange GW, Hintermeister RA, Schlegel T, Dillman CJ, and Steadman JR: Electromyographic and kinematic analysis of graded treadmill walking and the implications for knee rehabilitation, J Orthop Sports Phys Ther 23:294, 1996.

21. Laws K: *The physics of dance,* New York, 1984, Schirmer Books.

22. Linthorne NP: Optimum release angle in the shot put, J Sports Sci 19:359, 2001.

23. McCaw ST and Hoshizaki TB: A kinematic comparison of novice, intermediate, and elite ice skaters. In Jonsson B, ed: *Biomechanics X-B,* Champaign, IL, 1987, Human Kinetics.

24. Miller JA and Hay JG: Kinematics of a world record and other world-class performances in the triple jump, Int J Sport Biomech 2:272, 1986.

25. Miller S and Bartlett R: The relationship between basketball shooting kinematics, distance and playing position, J Sports Sci 14:243, 1996.

26. Morriss C and Bartlett R: Biomechanical factors critical for performance in the men's javelin throw, Sports Med 21:438, 1996.

27. Nilsson J, Tveit P, and Eikrehagen O: Effects of speed on temporal patterns in classical style and freestyle cross-country skiing, Sports Biomech 3:85, 2004.

28. Owings TM and Grabiner MD: Measuring step kinematic variability on an instrumented treadmill: how many steps are enough? J Biomech 36:1215, 2003.

29. Paradisis GP and Cooke CB: Kinematic and postural characteristics of spring running on sloping surfaces, J Sports Sci 19:149, 2001.

30. Ramos E, Latash MP, Hurvitz EA, and Brown SH: Quantification of upper extremity function using kinematic analysis, Arch Phys Med Rehabil 78:491, 1997.

31. Rojas FJ, Cepero M, Ona A, and Gutierrez M: Kinematic adjustments in basketball jump shot against an opponent, Ergonomics 43:1651, 2000.

32. Rundell KW and McCarthy JR: Effect of kinematic variables on performance in women during a cross-country ski race, Med Sci Sports Exerc 28:1413, 1996.

33. Seyfarth A, Blickhan R, and van Leeuwen JL: Optimum take-off techniques and muscle design for long jump, J Exp Biol 203:741, 2000.

34. Thompson KG, Haljand R, and MacLaren DP: AN analysis of selected kinematic variables in national and elite male and female 100-m and 200-m breaststroke swimmers.

35. Wakai M and Linthorne NP: Optimum take-off angle in the standing long jump, Hum Mov Sci 24:81, 2005.

36. Watanabe K: Ski-jumping, alpine, cross-country, and nordic combination skiing. In Vaughan CL, ed: Biomechanics of sport, Boca Raton, FL, 1989, CRC Press.

37. Wilson BD, McDonald M, and Neal RJ: Roller skating sprint technique. In Jonsson B, ed: Biomechanics X-B, Champaign, IL, 1987, Human Kinetics.

38. Yeadon MR: Theoretical models and their application to aerial movement. In Van Gheluwe B and Atha J, eds: Current research in sports biomechanics, Basel, 1987, Karger.

39. Yu B: Horizontal-to-vertical velocity conversion in the triple jump, J Sports Sci 17:221, 1999.

ANNOTATED READINGS

Hay JG: Citius, altius, longius (faster, higher, longer): the biomechanics of jumping for distance, J Biomech 26:7, 1993.
Discusses current research related to performance in the long jump and triple jump.

McCoy RL: *Modern exterior ballistics: the launch and flight dynamics of symmetric projectiles,* New York, 1999, Schiffer.
Provides a historical perspective on early technological developments in the nineteenth century, including the first ballistic firing tables.

Saunders PU, Pyne DB, Telford RD, and Hawley JA: Factors affecting running economy in trained distance runners, Sports Med 34:465, 2004.
Reviews current knowledge about kinematic and other factors that may contribute to economy during running.

Townend MS: Throwing. In Townend MS: *Mathematics in sport,* New York, 1984, John Wiley & Sons.
Provides an in-depth mathematical analysis of the mechanical principles of relevance in projecting the shot, hammer, discus, javelin, and basketball.

RELATED WEB SITES

Physics Classroom: Kinematics
www.physicsclassroom.com/Class/1DKin/1DKinTOC.html
   High-school-level tutorial on kinematics, including text and graphs.
Physics Classroom: Projectile Motion
www.physicsclassroom.com/Class/vectors/U3L2a.html
   High-school-level tutorial on projectile motion, including animations.
Physics of Projectile Motion
library.thinkquest.org/2779/
   Provides textual information and historical drawings of the first accurate description of projectile motion by Galileo, plus links to projectile animations, including a projectile water balloon game with sound effects.
Programming Example: Projectile Motion
www.cs.mtu.edu/~shene/COURSES/cs201/NOTES/chap02/projectile.html
   Provides a documented, downloadable computer program for calculating horizontal and vertical displacements, resultant velocity, and direction of a projectile.
Projectile Motion
galileo.phys.virginia.edu/classes/109N/more_stuff/Applets/ProjectileMotion/jarapplet.html
   Shows the trajectory of a projectile when the user enters the projection speed, angle, and height.

KEY TERMS

angle of projection	the direction at which a body is projected with respect to the horizontal
apex	the highest point in the trajectory of a projectile
average	occurring over a designated time interval
initial velocity	vector quantity incorporating both angle and speed of projection
instantaneous	occurring during a small interval of time
kinematics	the form, pattern, or sequencing of movement with respect to time
laws of constant acceleration	formulas relating displacement, velocity, acceleration, and time when acceleration is unchanging
linear acceleration	the rate of change in linear velocity
linear displacement	change in location, or the directed distance from initial to final location
linear velocity	the rate of change in location
meter	the most common international unit of length, on which the metric system is based
projectile	body in free fall that is subject only to the forces of gravity and air resistance
projection speed	the magnitude of projection velocity
range	the horizontal displacement of a projectile at landing
relative projection height	the difference between projection height and landing height
trajectory	the flight path of a projectile

11

Angular Kinematics of Human Movement

After completing this chapter, you will be able to:

Distinguish angular motion from rectilinear and curvilinear motion.

Discuss the relationships among angular kinematic variables.

Correctly associate angular kinematic quantities with their units of measure.

Explain the relationships between angular and linear displacement, angular and linear velocity, and angular and linear acceleration.

Solve quantitative problems involving angular kinematic quantities and the relationships between angular and linear kinematic quantities.

Visit the Online Learning Center at www.mhhe.com/hall5e to access the Online Lab Manual and many additional resources.

360   BASIC BIOMECHANICS

W hy is a driver longer than a 9-iron? Why do batters slide their hands up the handle of the bat to lay down a bunt but not to drive the ball? How does the angular motion of the discus or hammer during the windup relate to the linear motion of the implement after release?

These questions relate to angular motion, or rotational motion around an axis. The axis of rotation is a line, real or imaginary, oriented perpendicular to the plane in which the rotation occurs, like the axle for the wheels of a cart. In this chapter, we discuss angular motion, which, like linear motion, is a basic component of general motion. .

OBSERVING THE ANGULAR KINEMATICS OF HUMAN MOVEMENT

Understanding angular motion is particularly important for the student of human movement, because most volitional human movement involves rotation of one or more body segments around the joints at which they articulate. Translation of the body as a whole during gait occurs by virtue of rotational motions taking place at the hip, knee, and ankle around imaginary mediolateral axes of rotation. During the performance of jumping jacks, both the arms and the legs rotate around imaginary anteroposterior axes passing through the shoulder and hip joints. The angular motion of sport implements such as golf clubs, baseball bats, and hockey sticks, as well as household and garden tools, is also often of interest.

As discussed in Chapter 2, clinicians, coaches, and teachers of physical activities routinely analyze human movement based on visual observation. What is actually observed in such situations is the angular kinematics of human movement. Based on observation of the timing and range of motion (ROM) of joint actions, the experienced analyst can make inferences about the coordination of muscle activity producing the joint actions and the forces resulting from those joint actions.

Much of the reported description of the developmental stages of motor skills is based on analysis of angular kinematics. For example, three developmental stages for kicking among children age 2–6 have been identified (2). In stage 1, the child kicks using a small ROM of hip flexion, with no coordinated motion apparent at any other joint. In stage 2, knee extension is coordinated with hip flexion, and the arms are abducted at the shoulders to promote balance. Stage 3 is characterized by increased hip flexion and knee extension, and elbow flexion is present in addition to shoulder abduction to improve balance. The knowledgeable analyst can obtain a great deal of information about the relative developmental and skill levels of the performer through careful observation of angular kinematics.

MEASURING ANGLES

As reviewed in Appendix A, an angle is composed of two sides that intersect at a vertex. Quantitative kinematic analysis can be achieved by projecting·filmed images of the human body onto a piece of paper, with joint centers then marked with dots and the dots connected with lines representing the longitudinal axes of the body segments (Figure 11-1). A protractor can be used to make hand measurements of angles of interest from this representation, with the joint centers forming the vertices of the angles between adjacent body segments. (The procedure for measuring angles with a protractor is reviewed in Appendix A.) Videos and films of human movement can also be analyzed using this same basic procedure to evaluate the angles present at the joints of the human body and the

For the human body, joint centers form the vertices of body segment angles.

angular orientations of the body segments. The angle assessments are usually done with computer software from stick figure representations of the human body constructed in computer memory.

Relative versus Absolute Angles

Assessing the angle at a joint involves measuring the angle of one body segment relative to the other body segment articulating at the joint. The relative angle at the knee is the angle formed between the longitudinal axis of the thigh and the longitudinal axis of the lower leg (Figure 11-2). When joint ROM is quantified, it is the relative joint angle that is measured.

The convention used for measuring relative joint angles is that in anatomical reference position, all joint angles are at 0°. As discussed in Chapter 5, joint motion is then measured directionally. For example, when the extended arm is elevated 30° in front of the body in the sagittal plane, the arm is in 30° of flexion at the shoulder. When the leg is abducted at the hip, the ROM in abduction is likewise measured from 0° in anatomical reference position.

Other angles of interest are often the orientations of the body segments themselves. As discussed in Chapter 9, when the trunk is in flexion, the angle of inclination of the trunk directly affects the amount of force that must be generated by the trunk extensor muscles to support the trunk in the position assumed. The angle of inclination of a body segment, referred to as its absolute angle, is measured with respect to an absolute reference line, usually either horizontal or vertical. Figure 11-3 shows quantification of segment angles with respect to the right horizontal.

relative angle
angle at a joint formed between the longitudinal axes of adjacent body segments

● Relative angles should consistently be measured on the same side of a given joint.

● The straight, fully extended position at a joint is regarded as 0°.

absolute angle
angular orientation of a body segment with respect to a fixed line of reference

● Absolute angles should consistently be measured in the same direction from a single reference—either horizontal or vertical.

362   BASIC BIOMECHANICS

FIGURE 11-2

Angles measured at joints are
the angles between adjacent
body segments.

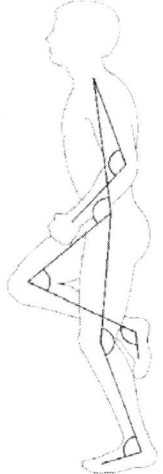

Tools for Measuring Body Angles

Goniometers are commonly used by clinicians for direct measurement of
relative joint angles on a live human subject. A goniometer is essentially
a protractor with two long arms attached. One arm is fixed so that it extends from the protractor at an angle of 0°. The other arm extends from
the center of the protractor and is free to rotate. The center of the protractor is aligned over the joint center, and the two arms are aligned over the
longitudinal axes of the two body segments that connect at the joint. The
angle at the joint is then read at the intersection of the freely rotating
arm and the protractor scale. The accuracy of the reading depends on the
accuracy of the positioning of the goniometer. Knowledge of the underly-

FIGURE 11-3

Angles of orientation of
individual body segments
are measured with respect
to an absolute (fixed) line of
reference.

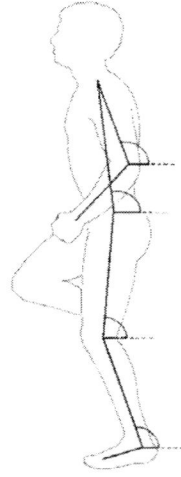

*The relative angle at the knee
(measured between adjacent
body segments) and the
absolute angle of the trunk
(measured with respect to the
right horizontal).*

ing joint anatomy is essential for proper location of the joint center of rotation. Placing marks on the skin to identify the location of the center of rotation at the joint and the longitudinal axes of the body segments before aligning the goniometer is sometimes helpful, particularly if repeated measurements are being taken at the same joint.

Other instruments available for quantifying angles relative to the human body are the electrogoniometer and various inclinometers. The electrogoniometer (referred to as an *elgon*) was developed by Peter Karpovich in

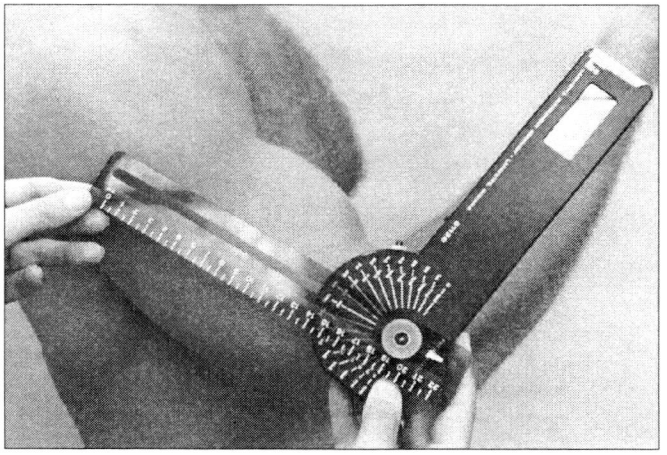

*A goniometer is used to
measure joint angles.*

FIGURE 11-4

The path of the instant center at the knee during knee extension.

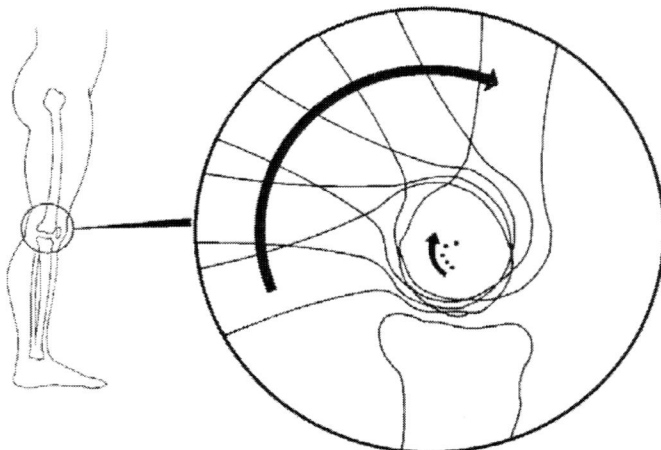

the late 1950s. An elgon is simply a goniometer with an electrical potentiometer at its vertex. When the arms of the elgon are attached with tape or velcro straps over a joint center, changes in the relative angle at the joint cause proportional changes in the electrical current emitted by the elgon. Inclinometers are other devices used for direct assessment of human body segment angles. These are usually gravitationally based instruments that identify the absolute angle of orientation of a body segment. Because accurate positioning of inclinometers is critical to the accuracy of the readings obtained, the measurement validity and reliability of these devices is controversial, particularly for measuring spinal orientation (11).

Instant Center of Rotation

Quantification of joint angles is complicated by the fact that joint motion is often accompanied by displacement of one bone with respect to the articulating bone at the joint. This phenomenon is caused by normal asymmetries in the shapes of the articulating bone surfaces. One example is the tibiofemoral joint, at which medial rotation and anterior displacement of the femur on the tibial plateau accompany flexion (Figure 11-4). As a result, the location of the exact center of rotation at the joint changes slightly when joint angle changes. The center of rotation at a given joint angle, or at a given instant in time during a dynamic movement, is called the instant center. The exact location of the instant center for a given joint may be determined through measurements taken from roentgenograms (X rays), which are usually taken at 10° intervals throughout the ROM at the joint (12). The instant center at the tibiofemoral joint of the knee shifts during angular movement at the knee due to the ellipsoid shapes of the femoral condyles (13).

instant center
precisely located center of rotation at a joint at a given instant in time

ANGULAR KINEMATIC RELATIONSHIPS

The interrelationships among angular kinematic quantities are similar to those discussed in Chapter 10 for linear kinematic quantities. Although

When the forearm returns to its original position at the completion of a curl exercise, the angular displacement at the elbow is zero.

the units of measure associated with the angular kinematic quantities are different from those used with their linear counterparts, the relationships among angular units also parallel those present among linear units.

Angular Distance and Displacement

Consider a pendulum swinging back and forth from a point of support. The pendulum is rotating around an axis passing through its point of support perpendicular to the plane of motion. If the pendulum swings through an arc of 60°, it has swung through an angular distance of 60°. If the pendulum then swings back through 60° to its original position, it has traveled an angular distance totaling 120° (60° + 60°). Angular distance is measured as the sum of all angular changes undergone by a rotating body.

The same procedure may be used for quantifying the angular distances through which the segments of the human body move. If the angle at the elbow joint changes from 90° to 160° during the flexion phase of a forearm curl exercise, the angular distance covered is 70°. If the extension phase of the curl returns the elbow to its original position of 90°, an additional 70° have been covered, resulting in a total angular distance of 140° for the complete curl. If 10 curls are performed, the angular distance transcribed at the elbow is 1400° (10 × 140°).

Just as with its linear counterpart, angular displacement is assessed as the difference in the initial and final positions of the moving body. If the angle at the knee of the support leg changes from 5° to 12° during the initial support phase of a running stride, the angular distance and the angular displacement at the knee are 7°. If extension occurs at the knee, returning the joint to its original 5° position, angular distance totals 14° (7° + 7°), but angular displacement is 0°, because the final position of the joint is the same as its original position. The relationship between angular distance and angular displacement is represented in Figure 11-5.

Like linear displacement, angular displacement is defined by both magnitude and direction. Since rotation observed from a side view occurs in either a clockwise or a counterclockwise direction, the direction of angular displacement may be indicated using these terms. The counterclockwise direction is conventionally designated as positive (+), and the

angular displacement
change in the angular position or orientation of a line segment

• *The counterclockwise direction is regarded as positive, and the clockwise direction is regarded as negative.*

366   BASIC BIOMECHANICS

FIGURE 11-5

A. The path of motion of a swinging pendulum. **B.** The angular distance is the sum of all angular changes that have occurred; the angular displacement is the angle between the initial and final positions.

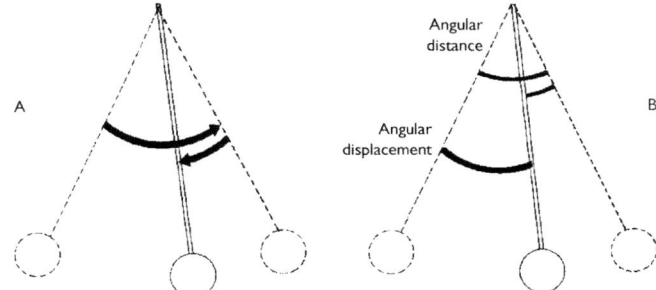

clockwise direction as negative $(-)$ (Figure 11-6). With the human body, it is also appropriate to indicate the direction of angular displacement with joint-related terminology such as flexion or abduction.

Three units of measure are commonly used to represent angular distance and angular displacement. The most familiar of these units is the degree. A complete circle of rotation transcribes an arc of 360°, an arc of 180° subtends a straight line, and 90° forms a right angle between perpendicular lines (Figure 11-7).

Another unit of angular measure sometimes used in biomechanical analyses is the radian. A line connecting the center of a circle to any point on the circumference of the circle is a radius. A radian is defined as the size of the angle subtended at the center of a circle by an arc equal in length to the radius of the circle (Figure 11-8). One complete circle is an arc of 2π radians, or 360°. Because 360° divided by 2π is 57.3°, one radian is equivalent to 57.3°. Because a radian is much larger than a degree, it is a more convenient unit for the representation of extremely large angular distances or displacements. Radians are often quantified in multiples of pi (π).

The third unit sometimes used to quantify angular distance or displacement is the revolution. One revolution transcribes an arc equal to a circle. Dives and some gymnastic skills are often described by the number of revolutions the human body undergoes during their execution. The

radian

unit of angular measure used in angular-linear kinematic quantity conversions; equal to 57.3°

●*Pi (π) is a mathematical constant equal to approximately 3.14, which is the ratio of the circumference to the diameter of a circle.*

FIGURE 11-6

The direction of rotational motion is commonly identified as counterclockwise (or positive) versus clockwise (or negative).

Clockwise   Counterclockwise

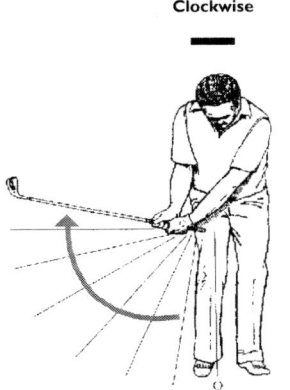

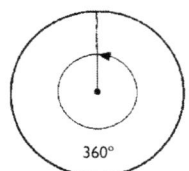

FIGURE 11-7

Angles measured in degrees.

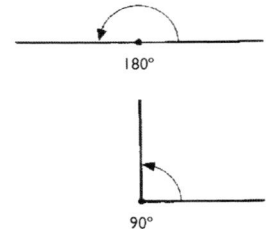

FIGURE 11-8

A radian is defined as the size of the angle subtended at the center of a circle by an arc equal in length to the radius of the circle.

one-and-a-half forward somersault dive is a descriptive example. Figure 11-9 illustrates the way in which degrees, radians, and revolutions compare as units of angular measure.

Angular Speed and Velocity

Angular speed is a scalar quantity and is defined as the angular distance covered divided by the time interval over which the motion occurred:

$$\text{angular speed} = \frac{\text{angular distance}}{\text{change in time}}$$

$$\sigma = \frac{\phi}{\Delta t}$$

The lowercase Greek letter sigma (σ) represents angular speed, the lowercase Greek letter phi (ϕ) represents angular distance, and t represents time.

368   BASIC BIOMECHANICS

Comparison of degrees, radians, and revolutions.

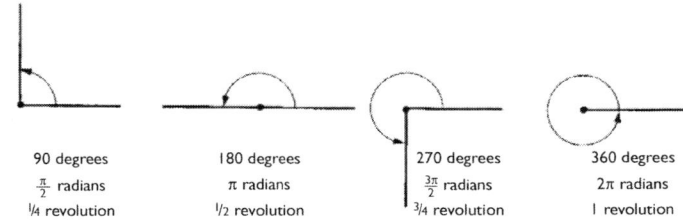

90 degrees
$\frac{\pi}{2}$ radians
¼ revolution

180 degrees
π radians
½ revolution

270 degrees
$\frac{3\pi}{2}$ radians
¾ revolution

360 degrees
2π radians
1 revolution

angular velocity
rate of change in the angular position or orientation of a line segment

Angular velocity is calculated as the change in angular position, or the angular displacement, that occurs during a given period of time:

$$\text{angular velocity} = \frac{\text{change in angular position}}{\text{change in time}}$$

$$\omega = \frac{\Delta \text{ angular position}}{\Delta \text{ time}}$$

$$\text{angular velocity} = \frac{\text{angular displacement}}{\text{change in time}}$$

$$\omega = \frac{\theta}{\Delta t}$$

The lowercase Greek letter omega (ω) represents angular velocity, the capital Greek letter theta (θ) represents angular displacement, and t represents the time elapsed during the velocity assessment. Another way to express change in angular position is angular position$_2$ − angular position$_1$, in which angular position$_1$ represents the body's position at one point in time and angular position$_2$ represents the body's position at a later point:

$$\omega = \frac{\text{angular position}_2 - \text{angular position}_1}{\text{time}_2 - \text{time}_1}$$

Because angular velocity is based on angular displacement, it must include an identification of the direction (clockwise or counterclockwise, negative or positive) in which the angular displacement on which it is based occurred.

Units of angular speed and angular displacement are units of angular distance or angular displacement divided by units of time. The unit of time most commonly used is the second. Units of angular speed and angular velocity are degrees per second (deg/s), radians per second (rad/s), revolutions per second (rev/s), and revolutions per minute (rpm).

Moving the body segments at a high rate of angular velocity is a characteristic of skilled performance in many sports. Angular velocities at the joints of the throwing arm in Major League Baseball pitchers have been reported to reach 2320 deg/s in elbow extension and 7240 deg/s in internal rotation (5). Interestingly, these values are also high in the throwing arms of youth pitchers, with 2230 deg/s in elbow extension and 6900 deg/s in internal rotation documented (5). Comparison of different types of pitches thrown by collegiate baseball pitchers showed internal rotation values of 7550 deg/s for fastballs, 6680 deg/s for change-ups, 7120 deg/s for curveballs, and 7920 deg/s for sliders (4). Figures 11-10 to 11-13 display the patterns of joint angle and joint angular velocity at the elbow and shoulder during underhand and overhand throws executed by collegiate

Joint angles of the elbow

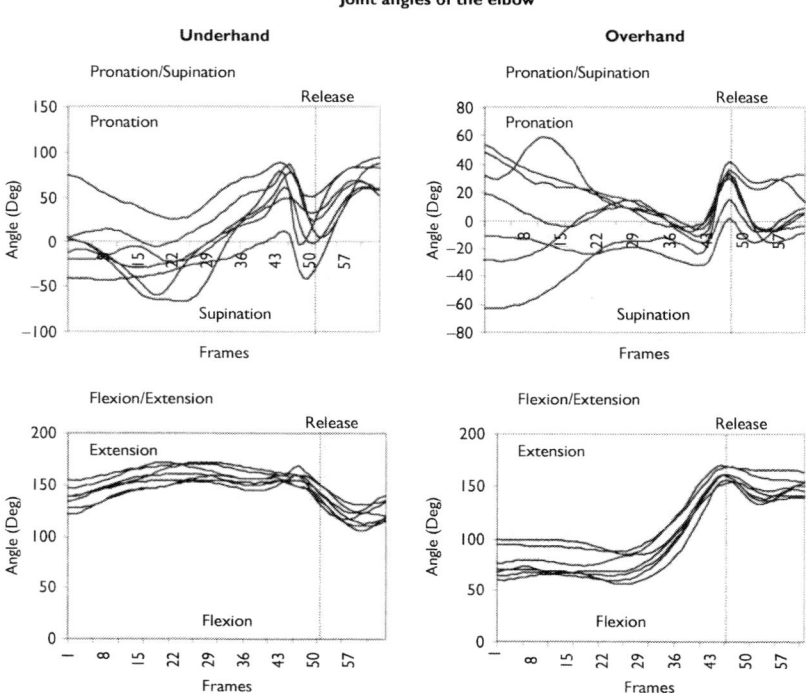

FIGURE 11-10   Elbow angles exhibited by seven collegiate softball players during fast-pitch strikes.
Graphs courtesy of Kim Hudson and James Richards.

softball players. A study of world-class male and female tennis players has documented a sequential rotation of segmental rotations. Analysis of the cocked, preparatory position showed the elbow flexed to an average of 104° and the upper arm rotated to about 172° of external rotation at the shoulder. Proceeding from this position, there was a rapid sequence of segmental rotations, with averages of trunk tilt of 280 deg/s, upper torso rotation of 870 deg/s, pelvis rotation of 440 deg/s, elbow extension of 1510 deg/s, wrist flexion of 1950 deg/s, and shoulder internal rotation of 2420 deg/s for males and 1370 deg/s, for females (6). Angular velocity of the racket during serves executed by professional male tennis players has been found to range from 1900 to 2200 deg/s (33.2 to 38.4 rad/s) just before ball impact (3).

As discussed in Chapter 10, when the human body becomes a projectile during the execution of a jump, the height of the jump determines the amount of time the body is in the air. When figure skaters perform a triple or quadruple axel, as compared to a axel or double axel, this means that either jump height or rotational velocity of the body must be greater. Measurements of these two variables indicate that it is the skater's angular velocity that increases, with skilled skaters rotating their bodies in

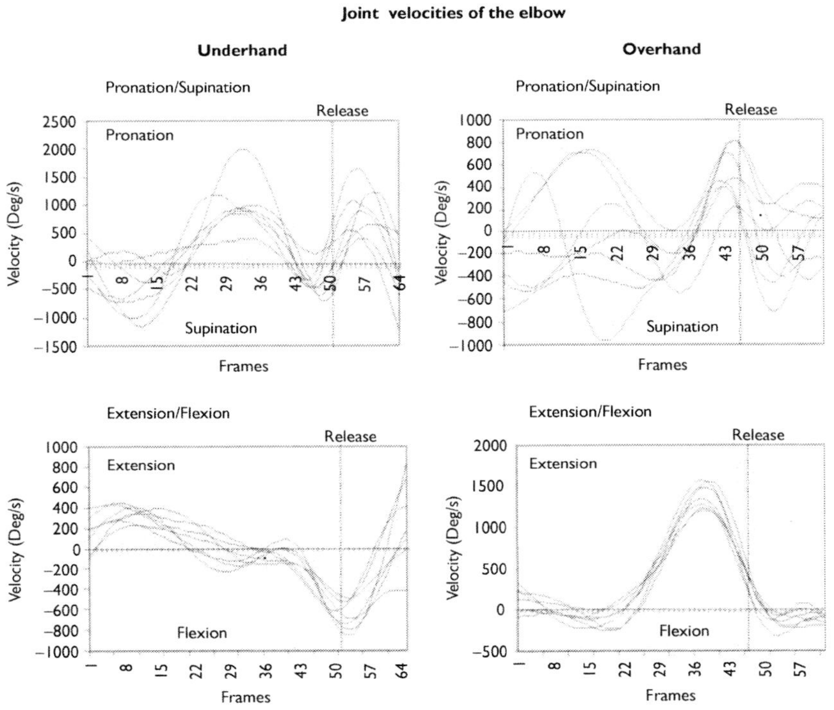

Joint velocities of the elbow

FIGURE 11-11   Elbow velocities exhibited by seven collegiate softball players during fast-pitch strikes. Graphs courtesy of Kim Hudson and James Richards.

excess of 5 rev/s while airborne during the triple axel (10). Higher rotational velocities of the body with increasing skill difficulty have also been documented in gymnastics, with representative values of 6.80 rad/s for the handspring, 7.77 rad/s for the handspring incorporating a somersault and one-half twist, and 10.2 rad/s for the backward somersault layout with two twists (1).

Angular Acceleration

angular acceleration
rate of change in angular velocity

Angular acceleration is the rate of change in angular velocity, or the change in angular velocity occurring over a given time. The conventional symbol for angular acceleration is the lowercase Greek letter alpha (α):

$$\text{angular acceleration} = \frac{\text{change in angular velocity}}{\text{change in time}}$$

$$\alpha = \frac{\Delta \omega}{\Delta t}$$

The calculation formula for angular acceleration is therefore the following:

$$\alpha = \frac{\omega_2 - \omega_1}{t_2 - t_1}$$

Joint angles of the shoulder

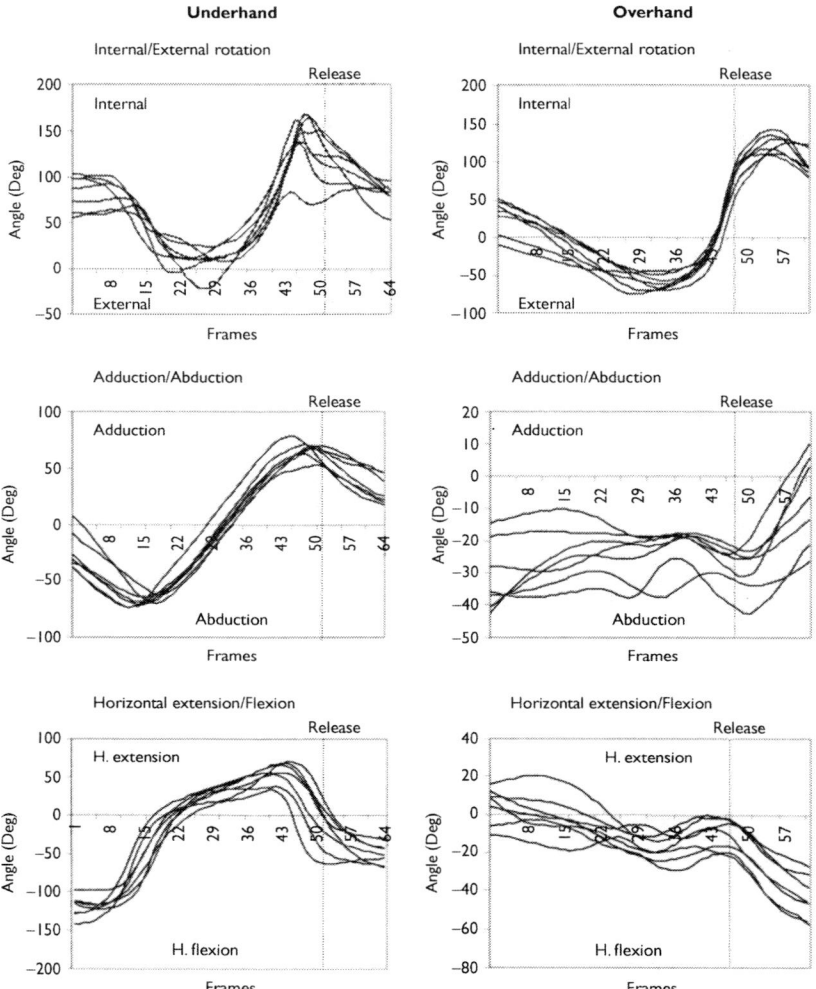

FIGURE 11-12 Shoulder angles exhibited by seven collegiate softball players during fast-pitch strikes. Graphs courtesy of Kim Hudson and James Richards.

In this formula, ω_1 represents angular velocity at an initial point in time, ω_2 represents angular velocity at a second or final point in time, and t_1 and t_2 are the times at which velocity was assessed. Use of this formula is illustrated in Sample Problem 11.1.

Just as with linear acceleration, angular acceleration may be positive, negative, or zero. When angular acceleration is zero, angular velocity is constant. Just as with linear acceleration, positive angular acceleration

•*Human movement rarely involves constant velocity or constant acceleration.*

372 BASIC BIOMECHANICS

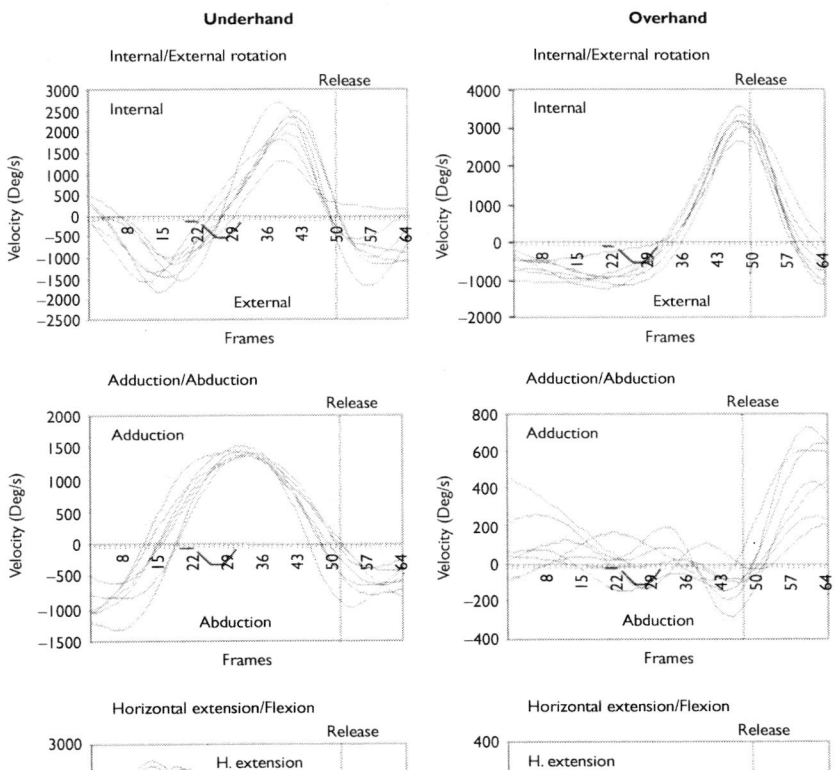

FIGURE 11-13 Shoulder velocities exhibited by seven collegiate softball players during fast-pitch strikes. Graphs courtesy of Kim Hudson and James Richards.

may indicate either increasing angular velocity in the positive direction or decreasing angular velocity in the negative direction. Similarly, a negative value of angular acceleration may represent either decreasing angular velocity in the positive direction or increasing angular velocity in the negative direction.

Units of angular acceleration are units of angular velocity divided by units of time. Common examples are degrees per second squared (deg/s^2), radians per second squared (rad/s^2), and revolutions per second squared

SAMPLE PROBLEM 11.1

A golf club is swung with an average angular acceleration of 1.5 rad/s². What is the angular velocity of the club when it strikes the ball at the end of a 0.8 s swing? (Provide an answer in both radian and degree-based units.)

Known

$$\alpha = 1.5 \text{ rad/s}^2$$
$$t = 0.8 \text{ s}$$

Solution

The formula to be used is the equation relating angular acceleration, angular velocity, and time:

$$\alpha = \frac{\omega_2 - \omega_1}{t}$$

Substituting in the known quantities yields the following:

$$1.5 \text{ rad/s}^2 = \frac{\omega_2 - \omega_1}{0.8 \text{ s}}$$

It may also be deduced that the angular velocity of the club at the beginning of the swing was zero:

$$1.5 \text{ rad/s}^2 = \frac{\omega_2 - 0}{0.8 \text{ s}}$$

$$(1.5 \text{ rad/s}^2)(0.8 \text{ s}) = \omega_2 - 0$$

$$\omega_2 = 1.2 \text{ rad/s}$$

In degree-based units:

$$\omega_2 = (1.2 \text{ rad/s})(57.3 \text{ deg/rad})$$

$$\omega_2 = 68.8 \text{ deg/s}$$

(rev/s²). Units of angular and linear kinematic quantities are compared in Table 11-1.

Angular Motion Vectors

Because representing angular quantities using symbols such as curved arrows would be impractical, angular quantities are represented with conventional straight vectors, using what is called the right hand rule. According to this rule, when the fingers of the right hand are curled in the direction of an angular motion, the vector used to represent the

right hand rule
procedure for identifying the direction of an angular motion vector

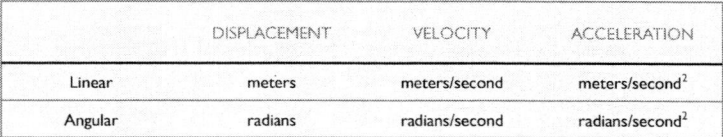

	DISPLACEMENT	VELOCITY	ACCELERATION
Linear	meters	meters/second	meters/second²
Angular	radians	radians/second	radians/second²

TABLE 11-1

Common Units of Kinematic Measure

374 BASIC BIOMECHANICS

FIGURE 11-14

An angular motion vector is oriented perpendicular to the linear displacement (d) of a point on a rotating body.

motion is oriented perpendicular to the plane of rotation, in the direction the extended thumb points in (Figure 11-14). The magnitude of the quantity may be indicated through proportionality to the vector's length.

Average versus Instantaneous Angular Quantities

Angular speed, velocity, and acceleration may be calculated as instantaneous or average values, depending on the length of the time interval selected. The instantaneous angular velocity of a baseball bat at the instant of contact with a ball is typically of greater interest than the average angular velocity of the swing, because the former directly affects the resultant velocity of the ball.

RELATIONSHIPS BETWEEN LINEAR AND ANGULAR MOTION

Linear and Angular Displacement

The greater the radius is between a given point on a rotating body and the axis of rotation, the greater is the linear distance undergone by

FIGURE 11-15

The larger the radius of rotation (r), the greater the linear distance (s) traveled by a point on a rotating body.

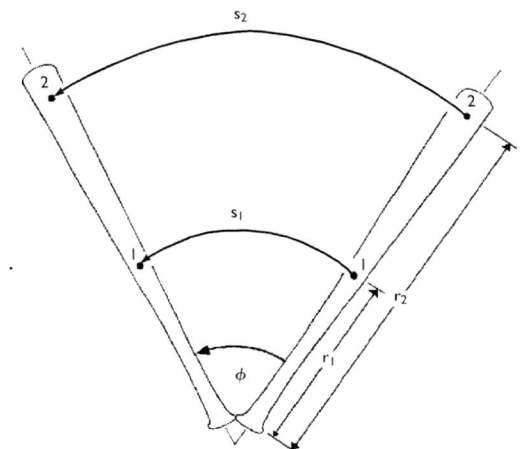

that point during an angular motion (Figure 11-15). This observation is expressed in the form of a simple equation:

$$s = r\phi$$

The curvilinear distance traveled by the point of interest s is the product of r, the point's radius of rotation, and ϕ, the angular distance through which the rotating body moves, which is quantified in radians.

For this relationship to be valid, two conditions must be met: (a) The linear distance and the radius of rotation must be quantified in the same units of length, and (b) angular distance must be expressed in radians. Although units of measure are normally balanced on opposite sides of an equal sign when a valid relationship is expressed, this is not the case here. When the radius of rotation (expressed in meters) is multiplied by angular displacement in radians, the result is linear displacement in meters. Radians disappear on the right side of the equation in this case because, as may be observed from the definition of the radian, the radian serves as a conversion factor between linear and angular measurements.

Linear and Angular Velocity

The same type of relationship exists between the angular velocity of a rotating body and the linear velocity of a point on that body at a given instant in time. The relationship is expressed as the following:

$$v = r\omega$$

The linear (tangential) velocity of the point of interest is v, r is the radius of rotation for that point, and ω is the angular velocity of the rotating body. For the equation to be valid, angular velocity must be expressed in radian-based units (typically rad/s), and velocity must be expressed in the units of the radius of rotation divided by the appropriate units of time. Radians are again used as a linear-angular conversion factor, and are not balanced on opposite sides of the equals sign:

$$m/s = (m) (rad/s)$$

The use of radian-based units for conversions between linear and angular velocities is shown in Sample Problem 11.2.

During several sport activities, an immediate performance goal is to direct an object such as a ball, shuttlecock, or hockey puck accurately, while imparting a relatively large amount of velocity to it with a bat, club, racket, or stick. In baseball batting, the initiation of the swing and the angular velocity of the swing must be timed precisely to make contact with the ball and direct it into fair territory. A 40 m/s pitch reaches the batter 0.41 s after leaving the pitcher's hand. It has been estimated that a difference of 0.001 s in the time of initiation of the swing can determine whether the ball is directed to center field or down the foul line, and that a swing initiated 0.003 s too early or too late will result in no contact with the ball (7). Similarly, there is a very small window of time during which gymnasts on the high bar can release from the bar to execute a skillful dismount. For high-bar finalists in the 2000 Olympic Games in Sydney, the release window was an average of 0.055 s (8).

With all other factors held constant, the greater the radius of rotation at which a swinging implement hits a ball, the greater the linear velocity imparted to the ball. In golf, longer clubs are selected for longer shots, and shorter clubs are selected for shorter shots. However, the magnitude of the angular velocity figures as heavily as the length of the radius of rotation in

radius of rotation
distance from the axis of rotation to a point of interest on a rotating body

Timing is important in the execution of a ground stroke in tennis. If the ball is contacted too soon or too late, it may be hit out of bounds.

● *Skilled performances of high-velocity movements are characterized by precisely coordinated timing of body segment rotations.*

SAMPLE PROBLEM 11.2

Two baseballs are consecutively hit by a bat. The first ball is hit 20 cm from the bat's axis of rotation, and the second ball is hit 40 cm from the bat's axis of rotation. If the angular velocity of the bat was 30 rad/s at the instant that both balls were contacted, what was the linear velocity of the bat at the two contact points?

Known

$$r_1 = 20 \text{ cm}$$
$$r_2 = 20 \text{ cm}$$
$$\omega_1 = \omega_2 = 30 \text{ rad/s}$$

Solution

The formula to be used is the equation relating linear and angular velocities:

$$v = r\omega$$

For ball 1:

$$v_1 = (0.20 \text{ m}) (30 \text{ rad/s})$$
$$v_1 = 6 \text{ m/s}$$

For ball 2:

$$v_2 = (0.40 \text{ m}) (30 \text{ rad/s})$$
$$v_2 = 12 \text{ m/s}$$

determining the linear velocity of a point on a swinging implement. Little Leaguers often select long bats, which increase the potential radius of rotation if a ball is contacted, but are also too heavy for the young players to swing as quickly as shorter, lighter bats. The relationship between the

The greater the angular velocity of a baseball bat, the farther a struck ball will travel, other conditions being equal.

Top view

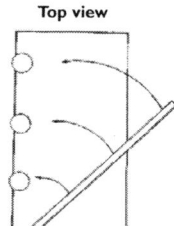

FIGURE 11-16

A simple experiment in which a rotating stick strikes three balls demonstrates the significance of the radius of rotation.

Side view

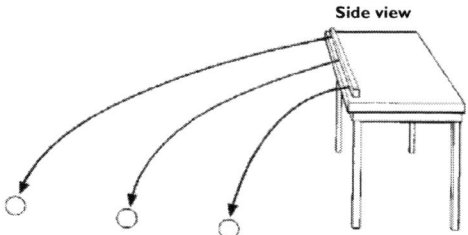

radius of rotation of the contact point between a striking implement and a ball and the subsequent velocity of the ball is shown in Figure 11-16.

It is important to recognize that the linear velocity of a ball struck by a bat, racket, or club is *not* identical to the linear velocity of the contact point on the swinging implement. Other factors, such as the directness of the hit and the elasticity of the impact, also influence ball velocity.

Linear and Angular Acceleration

The acceleration of a body in angular motion may be resolved into two perpendicular linear acceleration components. These components are directed along and perpendicular to the path of angular motion at any point in time (Figure 11-17).

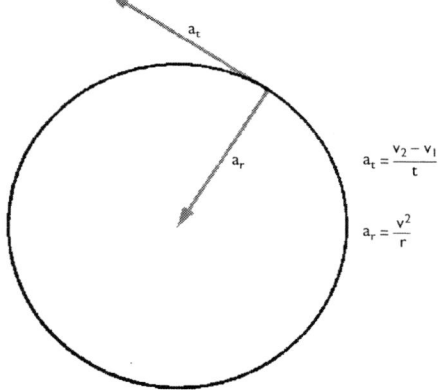

$$a_t = \frac{v_2 - v_1}{t}$$

$$a_r = \frac{v^2}{r}$$

FIGURE 11-17

Tangential and radial acceleration vectors shown relative to a circular path of motion.

378   BASIC BIOMECHANICS

tangential acceleration
component of acceleration of a body in angular motion directed along a tangent to the path of motion; represents change in linear speed

The component directed along the path of angular motion takes its name from the term *tangent*. A tangent is a line that touches, but does not cross, a curve at a single point. The tangential component, known as tangential acceleration, represents the change in linear speed for a body traveling on a curved path. The formula for tangential acceleration is the following:

$$a_t = \frac{v_2 - v_1}{t}$$

Tangential acceleration is a_t, v_1 is the tangential linear velocity of the moving body at an initial time, v_2 is the tangential linear velocity of the moving body at a second time, and t is the time interval over which the velocities are assessed.

When a ball is thrown, the ball follows a curved path as it is accelerated by the muscles of the shoulder, elbow, and wrist. The tangential component of ball acceleration represents the rate of change in the linear speed of the ball. Because the speed of projection greatly affects a projectile's range, tangential velocity should be maximum just before ball release if the objective is to throw the ball fast or far. Once ball release occurs, tangential acceleration is zero, because the thrower is no longer applying a force.

● *At the instant that a thrown ball is released, its tangential and radial accelerations become equal to zero, because a thrower is no longer applying force.*

The relationship between tangential acceleration and angular acceleration is expressed as follows:

$$a_t = r\alpha$$

Linear acceleration is a_t, r is the radius of rotation, and α is angular acceleration. The units of linear acceleration and the radius of rotation must be compatible, and angular acceleration must be expressed in radian-based units for the relationship to be accurate.

Although the linear speed of an object traveling along a curved path may not change, its direction of motion is constantly changing. The second component of angular acceleration represents the rate of change in direction of a body in angular motion. This component is called radial acceleration, and it is always directed toward the center of curvature. Radial acceleration may be quantified by using the following formula:

radial acceleration
component of acceleration of a body in angular motion directed toward the center of curvature; represents change in direction

$$a_r = \frac{v^2}{r}$$

Radial acceleration is a_r, v is the tangential linear velocity of the moving body, and r is the radius of rotation. An increase in linear velocity or a decrease in the radius of curvature increases radial acceleration. Thus, the smaller the radius of curvature (the tighter the curve) is, the more difficult it is for a cyclist to negotiate the curve at a high velocity (see Chapter 14).

During execution of a ball throw, the ball follows a curved path because the thrower's arm and hand restrain it. This restraining force causes radial acceleration toward the center of curvature throughout the motion. When the thrower releases the ball, radial acceleration no longer exists, and the implement follows the path of the tangent to the curve at that instant. The timing of release is therefore critical: If release occurs too soon or too late, the ball will be directed to the left or the right rather than straight ahead. Sample Problem 11.3 demonstrates the effects of the tangential and radial components of acceleration.

Both tangential and radial components of motion can contribute to the resultant linear velocity of a projectile at release. For example, during somersault dismounts from the high bar in gymnastics routines, although

SAMPLE PROBLEM 11.3

A windmill-style softball pitcher executes a pitch in 0.65 s. If her pitching arm is 0.7 m long, what are the magnitudes of the tangential and radial accelerations on the ball just before ball release, when tangential ball speed is 20 m/s? What is the magnitude of the total acceleration on the ball at this point?

Known

$$t = 0.65 \text{ s}$$
$$r = 0.7 \text{ m}$$
$$v_2 = 20 \text{ m/s}$$

Solution

To solve for tangential acceleration, use the following formula:

$$a_t = \frac{v_2 - v_1}{t}$$

Substitute in what is known and assume that $v_1 = 0$:

$$a_t = \frac{20 \text{ m/s} - 0}{0.65 \text{ s}}$$
$$a_t = 30.8 \text{ m/s}^2$$

To solve for radial acceleration, use the following formula:

$$a_r = \frac{v^2}{r}$$

Substitute in what is known:

$$a_r = \frac{(20 \text{ m/s})^2}{0.7 \text{m}}$$
$$a_r = 571.4 \text{ m/s}^2$$

To solve for total acceleration, perform vector composition of tangential and radial acceleration. Since tangential and radial acceleration are oriented perpendicular to each other, the Pythagorean theorem can be used to calculate the magnitude of total acceleration.

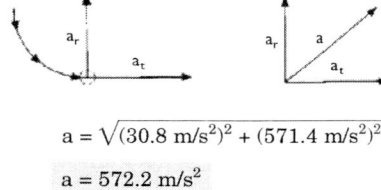

$$a = \sqrt{(30.8 \text{ m/s}^2)^2 + (571.4 \text{ m/s}^2)^2}$$

$$a = 572.2 \text{ m/s}^2$$

---

the primary contribution to linear velocity of the body's center of gravity is generally from tangential acceleration, the radial component can contribute up to 50% of the resultant velocity (9). The size of the contribution from the radial component, and whether the contribution is positive or negative, varies with the performer's technique.

SUMMARY

An understanding of angular motion is an important part of the study of biomechanics, because most volitional motion of the human body involves the rotation of bones around imaginary axes of rotation passing through the joint centers at which the bones articulate. The angular kinematic quantities—angular displacement, angular velocity, and angular acceleration—possess the same interrelationships as their linear counterparts, with angular displacement representing change in angular position, angular velocity defined as the rate of change in angular position, and angular acceleration indicating the rate of change in angular velocity during a given time. Depending on the selection of the time interval, either average or instantaneous values of angular velocity and angular acceleration may be quantified.

Angular kinematic variables may be quantified for the relative angle formed by the longitudinal axes of two body segments articulating at a joint, or for the absolute angular orientation of a single body segment with respect to a fixed reference line. Different instruments are available for direct measurement of angles on a human subject.

INTRODUCTORY PROBLEMS

1. The relative angle at the knee changes from 08 to 858 during the knee flexion phase of a squat exercise. If 10 complete squats are performed, what is the total angular distance and the total angular displacement undergone at the knee? (Provide answers in both degrees and radians.) (Answer: $\phi = 1700°$, 29.7 rad; $\theta = 0$)
2. Identify the angular displacement, the angular velocity, and the angular acceleration of the second hand on a clock over the time interval in which it moves from the number 12 to the number 6. Provide answers in both degree- and radian-based units. (Answer: $\theta = -180°$, $-\pi$ rad; $\omega = -6$ deg/s, $-\pi/30$ rad/s; $\alpha = 0$)
3. How many revolutions are completed by a top spinning with a constant angular velocity of 3π rad/s during a 20 s time interval? (Answer: 30 rev)
4. A kicker's extended leg is swung for 0.4 s in a counterclockwise direction while accelerating at 200 deg/s². What is the angular velocity of the leg at the instant of contact with the ball? (Answer: 80 deg/s, 1.4 rad/s)
5. The angular velocity of a runner's thigh changes from 3 rad/s to 2.7 rad/s during a 0.5 s time period. What has been the average angular acceleration of the thigh? (Answer: -0.6 rad/s², -34.4 deg/s²)
6. Identify three movements during which the instantaneous angular velocity at a particular time is the quantity of interest. Explain your choices.
7. Fill in the missing corresponding values of angular measure in the table below.

DEGREES	RADIANS	REVOLUTIONS
90	?	?
?	1	?
180	?	?
?	?	1

8. Measure and record the following angles for the drawing shown below:

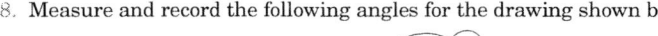

   a. The relative angle at the shoulder
   b. The relative angle at the elbow
   c. The absolute angle of the upper arm
   d. The absolute angle of the forearm
   Use the right horizontal as your reference for the absolute angles.

9. Calculate the following quantities for the diagram shown below:
   a. The angular velocity at the hip over each time interval
   b. The angular velocity at the knee over each time interval
   Would it provide meaningful information to calculate the average angular velocities at the hip and knee for the movement shown? Provide a rationale for your answer.

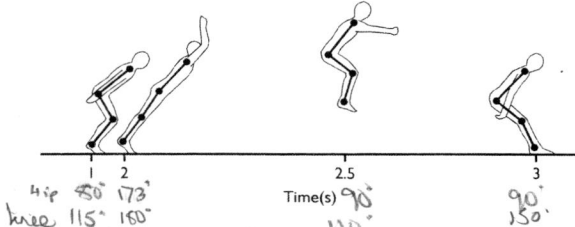

10. A tennis racket swung with an angular velocity of 12 rad/s strikes a motionless ball at a distance of 0.5 m from the axis of rotation. What is the linear velocity of the racket at the point of contact with the ball? (Answer: 6 m/s)

ADDITIONAL PROBLEMS

1. A 1.2 m golf club is swung in a planar motion by a right-handed golfer with an arm length of 0.76 m. If the initial velocity of the golf ball is 35 m/s, what was the angular velocity of the left shoulder at the point of ball contact? (Assume that the left arm and the club form a straight line, and that the initial velocity of the ball is the same as the linear velocity of the club head at impact.) (Answer: 17.86 rad/s)

2. David is fighting Goliath. If David's 0.75 m sling is accelerated for 1.5 s at 20 rad/s², what will be the initial velocity of the projected stone? (Answer: 22.5 m/s)

3. A baseball is struck by a bat 46 cm from the axis of rotation when the angular velocity of the bat is 70 rad/s. If the ball is hit at a height of 1.2 m at a 45° angle, will the ball clear a 1.2 m fence 110 m away? (Assume that the initial linear velocity of the ball is the same as the linear velocity of the bat at the point at which it is struck.) (Answer: No, the ball will fall through a height of 1.2 m at a distance of 105.7 m.)

4. A polo player's arm and stick form a 2.5 m rigid segment. If the arm and stick are swung with an angular speed of 1.0 rad/s as the player's horse gallops at 5 m/s, what is the resultant velocity of a motionless ball that is struck head-on? (Assume that ball velocity is the same as the linear velocity of the end of the stick.) (Answer: 7.5 m/s)

5. Explain how the velocity of the ball in Problem 4 would differ if the stick were swung at a 30° angle to the direction of motion of the horse.

6. List three movements for which a relative angle at a particular joint is important and three movements for which the absolute angle of a body segment is important. Explain your choices.

7. A majorette in the Rose Bowl Parade tosses a baton into the air with an initial angular velocity of 2.5 rev/s. If the baton undergoes a constant acceleration while airborne of -0.2 rev/s^2 and its angular velocity is 0.8 rev/s when the majorette catches it, how many revolutions does it make in the air? (Answer: 14 rev)

8. A cyclist enters a curve of 30 m radius at a speed of 12 m/s. As the brakes are applied, speed is decreased at a constant rate of 0.5 m/s^2. What are the magnitudes of the cyclist's radial and tangential accelerations when his speed is 10 m/s? (Answer: $a_r = 3.33$ m/s^2; $a_t = -0.5$ m/s^2)

9. A hammer is being accelerated at 15 rad/s^2. Given a radius of rotation of 1.7 m, what are the magnitudes of the radial and tangential components of acceleration when tangential hammer speed is 25 m/s? (Answer: $a_r = 367.6$ m/s^2; $a_t = 25.5$ m/s^2)

10. A speed skater increases her speed from 10 m/s to 12.5 m/s over a period of 3 s while coming out of a curve of 20 m radius. What are the magnitudes of her radial, tangential, and total accelerations as she leaves the curve? (Remember that a_r and a_t are the vector components of total acceleration.) (Answer: $a_r = 7.81$ m/s^2; $a_t = 0.83$ m/s^2; $a = 7.85$ m/s^2)

relative RoM

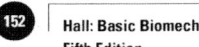
NAME _____

DATE _____

LABORATORY EXPERIENCES

1. Perform the experiment shown in Sample Problem 11.1 in this chapter. Record the linear distances traveled by the three balls, and write a brief explanation.

Distances: _____

Explanation: _____

_____

_____

2. With a partner, use a goniometer to measure range of motion for wrist flexion and hyperextension, for ankle plantar flexion and dorsiflexion, and for shoulder flexion and hyperextension. Provide an explanation for differences in these ranges of motion between your partner and yourself.

	Yourself	**Your Partner**
Wrist flexion	_____	_____
Wrist hyperextension	_____	_____
Plantar flexion	_____	_____
Dorsiflexion	_____	_____
Shoulder flexion	_____	_____
Shoulder hyperextension	_____	_____

Explanation: _____

_____

_____

3. Observe a young child executing a kick or a throw. Write a brief description of the angular kinematics of the major joint actions. What features distinguish the performance from that of a reasonably skilled adult?

Hip kinematics: _____

_____

_____

Knee kinematics: _____

_____

_____

Foot/ankle kinematics: _____

_____

_____

4. Working in a small group, observe from a side view two volunteers performing simultaneous maximal vertical jumps. Either video (and replay) the jumps or have the subjects repeat the jumps several times. Write a comparative description of the angular kinematics of the jumps, including both relative and absolute angles of importance. Does your description suggest a reason one jump is higher than the other?

Performer 1   **Performer 2**

_____   _____

_____   _____

_____   _____

_____   _____

_____   _____

_____   _____

_____   _____

_____   _____

_____   _____

_____   _____

_____   _____

_____   _____

_____   _____

_____   _____

_____   _____

_____   _____

5. Tape a piece of tracing paper over the monitor of a videocassette recorder. Using the single-frame advance button, draw at least three sequential stick figure representations of a person performing a movement of interest. (If the movement is slow, you may need to skip a consistent number of frames between tracings.) Use a protractor to measure the angle present at one major joint of interest on each figure. Given 1/30 s between adjacent video pictures, calculate the angular velocity at the joints between pictures 1 and 2 and between pictures 2 and 3. Record your answers in both degree- and radian-based units.

Joint selected: _____

Angle 1: _____ angle 2: _____ angle 3: _____

Number of frames skipped between tracings: _____

Calculation:

REFERENCES

1. Bruggemann G-P: Biomechanics in gymnastics. In Van Gheluwe B and Atha J: *Current research in sports biomechanics,* Basel, 1987, Karger.
2. Deach D: Genetic development of motor skills in children two through six years of age. Unpublished doctoral dissertation, University of Michigan, 1950.
3. Elliott BC: Tennis strokes and equipment. In Vaughan CL, ed: *Biomechanics of sport,* Boca Raton, FL, 1989, CRC Press.
4. Escamilla RF, Fleisig GS, Barrentine SW, Zheng N, and Andrews JR: Kinematic comparisons of throwing different types of baseball pitches, J Appl Biomech 14:1, 1998.
5. Fleisig GS, Barrentine SW, Zheng N, Escamilla RF, and Andrews JR: Kinematic and kinetic comparison of baseball pitching among various levels of development, J Biomech 32:1371, 1999.
6. Fleisig G, Nicholls R, Elliott B, and Escamilla R: Kinematics used by world class tennis players to produce high-velocity serves, Sports Biomech 2:51, 2003.
7. Gutman D: The physics of foul play, Discover, p 70, Apr 1988.
8. Hiley MJ and Yeadon MR: Maximal dismounts from high bar, J Biomech 38:2221, 2005.
9. Kerwin DG, Yeadon MR, and Harwood MJ: High bar release in triple somersault dismounts, J Appl Biomech 9:279, 1993.
10. King D, Arnold A, and Smith S: A biomechanical comparison of single, double, and triple axels. In Hamill J, Derrick TR, and Elliott EH, eds: *Biomechanics in sports XI,* Amherst, MA, 1993, International Society of Biomechanics in Sports.
11. Mayer TG, Kondraske G, Beals SB, and Gatchel RJ: Spinal range of motion: accuracy and sources of error with inclinometric measurement, Spine 22:1976, 1997.
12. Nordin M and Frankel VH: Biomechanics of the knee. In Nordin M and Frankel VH, eds: *Biomechanics of the musculoskeletal system* (3rd ed), Philadelphia, 2001, Lippincott Williams & Wilkins.
13. Smith PN, Refshauge KM, and Scarvell JM: Arch Phys Med Rehabil 84:1895, 2003.

ANNOTATED READINGS

Bruggemann G-P: Biomechanics in gymnastics. In Van Gheluwe B and Atha J: *Current research in sports biomechanics,* Basel, 1987, Karger.
Presents research on kinematic and other aspects of human body rotation in gymnastics.
Fleisig GS, Jameson EG, Dillman CJ, and Andrews JR: Biomechanics of overhead sports. In Garrett WE Jr. and Kirkendall DT: *Exercise and sport science,* Philadelphia, 2000, Lippincott Williams & Wilkins.
Includes a chapter on kinematic and other aspects of throwing and related movements.
Gregor RJ: Biomechanics of cycling. In Garrett WE Jr and Kirkendall DT: *Exercise and sport science,* Philadelphia, 2000, Lippincott Williams & Wilkins.
Includes a comprehensive review of kinematic and other aspects of cycling.
Zatsiorsky VM: *Kinematics of Human Motion,* Champaign, IL, 1998 Human Kinetics.
Contains chapters on joint kinematics and the kinematics of individual joints.

386   BASIC BIOMECHANICS

RELATED WEB SITES

Exploratorium: Science of Baseball
www.exploratorium.edu/baseball/index.html
   Explains scientific concepts related to baseball pitching and hitting.
Exploratorium: Science of Cycling
www.exploratorium.edu/cycling/index.html
   Explains scientific concepts related to bicycle wheels and gear ratios.
Exploratorium's Science of Hockey
www.exploratorium.edu/hockey/index.html
   Explains scientific concepts related to hockey, including how to translate rotational motion of the arms into linear motion of the puck.
Kinematics
guardian.curtin.edu.au/cga/teach-in/kinematics.html
   Defines terminology and uses a series of diagrams to discuss the angular kinematics of human gait.

KEY TERMS

absolute angle	angular orientation of a body segment with respect to a fixed line of reference
angular acceleration	rate of change in angular velocity
angular displacement	change in the angular position or orientation of a line segment
angular velocity	rate of change in the angular position or orientation of a line segment
instant center	precisely located center of rotation at a joint at a given instant in time
radial acceleration	component of acceleration of a body in angular motion directed toward the center of curvature; represents change in direction
radian	unit of angular measure used in angular-linear kinematic quantity conversions; equal to 57.3°
radius of rotation	distance from the axis of rotation to a point of interest on a rotating body
relative angle	angle at a joint formed between the longitudinal axes of adjacent body segments
right hand rule	procedure for identifying the direction of an angular motion vector
tangential acceleration	component of acceleration of a body in angular motion directed along a tangent to the path of motion; represents change in linear speed

12

Linear Kinetics of Human Movement

After completing this chapter, you will be able to:

Identify Newton's laws of motion and gravitation, and describe practical illustrations of the laws.

Explain what factors affect friction, and discuss the role of friction in daily activities and sports.

Define impulse and momentum, and explain the relationship between them.

Explain what factors govern the outcome of a collision between two bodies.

Discuss the relationships among mechanical work, power, and energy.

Solve quantitative problems related to kinetic concepts.

Visit the Online Learning Center at www.mhhe.com/hall5e to access the Online Lab Manual and many additional resources.

W hat can people do to improve traction when walking on icy streets? Why do some balls bounce higher on one surface than on another? How can football linemen push larger opponents backward? In this chapter, we introduce the topic of kinetics with a discussion of some important basic concepts and principles relating to linear kinetics.

NEWTON'S LAWS

Sir Isaac Newton (1642–1727) discovered many of the fundamental relationships that form the foundation for the field of modern mechanics. These principles highlight the interrelationships among the basic kinetic quantities introduced in Chapter 3.

Law of Inertia

Newton's first law of motion is known as the *law of inertia*. This law states the following:

> A body will maintain a state of rest or constant velocity unless acted on by an external force that changes the state.

In other words, a motionless object will remain motionless unless there is a net force (a force not counteracted by another force) acting on it. Similarly, a body traveling with a constant speed along a straight path will continue its motion unless acted on by a net force that alters either the speed or the direction of the motion.

It seems intuitively obvious that an object in a static (motionless) situation will remain motionless barring the action of some external force. We assume that a piece of furniture such as a chair will maintain a fixed position unless pushed or pulled by a person exerting a net force to cause its motion. When a body is traveling with a constant velocity, however, the enactment of the law of inertia is not so obvious, because, in most situations, external forces do act to reduce velocity. For example, the law of inertia implies that a skater gliding on ice will continue gliding with the same speed and in the same direction, barring the action of an external force. But in reality, friction and air resistance are two forces normally present that act to slow skaters and other moving bodies.

A skater has a tendency to continue gliding with constant speed and direction because of inertia.

Law of Acceleration

Newton's second law of motion is an expression of the interrelationships among force, mass, and acceleration. This law, known as the *law of acceleration,* may be stated as follows for a body with constant mass:

> A force applied to a body causes an acceleration of that body of a magnitude proportional to the force, in the direction of the force, and inversely proportional to the body's mass.

When a ball is thrown, kicked, or struck with an implement, it tends to travel in the direction of the line of action of the applied force. Similarly, the greater the amount of force applied, the greater the speed the ball has. The algebraic expression of the law is a well-known formula that expresses the quantitative relationships among an applied force, a body's mass, and the resulting acceleration of the body:

$$F = ma$$

Thus, if a 1 kg ball is struck with a force of 10 N, the resulting acceleration of the ball is 10 m/s^2. If the ball has a mass of 2 kg, the application of the same 10 N force results in an acceleration of only 5 m/s^2.

Newton's second law also applies to a moving body. When a defensive football player running down the field is blocked by an opposing player, the velocity of the defensive player following contact is a function of the player's original direction and speed and the direction and magnitude of the force exerted by the offensive player.

Law of Reaction

The third of Newton's laws of motion states that every applied force is accompanied by a reaction force:

> For every action, there is an equal and opposite reaction.

In terms of forces, the law may be stated as follows:

> When one body exerts a force on a second, the second body exerts a reaction force that is equal in magnitude and opposite in direction on the first body.

When a person leans with a hand against a rigid wall, the wall pushes back on the hand with a force that is equal and opposite to that exerted by the hand on the wall. The harder the hand pushes against the wall, the greater is the amount of pressure felt across the surface of the hand where it contacts the wall. Another illustration of Newton's third law of motion is found in Sample Problem 12.1.

During gait, every contact of a foot with the floor or ground generates an upward reaction force. Researchers and clinicians measure and study these ground reaction forces (GRFs) in analyzing differences in gait patterns across the life span and among individuals with handicapping conditions. Research in this area shows that young children achieve an adultlike gait pattern with a significant heel strike between 2 and 3 (36). For children age 5–12, it has been shown that the magnitudes of GRFs are related to gait speed and not to age (42).

In accordance with Newton's third law of motion, ground reaction forces are sustained with every footfall during running.

SAMPLE PROBLEM 12.1

A 90 kg ice hockey player collides head-on with an 80 kg player. If the first player exerts a force of 450 N on the second player, how much force is exerted by the second player on the first?

Known

$$m_1 = 90 \text{ kg}$$
$$m_2 = 80 \text{ kg}$$
$$F_1 = 450 \text{ N}$$

Solution

This problem does not require computation. According to Newton's third law of motion, for every action, there is an equal and opposite reaction. If the force exerted by the first player on the second has a magnitude of 450 N and a positive direction, then the force exerted by the second player on the first has a magnitude of 450 N and a negative direction.

$$-450 \text{ N}$$

FIGURE 12-1

Typical ground reaction force patterns for rearfoot strikers and others. Runners may be classified as rearfoot, midfoot, or forefoot strikers according to the portion of the shoe that usually contacts the ground first.

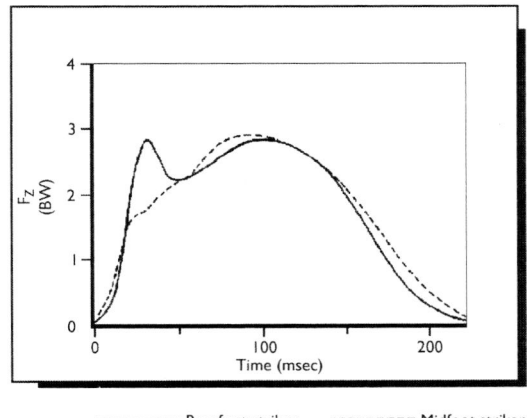

——————— Rearfoot striker   – – – – – – – Midfoot striker

Researchers have studied the GRFs that are sustained with every footfall during running to investigate factors related to both performance and running-related injuries. The magnitude of the vertical component of the GRF during running on a level surface is generally two to three times the runner's body weight, with the pattern of force sustained during ground contact varying with running style. Runners are classified as rearfoot, midfoot, or forefoot strikers, according to the portion of the shoe first making contact with the ground. Typical vertical GRF patterns for rearfoot strikers and others are shown in Figure 12-1. Runners who toe out generate greater mediolateral GRF than those who do not (41).

Other factors influencing GRF patterns include running speed, running duration, knee flexion angle at contact, stride length, fatigue, footwear, surface stiffness, surface smoothness, light intensity, and grade (13). During treadmill running at 3 m/s at a grade of −9°, impacts perpendicular to the surface increase on the order of 54% compared to level running, significantly increasing the potential for stress-related injury (16). The presence of fatigue, on the other hand, slightly reduces peak impact forces, secondary to reduced step length and increased knee flexion at contact (15).

Although it may seem logical that harder running surfaces would generate larger ground reaction forces, this has not been documented. When encountering surfaces of different stiffness, runners typically make individual adjustments in running kinematics that tend to maintain GRFs at a constant level (14). This may be explained to some extent by runners' sensitivity to the shock waves resulting from every heel strike that propagate upward, dynamically loading the musculoskeletal system. There is evidence that when the magnitude of the GRF increases, dynamic loading of the musculoskeletal system increases at five times the rate of the increase in the GRF (48). Research has shown that muscle activity is elicited to minimize soft-tissue vibrations arising from impact forces during running, another sign of runners' sensitivity to dynamic loading (33, 34).

As discussed in Chapter 10, runners generally increase stride length as running speed increases over the slow-to-moderate speed range. Longer strides tend to generate GRFs with larger retarding horizontal compo-

•*Since the ground reaction force is an external force acting on the human body, its magnitude and direction affect the body's velocity.*

FIGURE 12-2

Use of a longer stride length during running increases the retarding horizontal component (F_H) of the ground reaction force (R).

nents (Figure 12-2). This is one reason that overstriding can be counterproductive. Research has shown that a retarding horizontal force of 6% body weight increases the metabolic cost of running by 30% (7). With longer stride lengths and more extended knee angles at contact, muscles crossing the knee also absorb more of the shock that is transmitted upward through the musculoskeletal system, which may translate to additional stress being placed on the knees (12).

Since the GRF is an external force acting on the human body, its magnitude and direction have implications for performance in many sporting events. In the high jump, for example, skilled performers are moving with a large horizontal velocity and a slight downwardly directed vertical velocity at the beginning of the stride before takeoff. The GRF reduces the jumper's horizontal velocity and creates an upwardly directed vertical velocity (Figure 12-3). Better jumpers not only enter the takeoff phase of the jump with high horizontal velocities but also effectively use the GRF to convert horizontal velocity to upward vertical velocity (9). Skilled performance in baseball pitching is characterized by ground reaction shear forces of 35% of body weight in the direction of the pitch with the push-off leg, which emphasizes the importance of the lower-extremity contribution to the throwing motion (29). Maximizing the distance of drives in golf requires generation of large GRFs, with a greater proportion of the GRF on the back foot during the backswing and transfer of this proportion to the front foot during the downswing (23).

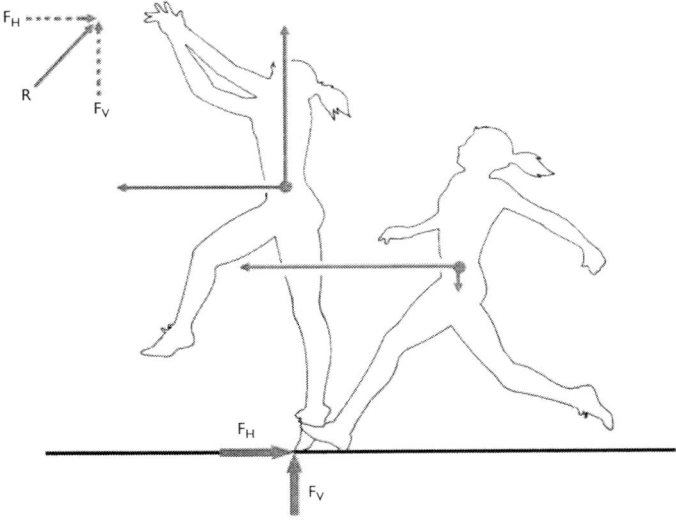

FIGURE 12-3

During the high jump takeoff, the horizontal component (F_H) of the ground reaction force (R) decreases the performer's horizontal velocity, and the vertical component (F_V) can contribute to upward vertical velocity.

Law of Gravitation

Newton's discovery of the law of universal gravitation was one of the most significant contributions to the scientific revolution and is considered by many to mark the beginning of modern science (8). According to legend, Newton's thoughts on gravitation were provoked either by his observation of a falling apple or by his actually being struck on the head by a falling apple. In his writings on the subject, Newton used the example of the falling apple to illustrate the principle that every body attracts every other body (6). Newton's law of gravitation states the following:

> All bodies are attracted to one another with a force proportional to the product of their masses and inversely proportional to the square of the distance between them.

Stated algebraically, the law is the following:

$$F_g = G\frac{m_1 m_2}{d^2}$$

The force of gravitational attraction is F_g, G is a numerical constant, m_1 and m_2 are the masses of the bodies, and d is the distance between the mass centers of the bodies.

For the example of the falling apple, Newton's law of gravitation indicates that just as the earth attracts the apple, the apple attracts the earth, although to a much smaller extent. As the formula for gravitational force shows, the greater the mass of either body, the greater the attractive force between the two. Similarly, the greater the distance between the bodies, the smaller the attractive force between them.

For biomechanical applications, the only gravitational attraction of consequence is that generated by the earth because of its extremely large mass. The rate of gravitational acceleration at which bodies are attracted toward the surface of the earth (9.81 m/s^2) is based on the earth's mass and the distance to the center of the earth.

MECHANICAL BEHAVIOR OF BODIES IN CONTACT

According to Newton's third law of motion, for every action there is an equal and opposite reaction. However, consider the case of a horse hitched to a cart. According to Newton's third law, when the horse exerts a force on the cart to cause forward motion, the cart exerts a backward force of equal magnitude on the horse (Figure 12-4). Considering the horse and the cart as a single mechanical system, if the two forces are equal in magnitude and opposite in direction, their vector sum is zero. How does the horse-and-cart system achieve forward motion? The answer relates to the presence of another force that acts with a different magnitude on the cart than on the horse: the force of friction.

Friction

Friction is a force that acts at the interface of surfaces in contact in the direction opposite the direction of motion or impending motion. Because friction is a force, it is quantified in units of force (N). The magnitude of the generated friction force determines the relative ease or difficulty of motion for two objects in contact.

Consider the example of a box sitting on a level tabletop (Figure 12-5). The two forces acting on the undisturbed box are its own weight and a reaction force (R) applied by the table. In this situation, the reaction force is equal in magnitude and opposite in direction to the box's weight.

When an extremely small horizontal force is applied to this box, it remains motionless. The box can maintain its static position because the applied force causes the generation of a friction force at the box/table interface that is equal in magnitude and opposite in direction to the small applied force. As the magnitude of the applied force becomes greater and greater, the magnitude of the opposing friction force also increases to a certain critical point. At that point, the friction force present is termed maximum static friction (F_m). If the magnitude of the applied force is increased beyond this value, motion will occur (the box will slide).

Once the box is in motion, an opposing friction force continues to act. The friction force present during motion is referred to as kinetic friction (F_k). Unlike static friction, the magnitude of kinetic friction remains at a constant value that is *less than* the magnitude of maximum static friction. Regardless of the amount of the applied force or the speed of the occurring motion, the kinetic friction force remains the same. Figure 12-6 illustrates the relationship between friction and an applied external force.

What factors determine the amount of applied force needed to move an object? More force is required to move a refrigerator than to move

friction
force acting over the area of contact between two surfaces in the direction opposite that of motion or motion tendency

maximum static friction
maximum amount of friction that can be generated between two static surfaces

kinetic friction
constant-magnitude friction generated between two surfaces in contact during motion

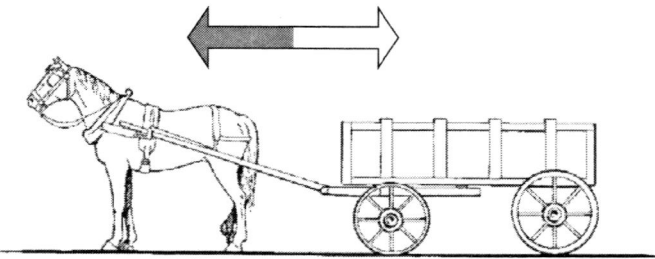

When a horse attempts to pull a cart forward, the cart exerts an equal and opposite force on the horse, in accordance with Newton's third law.

394   BASIC BIOMECHANICS

FIGURE 12-5

The magnitude of the friction force changes with increasing amounts of applied force.

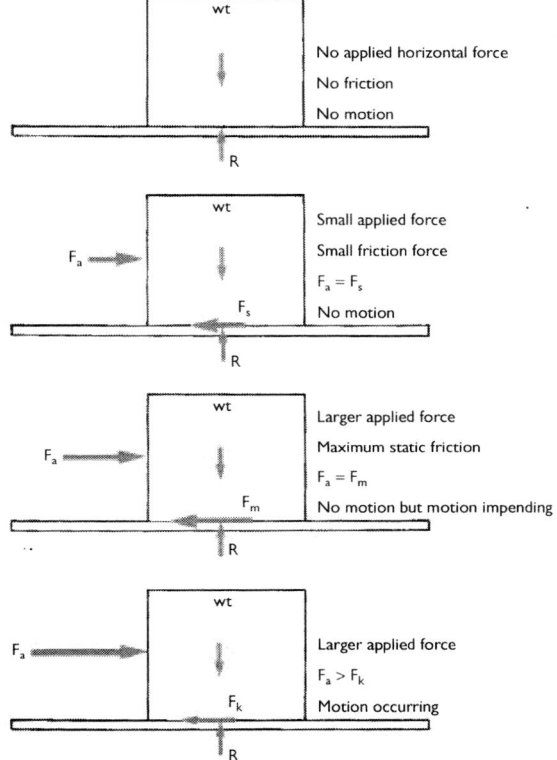

coefficient of friction
number that serves as an index of the interaction between two surfaces in contact

normal reaction force
force acting perpendicular to two surfaces in contact

the empty box in which the refrigerator was delivered. More force is also needed to slide the refrigerator across a carpeted floor than to do so across a smooth linoleum floor. Two factors govern the magnitude of the force of maximum static friction or kinetic friction in any situation: the coefficient of friction, represented by the lowercase Greek letter mu (μ), and the normal (perpendicular) reaction force (R):

$$F = \mu R$$

FIGURE 12-6

As long as a body is static, the magnitude of the friction force developed is equal to that of an applied external force. Once motion is initiated, the magnitude of the friction force remains at a constant level below that of maximum static friction.

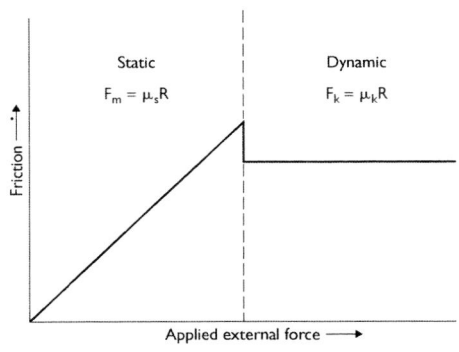

The coefficient of friction is a unitless number indicating the relative ease of sliding, or the amount of mechanical and molecular interaction between two surfaces in contact. Factors influencing the value of μ are the relative roughness and hardness of the surfaces in contact and the type of molecular interaction between the surfaces. The greater the mechanical and molecular interaction, the greater the value of μ. For example, the coefficient of friction between two blocks covered with rough sandpaper is larger than the coefficient of friction between a skate and a smooth surface of ice. The coefficient of friction describes the interaction between two surfaces in contact and is not descriptive of either surface alone. The coefficient of friction for the blade of an ice skate in contact with ice is different from that for the blade of the same skate in contact with concrete or wood.

The coefficient of friction between two surfaces assumes one or two different values, depending on whether the bodies in contact are motionless (static) or in motion (kinetic). The two coefficients are known as the *coefficient of static friction* (μ_s) and the *coefficient of kinetic friction* (μ_k). The magnitude of maximum static friction is based on the coefficient of static friction:

$$F_m = \mu_s R$$

The magnitude of the kinetic friction force is based on the coefficient of kinetic friction:

$$F_k = \mu_k R$$

For any two bodies in contact, μ_k is always smaller than μ_s. Kinetic friction coefficients as low as 0.003 have been reported between the blade of a racing skate and a properly treated ice rink under optimal conditions (47). Use of the coefficients of static and kinetic friction is illustrated in Sample Problem 12.2.

The other factor affecting the magnitude of the friction force generated is the normal reaction force. If weight is the only vertical force acting on a body sitting on a horizontal surface, R is equal in magnitude to the weight. If the object is a football blocking sled with a 100 kg coach standing on it, R is equal to the weight of the sled plus the weight of the coach. Other vertically directed forces such as pushes or pulls can also affect the magnitude of R, which is always equal to the vector sum of all forces or force components acting normal to the surfaces in contact (Figure 12-7).

The magnitude of R can be intentionally altered to increase or decrease the amount of friction present in a particular situation. When a football coach stands on the back of a blocking sled, the normal reaction force exerted by the ground on the sled is increased, with a concurrent increase in the amount of friction generated, making it more difficult for a player to move the sled. Alternatively, if the magnitude of R is decreased, friction is decreased and it is easier to initiate motion.

How can the normal reaction force be decreased? Suppose you need to rearrange the furniture in a room. Is it easier to push or pull an object such as a desk to move it? When a desk is pushed, the force exerted is typically directed diagonally downward. In contrast, force is usually directed diagonally upward when a desk is pulled. The vertical component of the push or pull either adds to or subtracts from the magnitude of the normal reaction force, thus influencing the magnitude of the friction force generated and the relative ease of moving the desk (Figure 12-8).

The amount of friction present between two surfaces can also be changed by altering the coefficient of friction between the surfaces. For example, the use of gloves in sports such as golf and racquetball increases

• *Because μ_k is always smaller than μ_s, the magnitude of kinetic friction is always less than the magnitude of maximum static friction.*

• *It is advantageous to pull with a line of force that is directed slightly upward when moving a heavy object.*

396   BASIC BIOMECHANICS

SAMPLE PROBLEM 12.2

The coefficient of static friction between a sled and the snow is 0.18, with a coefficient of kinetic friction of 0.15. A 250 N boy sits on the 200 N sled. How much force directed parallel to the horizontal surface is required to start the sled in motion? How much force is required to keep the sled in motion?

Known

$$\mu_s = 0.18$$
$$\mu_k = 0.15$$
$$wt = 250\ N + 200\ N$$

Solution

To start the sled in motion, the applied force must exceed the force of maximum static friction:

$$F_m = \mu_s R$$
$$= (0.18)(250\ N + 200\ N)$$
$$= 81\ N$$

The applied force must be greater than 81 N.

To maintain motion, the applied force must equal the force of kinetic friction:

$$F_k = \mu_k R$$
$$= (0.15)(250\ N + 200\ N)$$
$$= 67.5\ N$$

The applied force must be at least 67.5 N.

FIGURE 12-7

As weight increases, the normal reaction force increases.

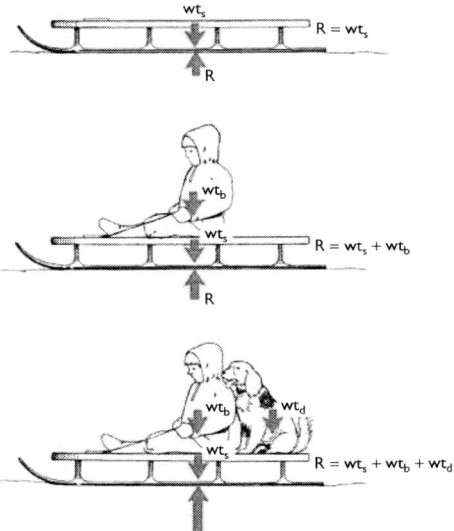

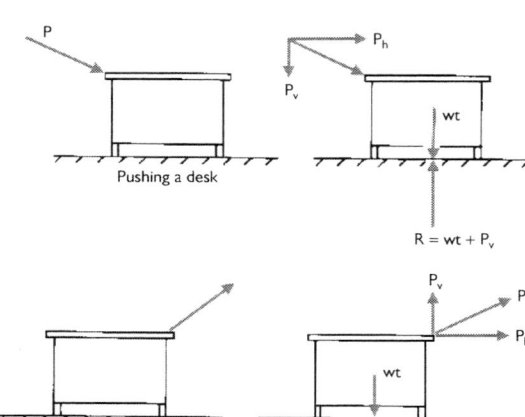

Pushing a desk

$R = wt + P_v$

Pulling a desk

$R = wt - P_v$

FIGURE 12-8

From a mechanical perspective, it is easier to pull than to push an object such as a desk, since pulling tends to decrease the magnitude of R and F, whereas pushing tends to increase R and F.

the coefficient of friction between the hand and the grip of the club or racquet. Similarly, lumps of wax applied to a surfboard increase the roughness of the board's surface, thereby increasing the coefficient of friction between the board and the surfer's feet. The application of a thin, smooth coat of wax to the bottom of cross-country skis is designed to decrease the coefficient of friction between the skis and the snow, with different waxes used for various snow conditions.

A widespread misconception about friction is that greater contact surface area generates more friction. Advertisements often imply that wide-track automobile tires provide better traction (friction) against the road than tires of normal width. However, the only factors known to affect friction are the coefficient of friction and the normal reaction force. Because wide-track tires typically weigh more than normal tires, they do increase friction to the extent that they increase R. However, the same effect can be achieved by carrying bricks or cinder blocks in the trunk of the car, a practice often followed by people who regularly drive on icy roads. Wide-track tires do tend to provide the advantages of increased lateral stability and increased wear, since larger surface area reduces the stress on a properly inflated tire.

Friction exerts an important influence during many daily activities. Walking depends on a proper coefficient of friction between a person's shoes and the supporting surface. If the coefficient of friction is too low, as when a person with smooth-soled shoes walks on a patch of ice, slip-page will occur. The bottom of a wet bathtub or shower stall should provide a coefficient of friction with the soles of bare feet that is sufficiently large to prevent slippage.

The amount of friction present between ballet shoes and the dance studio floor must be controlled so that movements involving some amount of sliding or pivoting—such as *glissades, assembles,* and *pirouettes*—can be executed smoothly but without slippage. Rosin is often applied to dance floors because it provides a large coefficient of static friction but a significantly smaller coefficient of dynamic friction (26). This helps to prevent slippage in static situations and allows desired movements to occur freely.

The amount of friction present during sport situations has engendered heated controversies. The National Football League Players Association

• *Racquetball and golf gloves are designed to increase the friction between the hand and the racquet or club, as are the grips on the handles of the rackets and clubs themselves.*

The coefficient of friction between a dancer's shoes and the floor must be small enough to allow freedom of motion but large enough to prevent slippage.

398   BASIC BIOMECHANICS

has attempted to have artificial turf declared a "hazardous substance" partly because the high coefficient of friction between artificial turf and a football shoe often does not allow rotation of a planted foot. Many knee injuries have been attributed to the immobility of a foot planted on artificial turf when a player is tackled. This possibility is heightened with increased turf temperature, since the coefficient of friction between football shoes and artificial turf increases with temperature (46). Football shoes that are not designed for use on artificial turf also tend to generate more friction on artificial turf than those shoes that are designed for such use (22). However, playing on artificial turf continues, because the Consumer Products Safety Commission has concluded that there is insufficient evidence supporting the NFL players' claim (39).

Another controversial disagreement occurred between Glenn Allison, a retired professional bowler and member of the American Bowling Congress Hall of Fame, and the American Bowling Congress. The dispute arose over the amount of friction present between Allison's ball and the lanes on which he bowled a perfect score of 300 in three consecutive games. According to the congress, his scores could not be recognized because the lanes he used did not conform to congress standards for the amount of conditioning oil present (25).

• *Rolling friction is influenced by the weight, radius, and deformability of the rolling object, as well as by the coefficient of friction between the two surfaces.*

The magnitude of the rolling friction present between a rolling object, such as a bowling ball or an automobile tire, and a flat surface is approximately one-hundredth to one-thousandth of that present between sliding surfaces. Rolling friction occurs because both the curved and the flat surfaces are slightly deformed during contact. The coefficient of friction between the surfaces in contact, the normal reaction force, and the size of the radius of curvature of the rolling body all influence the magnitude of rolling friction. For bicycle tires, rolling friction is inversely proportional to the wheel diameter (49). It decreases with bicycle tire width and increases with reduced tire pressure (35).

• *The synovial fluid present at many of the joints of the human body greatly reduces the friction between the articulating bones.*

The amount of friction present in a sliding or rolling situation is dramatically reduced when a layer of fluid, such as oil or water, intervenes between two surfaces in contact. The presence of synovial fluid serves to reduce the friction, and subsequently the mechanical wear, on the diarthrodial joints of the human body. The coefficient of friction in a total hip prosthesis is approximately 0.01 (40). Researchers attribute the extremely low coefficients of friction between speed skates and the ice to a liquid-like film layer on the surface of the ice (10). The amount of friction between a bowling ball and a properly oiled lane is also extremely small, and according to the American Bowling Congress, an insufficient amount of oil on the lanes gave Allison the unfair advantage of added ball traction (25).

Revisiting the question presented earlier about the horse and cart, the force of friction is the determining factor for movement. The system moves forward if the magnitude of the friction force generated by the horse's hooves against the ground exceeds that produced by the wheels of the cart against the ground (Figure 12-9). Because most horses are shod to increase the amount of friction between their hooves and the ground, and most cart wheels are round and smooth to minimize the amount of friction they generate, the horse is usually at an advantage. However, if the horse stands on a slippery surface or if the cart rests in deep sand or is heavily loaded, motion may not be possible.

Momentum

Another factor that affects the outcome of interactions between two bodies is momentum, a mechanical quantity that is particularly important

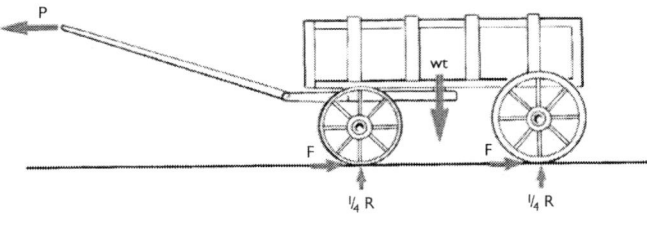

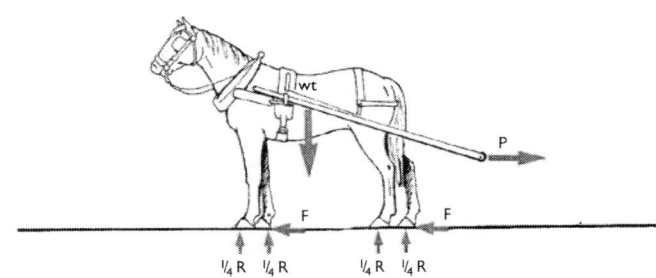

FIGURE 12-9

A horse can pull a cart if the horse's hooves generate more friction than the wheels of the cart.

in situations involving collisions. Momentum may be defined generally as the quantity of motion that an object possesses. More specifically, linear momentum is the product of an object's mass and its velocity:

$$M = mv$$

A static object (with zero velocity) has no momentum; that is, its momentum equals zero. A change in a body's momentum may be caused by either a change in the body's mass or a change in its velocity. In most human movement situations, changes in momentum result from changes in velocity. Units of momentum are units of mass multiplied by units of velocity, expressed in terms of kg · m/s. Because velocity is a vector quantity, momentum is also a vector quantity and is subject to the rules of vector composition and resolution.

When a head-on collision between two objects occurs, there is a tendency for both objects to continue moving in the direction of motion originally possessed by the object with the greatest momentum. If a 90 kg hockey player traveling at 6 m/s to the right collides head-on with an 80 kg player traveling at 7 m/s to the left, the momentum of the first player is the following:

$$M = mv$$
$$= (90 \text{ kg}) (6 \text{ m/s})$$
$$= 540 \text{ kg} \cdot \text{m/s}$$

The momentum of the second player is expressed as follows:

$$M = mv$$
$$= (80 \text{ kg}) (7 \text{ m/s})$$
$$= 560 \text{ kg} \cdot \text{m/s}$$

Since the second player's momentum is greater, both players would tend to continue moving in the direction of the second player's original velocity after the collision. Actual collisions are also affected by the extent to which

linear momentum
quantity of motion, measured as the product of a body's mass and its velocity

•*Momentum is a vector quantity.*

400   BASIC BIOMECHANICS

●*In the absence of external forces, momentum is conserved. However, friction and air resistance are forces that normally act to reduce momentum.*

the players become entangled, by whether one or both players remain on their feet, and by the elasticity of the collision.

Neglecting these other factors that may influence the outcome of the collision, it is possible to calculate the magnitude of the combined velocity of the two hockey players after the collision using a modified statement of Newton's first law of motion (see Sample Problem 12.3). Newton's first law may be restated as the *principle of conservation of momentum:*

In the absence of external forces, the total momentum of a given system remains constant.

The principle is expressed in equation format as the following:

$$M_1 = M_2$$
$$(mv)_1 = (mv)_2$$

SAMPLE PROBLEM 12.3

A 90 kg hockey player traveling with a velocity of 6 m/s collides head-on with an 80 kg player traveling at 7 m/s. If the two players entangle and continue traveling together as a unit following the collision, what is their combined velocity?

Known

$m_1 = 90$ kg
$v_1 = 6$ m/s
$m_2 = 80$ kg
$v_2 = -7$ m/s

m = 90 kg
v = 6 m/s

m = 80 kg
v = 7 m/s

Collision

m = (90 + 80) kg
v = ?

Solution

The law of conservation of momentum may be used to solve the problem, with the two players considered as the total system.

Before collision   After collision

$$m_1v_1 + m_2v_2 = (m_1 + m_2)(v)$$
$$(90 \text{ kg})(6 \text{ m/s}) + (80 \text{ kg})(-7 \text{ m/s}) = (90 \text{ kg} + 80 \text{ kg})(v)$$
$$540 \text{ kg} \cdot \text{m/s} - 560 \text{ kg} \cdot \text{m/s} = (170 \text{ kg})(v)$$
$$-20 \text{ kg} \cdot \text{m/s} = (170 \text{ kg})(v)$$

$v = 0.12$ m/s in the 80 kg player's original direction of travel.

Subscript 1 designates an initial point in time and subscript 2 represents a later time.

Applying this principle to the hypothetical example of the colliding hockey players, the vector sum of the two players' momenta before the collision is equal to their single, combined momentum following the collision (see Sample Problem 12.3). In reality, friction and air resistance are external forces that typically act to reduce the total amount of momentum present.

Impulse

When external forces do act, they change the momentum present in a system predictably. Changes in momentum depend not only on the magnitude of the acting external forces but also on the length of time over which each force acts. The product of force and time is known as impulse:

$$impulse = Ft$$

When an impulse acts on a system, the result is a change in the system's total momentum. The relationship between impulse and momentum is derived from Newton's second law:

$$F = ma$$

$$f = m\frac{(v_2 - v_1)}{t}$$

$$Ft = (mv)_2 - (mv)_1$$
$$Ft = \Delta M$$

Subscript 1 designates an initial time and subscript 2 represents a later time. An application of this relationship is presented in Sample Problem 12.4.

impulse
product of a force and the time interval over which the force acts

---

SAMPLE PROBLEM 12.4

A toboggan race begins with the two crew members pushing the toboggan to get it moving as quickly as possible before they climb in. If crew members apply an average force of 100 N in the direction of motion of the 90 kg toboggan for a period of 7 s before jumping in, what is the toboggan's speed (neglecting friction) at that point?

Known

$$F = 100 \text{ N}$$
$$t = 7 \text{ s}$$
$$m = 90 \text{ kg}$$

Solution

The crew members are applying an impulse to the toboggan to change the toboggan's momentum from zero to a maximum amount. The impulse–momentum relationship may be used to solve the problem.

$$Ft = (mv)_2 - (mv)_1$$
$$(100 \text{ N}) (7 \text{ s}) = (90 \text{ kg}) (v) - (90 \text{ kg}) (0)$$

$$v = 7.78 \text{ m/s in the direction of force application}$$

Significant changes in an object's momentum may result from a small force acting over a large time interval or from a large force acting over a small time interval. A golf ball rolling across a green gradually loses momentum because its motion is constantly opposed by the force of rolling friction. The momentum of a baseball struck vigorously by a bat also changes because of the large force exerted by the bat during the fraction of a second it is in contact with the ball.

The amount of impulse generated by the human body is often intentionally manipulated. When a vertical jump is performed on a force platform, a graphical display of the vertical GRF across time can be generated (Figure 12-10). Since impulse is the product of force and time, the impulse is the area under the force–time curve. The larger the impulse generated against the floor, the greater the change in the performer's momentum, and the higher the resulting jump. Theoretically, impulse can be increased by increasing either the magnitude of applied force or the time interval over which the force acts. Practically, however, when time of force application against the ground is prolonged during vertical jump execution, the magnitude of the force that can be generated is dramatically reduced,

FIGURE 12-10

Force–time histories for (**A**) high, and (**B**) low vertical jumps by the same performer. The shaded area represents the impulse generated against the floor during the jump.

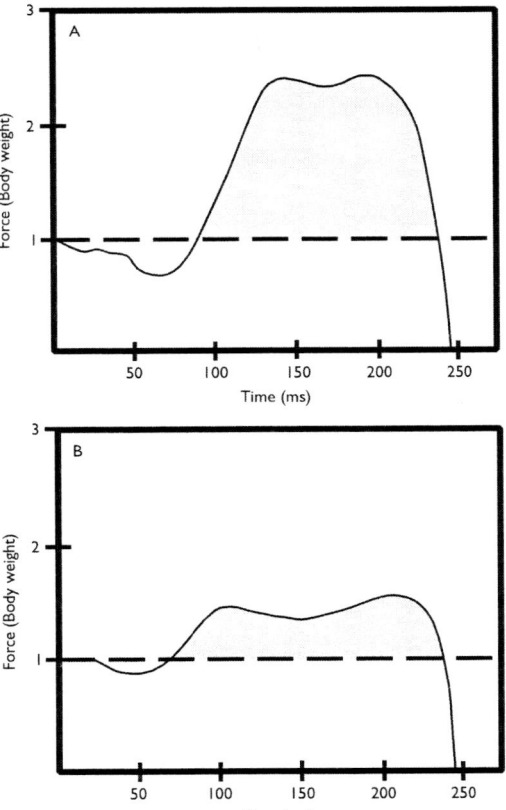

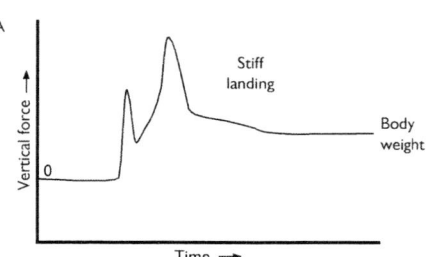

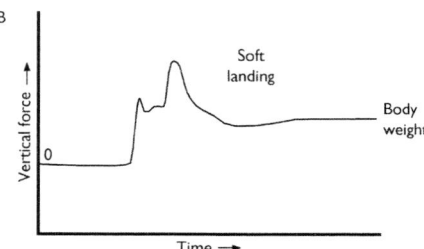

FIGURE 12-11

Representations of ground reaction forces during vertical jump performances: (**A**) a rigid landing, (**B**) a landing with hip, knee, and ankle flexion occurring. Note the differences in the magnitudes and times of the landing impulses.

with the ultimate result being a smaller impulse. For performing a maximal vertical jump, the performer must maximize impulse by optimizing the trade-off between applied force magnitude and force duration. The motion of the arms during a counter-movement jump contributes 12–13% of the total upward momentum, indicating the importance of arm motion when jumping for maximum height (27).

Impulse can also be intentionally manipulated during a landing from a jump (Figure 12-11). A performer who lands rigidly will experience a relatively large GRF sustained over a relatively short time interval. Alternatively, allowing the hip, knee, and ankle joints to undergo flexion during the landing increases the time interval over which the landing force is absorbed, thereby reducing the magnitude of the force sustained. Research has shown that females tend to land in a more erect posture than males, with greater shock absorption occurring in the knees and ankles, and a concomitant greater likelihood of lower-extremity injury (11). One-foot landings also tend to generate higher impact forces and faster loading rates than two-foot landings (45).

It is also useful to manipulate impulse when catching a hard-thrown ball. "Giving" with the ball after it initially contacts the hands or the glove before bringing the ball to a complete stop will prevent the force of the ball from causing the hands to sting. The greater the period is between making initial hand contact with the ball and bringing the ball to a complete stop, the smaller is the magnitude of the force exerted by the ball against the hand, and the smaller is the likelihood of experiencing a sting.

Impact

The type of collision that occurs between a struck baseball and a bat is known as an impact. An impact involves the collision of two bodies over an extremely small time interval during which the two bodies exert relatively large forces on each other. The behavior of two objects following an

impact
collision characterized by the exchange of a large force during a small time interval

404   BASIC BIOMECHANICS

"Giving" with the ball during a catch serves to lessen the magnitude of the impact force sustained by the catcher.

impact depends not only on their collective momentum but also on the nature of the impact.

For the hypothetical case of a perfectly elastic impact, the relative velocities of the two bodies after impact are the same as their relative velocities before impact. The impact of a superball with a hard surface approaches perfect elasticity, because the ball's speed diminishes little during its collision with the surface. At the other end of the range is the perfectly plastic impact, during which at least one of the bodies in contact deforms and does not regain its original shape, and the bodies do not separate. This occurs when modeling clay is dropped on a surface.

Most impacts are neither perfectly elastic nor perfectly plastic, but somewhere between the two. The coefficient of restitution describes the relative elasticity of an impact. It is a unitless number between 0 and 1. The closer the coefficient of restitution is to 1, the more elastic is the impact; and the closer the coefficient is to 0, the more plastic is the impact.

The coefficient of restitution governs the relationship between the relative velocities of two bodies before and after an impact. This relationship, which was originally formulated by Newton, may be stated as follows:

> When two bodies undergo a direct collision, the difference in their velocities immediately after impact is proportional to the difference in their velocities immediately before impact.

This relationship can also be expressed algebraically as the following:

$$-e = \frac{\text{relative velocity after impact}}{\text{relative velocity before impact}}$$

$$-e = \frac{v_1 - v_2}{u_1 - u_2}$$

In this formula, e is the coefficient of restitution, u_1 and u_2 are the velocities of the bodies just before impact, and v_1 and v_2 are the velocities of the bodies immediately after impact (Figure 12-12).

perfectly elastic impact
impact during which the velocity of the system is conserved

perfectly plastic impact
impact resulting in the total loss of system velocity

coefficient of restitution
number that serves as an index of elasticity for colliding bodies

Ball velocities before impact

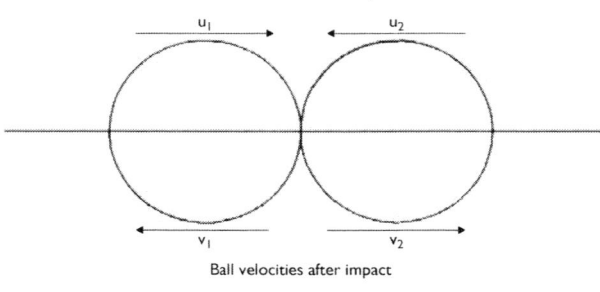

Ball velocities after impact

$$v_1 - v_2 = -e\,(u_1 - u_2)$$

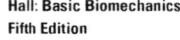

FIGURE 12-12

The differences in two ball's velocities before impact is proportional to the difference in their velocities after impact. The factor of proportionality is the coefficient of restitution.

In tennis, the nature of the game depends on the type of impacts between ball and racket and between ball and court. All other conditions being equal, a tighter grip on the racket increases the apparent coefficient of restitution between ball and racket (21). When a pressurized tennis ball is punctured, there is a reduction in the coefficient of restitution between ball and surface of 20% (20). Other factors of influence are racket size, shape, balance, flexibility, string type and tension, and swing kinematics (18, 19, 51).

The nature of impact between the bat and the ball is also an important factor in the sports of baseball and softball. The hitting surface of the bat is convex, in contrast to the surface of the tennis racquet, which deforms to a convex shape during ball contact. Consequently, hitting a baseball or softball in a direct, rather than a glancing, fashion is of paramount concern. Research has shown that aluminum baseball bats produce significantly higher batted ball speeds than do wood bats, which suggests that the coefficient of restitution between an aluminum bat and baseball is higher than that between a wood bat and baseball (17). The condition of the ball is also significant. Tests have shown that rebound from a surface is higher after 800 impacts than when a ball is new, because the loss of nap increases the coefficient of restitution between ball and surface, and decreases the ball's aerodynamic drag. However, the major factor affecting ball rebound is the amount of time the ball has been outside a pressurized can. A loss of rebound height for both used and unused balls occurs after five days out of a can (38). The surface of the court also influences ball rebound during play, with differences in the coefficients of restitution and friction between ball and surface making some courts "fast" and others "slow."

In the case of an impact between a moving body and a stationary one, Newton's law of impact can be simplified because the velocity of the stationary body remains zero. The coefficient of restitution between a ball and a flat, stationary surface onto which the ball is dropped may be approximated using the following formula:

$$e = \sqrt{\frac{h_b}{h_d}}$$

In this equation, e is the coefficient of restitution, h_d is the height from which the ball is dropped, and h_b is the height to which the ball bounces (see Sample Problem 12.5). The coefficient of restitution describes the interaction between two bodies during an impact; it is *not* descriptive of any

SAMPLE PROBLEM 12.5

A basketball is dropped from a height of 2 m onto a gymnasium floor. If the coefficient of restitution between ball and floor is 0.9, how high will the ball bounce?

Known

$$h_d = 2 \text{ m}$$
$$e = 0.9$$

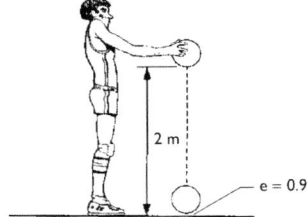

2 m

e = 0.9

Solution

$$e = \sqrt{\frac{h_b}{h_d}}$$

$$0.9 = \sqrt{\frac{h_b}{2 \text{ m}}}$$

$$0.81 = \frac{h_b}{2 \text{ m}}$$

$$h_b = 1.6 \text{ m}$$

single object or surface. Dropping a basketball, a golf ball, a racquetball, and a baseball onto several different surfaces demonstrates that some balls bounce higher on certain types of surfaces (Figure 12-13).

The coefficient of restitution is increased by increases in both impact velocity and temperature. In sports such as baseball and tennis, increases in both incoming ball velocity and bat or racket velocity increase the coefficient of restitution between bat or racket and ball, and contribute to a livelier ball rebound from the striking instrument. In racquetball and squash, where the ball is constantly being deformed against the wall, the ball's thermal energy (temperature) is increased over the course of play. As ball temperature increases, its rebound from both racquet and wall becomes more lively.

• *Increases in impact velocity and temperature increase the coefficient of restitution.*

FIGURE 12-13

Bounce heights of a basketball, golf ball, racquetball, and baseball all dropped onto the same surface from a height of 1 m.

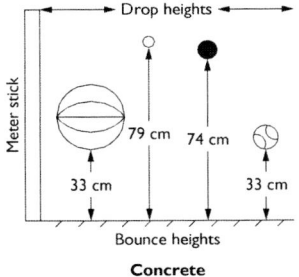

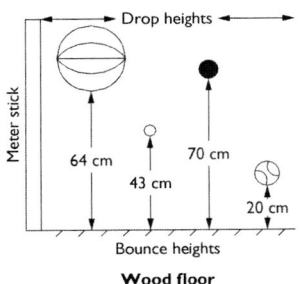

WORK, POWER, AND ENERGY RELATIONSHIPS

Work

The word *work* is commonly used in a variety of contexts. A person can speak of "working out" in the weight room, doing "yard work," or "working hard" to prepare for an exam. However, from a mechanical standpoint, work is defined as force applied against a resistance, multiplied by the displacement of the resistance in the direction of the force:

$$W = Fd$$

When a body is moved a given distance as the result of the action of an applied external force, the body has had work performed on it, with the quantity of work equal to the product of the magnitude of the applied force and the distance through which the body was moved. When a force is applied to a body but no net force results because of opposing forces such as friction or the body's own weight, no mechanical work has been done, since there has been no movement of the body.

When the muscles of the human body produce tension resulting in the motion of a body segment, the muscles perform work on the body segment, and the mechanical work performed may be characterized as either positive or negative work, according to the type of muscle action that predominates. When both the net muscle torque and the direction of angular motion at a joint are in the same direction, the work done by the muscles is said to be *positive*. Alternatively, when the net muscle torque and the direction of angular motion at a joint are in opposite directions, the work done by the muscles is considered to be *negative*. Although many movements of the human body involve co-contraction of agonist and antagonist muscle groups, when concentric contraction prevails the work is positive, and when eccentric contraction prevails the work is negative. During an activity such as running on a level surface, the net negative work done by the muscles is equal to the net positive work done by the muscles.

Performing positive mechanical work typically requires greater caloric expenditure than performing the same amount of negative mechanical work. However, no simple relationship between the caloric energy required for performing equal amounts of positive and negative mechanical work has been discovered, and the picture is complicated by the fact that agonist and other muscle groups often co-contract (1, 31). When individuals are monitored during performances of positive and negative mechanical work, energy expenditures vary considerably both across and within individual performances (3). Energy expenditure with the use of elbow crutches is 2–3 times higher than in normal walking, although the mechanical work is only 1.3–1.5 times greater (44). This indicates that use of elbow crutches is also accompanied by a decrease in the efficiency of mechanical work production. Similarly, researchers have calculated that walking on sand requires 1.6–2.5 times more mechanical work than walking on a hard surface, but 2.1–2.7 times more energy expenditure (28).

Units of work are units of force multiplied by units of distance. In the metric system, the common unit of force (N) multiplied by a common unit of distance (m) is termed the *joule* (J).

$$1 \text{ J} = 1 \text{ Nm}$$

work
in a mechanical context, force multiplied by the displacement of the resistance in the direction of the force

•*Mechanical work should not be confused with caloric expenditure.*

Power

power
rate of work production, calculated as work divided by the time during which the work was done

Another term used in different contexts is power. In mechanics, power refers to the amount of mechanical work performed in a given time:

$$\text{power} = \frac{\text{work}}{\text{change in time}}$$

$$P = \frac{W}{\Delta t}$$

Using the relationships previously described, power can also be defined as the following:

$$\text{power} = \frac{\text{force} \times \text{distance}}{\text{change in time}}$$

$$P = \frac{Fd}{\Delta t}$$

Because velocity equals the directed distance divided by the change in time, the equation can also be expressed as the following:

$$P = Fv$$

Units of power are units of work divided by units of time. In the metric system, joules divided by seconds are termed *watts* (W):

$$1 \text{ W} = 1 \text{ J/s}$$

• *The ability to produce mechanical power is critical for athletes competing in explosive track-and-field events.*

In activities such as throwing, jumping, and sprinting and in Olympic weight lifting, the athlete's ability to exert mechanical power or the combination of force and velocity is critical to successful performance. Peak power is strongly associated with maximum isometric strength (43). A problem involving mechanical work and power is shown in Sample Problem 12.6.

Energy

kinetic energy
energy of motion, calculated as $\frac{1}{2} mv^2$

potential energy
energy by virtue of a body's position or configuration, calculated as the product of weight and height

Energy is defined generally as the capacity to do work. Mechanical energy is therefore the capacity to do mechanical work. Units of mechanical energy are the same as units of mechanical work (joules, in the metric system). There are two forms of mechanical energy: kinetic energy and potential energy.

Kinetic energy (KE) is the energy of motion. A body possesses kinetic energy only when in motion. Formally, the kinetic energy of linear motion is defined as one-half of a body's mass multiplied by the square of its velocity:

$$KE = \tfrac{1}{2} mv^2$$

If a body is motionless (v = 0), its kinetic energy is also zero. Because velocity is squared in the expression for kinetic energy, increases in a body's velocity create dramatic increases in its kinetic energy. For example, a 2 kg ball rolling with a velocity of 1 m/s has a kinetic energy of 1 J:

$$
\begin{aligned}
KE &= \tfrac{1}{2} mv^2 \\
&= (0.5)\,(2 \text{ kg})\,(1 \text{ m/s})^2 \\
&= (1 \text{ kg})\,(1 \text{ m}^2/\text{s}^2) \\
&= 1 \text{ J}
\end{aligned}
$$

SAMPLE PROBLEM 12.6

A 580 N person runs up a flight of 30 stairs of riser (height) of 25 cm during a 15 s period. How much mechanical work is done? How much mechanical power is generated?

Known

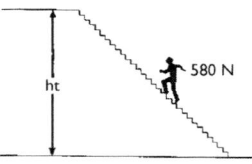

$$\text{wt (F)} = 580 \text{ N}$$
$$h = 30 \times 25 \text{ cm}$$
$$t = 15 \text{ s}$$

Solution

For mechanical work:

$$W = Fd$$
$$= (580 \text{ N}) (30 \times 0.25 \text{ m})$$
$$\boxed{W = 4350 \text{ J}}$$

For mechanical power:

$$P = \frac{W}{t}$$
$$= \frac{4350 \text{ J}}{15 \text{ s}}$$
$$\boxed{P = 290 \text{ watts}}$$

If the velocity of the ball is increased to 3 m/s, kinetic energy is significantly increased:

$$KE = \tfrac{1}{2} mv^2$$
$$= (0.5) (2 \text{ kg}) (3 \text{ m/s})^2$$
$$= (1 \text{ kg}) (9 \text{ m}^2/\text{s}^2)$$
$$= 9 \text{ J}$$

The other major category of mechanical energy is potential energy (PE), which is the energy of position. More specifically, potential energy is a body's weight multiplied by its height above a reference surface:

$$PE = \text{wt} \cdot h$$
$$PE = ma_g h$$

In the second formula, m represents mass, a_g is the acceleration of gravity, and h is the body's height. The reference surface is usually the floor or the ground, but in special circumstances, it may be defined as another surface.

Because in biomechanical applications the weight of a body is typically fixed, changes in potential energy are usually based on changes in the body's height. For example, when a 50 kg bar is elevated to a height of 1 m, its potential energy at that point is 490.5 J:

$$PE = ma_g h$$
$$= (50 \text{ kg}) (9.81 \text{ m/s}^2) (1 \text{ m})$$
$$= 490.5 \text{ J}$$

410   BASIC BIOMECHANICS

strain energy
capacity to do work by virtue of a deformed body's return to its original shape

During the pole vault, the bent pole stores strain energy for subsequent release as kinetic energy and heat.

Potential energy may also be thought of as stored energy. The term *potential* implies potential for conversion to kinetic energy. A special form of potential energy is called strain energy (SE), or elastic energy. Strain energy may be defined as follows:

$$SE = \tfrac{1}{2} kx^2$$

In this formula, k is a spring constant, representing a material's relative stiffness or ability to store energy on deformation, and x is the distance over which the material is deformed. When an object is stretched, bent, or otherwise deformed, it stores this particular form of potential energy for later use. For example, when the muscles and tendons of the human body are stretched, they store strain energy that is released to increase the force of subsequent contraction, as discussed in Chapter 6. During an activity such as a maximal-effort throw, stored energy in stretched musculotendinous units can contribute significantly to the force and power generated and to the resulting velocity of the throw (32). Because they are more extensible than muscle, it is primarily the tendons that store and return elastic energy, with longer tendons performing this function more effectively than shorter ones (5). Likewise, when the end of a diving board or a trampoline surface is depressed, strain energy is created. Subsequent conversion of the stored energy to kinetic energy enables the surface to return to its original shape and position. The poles used by vaulters store strain energy as they bend, and then release kinetic energy and increase the potential energy of the athlete as they straighten during the performance of the vault (2). In 1963, the increase of approximately 23 cm in the world record for the pole vault was attributed largely to the advent of vaulting poles made of fiberglass, a material capable of storing more strain energy than the bamboo, steel, or aluminum of which earlier poles were constructed (24).

Conservation of Mechanical Energy

Consider the changes that occur in the mechanical energy of a ball tossed vertically into the air (Figure 12-14). As the ball gains height, it also gains potential energy ($ma_g h$). However, since the ball is losing velocity with increasing height because of gravitational acceleration, it is also losing kinetic energy ($\tfrac{1}{2} mv^2$) At the apex of the ball's trajectory (the instant between rising and falling), its height and potential energy are at a maximum value, and its velocity and kinetic energy are zero. As the ball starts to fall, it progressively gains kinetic energy while losing potential energy.

The correlation between the kinetic and potential energies of the vertically tossed ball illustrates a concept that applies to all bodies when the only external force acting is gravity. The concept is known as the *law of conservation of mechanical energy*, which may be stated as follows:

> When gravity is the only acting external force, a body's mechanical energy remains constant.

Since the mechanical energy a body possesses is the sum of its potential and kinetic energies, the relationship may also be expressed as the following:

$$(PE + KE) = C$$

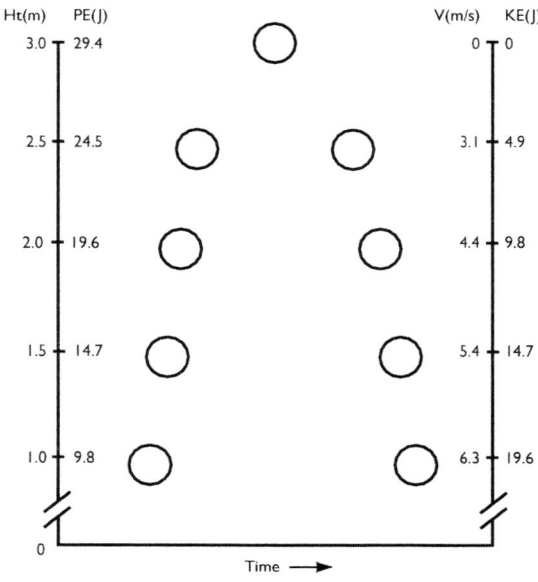

Ht(m)   PE(J)
3.0 — 29.4
2.5 — 24.5
2.0 — 19.6
1.5 — 14.7
1.0 — 9.8
0

V(m/s)   KE(J)
0 — 0
3.1 — 4.9
4.4 — 9.8
5.4 — 14.7
6.3 — 19.6

Time →

FIGURE 12-14

Height, velocity, potential energy, and kinetic energy change for a 1 kg ball tossed upward from a height of 1 m. Note that PE + KE = C (a constant) throughout the trajectory.

In this formula, C is a constant; that is, it is a number that remains constant throughout the period of time during which gravity is the only external force acting. Sample Problem 12.7 quantitatively illustrates this principle.

• When gravity is the only acting external force, any change in a body's potential energy necessitates a compensatory change in its kinetic energy.

Principle of Work and Energy

There is a special relationship between the quantities of mechanical work and mechanical energy. This relationship is described as the *principle of work and energy,* which may be stated as follows:

> The work of a force is equal to the change in energy that it produces in the object acted on.

Algebraically, the principle may be represented thus:

$$W = \Delta KE + \Delta PE + \Delta TE$$

In this formula, KE is kinetic energy, PE is potential energy, and TE is thermal energy (heat). The algebraic statement of the principle of work and energy indicates that the change in the sum of the forms of energy produced by a force is quantitatively equal to the mechanical work done by that force. When a tennis ball is projected into the air by a ball-throwing machine, the mechanical work performed on the ball by the machine results in an increase in the ball's mechanical energy. Prior to projection, the ball's potential energy is based on its weight and height, and its kinetic energy is zero. The ball-throwing machine increases the ball's total mechanical energy by imparting kinetic energy to it. In this situation, the change in the ball's thermal energy is negligible. Sample Problem 12.8 provides a quantitative illustration of the principle of work and energy.

The work–energy relationship is also evident during movements of the human body. For example, the arches in runners' feet act as a mechanical

412   BASIC BIOMECHANICS

SAMPLE PROBLEM 12.7

A 2 kg ball is dropped from a height of 1.5 m. What is its velocity immediately before impact with the floor?

Known

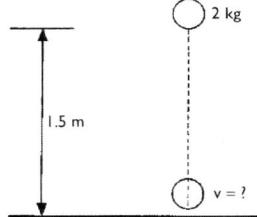

$$m = 2kg$$
$$h = 1.5 \text{ m}$$

Solution

The principle of the conservation of mechanical energy may be used to solve the problem. The total energy possessed by the ball when it is held at a height of 1.5 m is its potential energy. Immediately before impact, the ball's height (and potential energy) may be assumed to be zero, and 100% of its energy at that point is kinetic.

Total (constant) mechanical energy possessed by the ball:

$$PE + KE = C$$
$$(\text{wt})\,(h) + \tfrac{1}{2}\,mv^2 = C$$
$$(2 \text{ kg})\,(9.81 \text{ m/s}^2)\,(1.5 \text{ m}) + 0 = C$$
$$29.43 \text{ J} = C$$

Velocity of the ball before impact:

$$PE + KE = 29.43 \text{ J}$$
$$(\text{wt})\,(h) + \tfrac{1}{2}\,mv^2 = 29.43 \text{ J}$$
$$(2 \text{ kg})\,(9.81 \text{ m/s}^2)\,(0) + \tfrac{1}{2}\,(2 \text{ kg})\,v^2 = 29.43 \text{ J}$$
$$v^2 = 29.43 \text{ J/kg}$$
$$v = 5.42 \text{ m/s}$$

spring to store, and subsequently return, strain energy as they cyclically deform and then regain their resting shapes. For a 70 kg man running at 4.5 m/s, each arch stores approximately 17 J of energy at midstance. Combined with the estimated 35 J stored by each of the Achilles tendons, this equals a storage and partial return of approximately one-half of the mechanical energy expended, or one-half of the mechanical work required of the muscles during the stance phase (4). The ability of the arches to function as a spring reduces the amount of mechanical work that would otherwise be required during running.

Two-joint muscles in the human body also serve to transfer mechanical energy from one joint to another, thereby reducing the mechanical work required of the muscles crossing the second joint during a given

SAMPLE PROBLEM 12.8

How much mechanical work is required to catch a 1.3 kg ball traveling at a velocity of 40 m/s?

Known

$$m = 1.3 \text{ kg}$$
$$v = 40 \text{ m/s}$$

v = 40 m/s

1.3 kg

Solution

The principle of work and energy may be used to calculate the mechanical work required to change the ball's kinetic energy to zero. Assume that the potential energy and thermal energy of the ball do not change:

$$W = \Delta Ke$$
$$= (\tfrac{1}{2} mv^2)_2 - (\tfrac{1}{2} mv^2)_1$$
$$= 0 - (\tfrac{1}{2})(1.3 \text{ kg})(40 \text{ m/s})^2$$

$$W = 1040 \text{ J}$$

movement. For example, during takeoff for a vertical jump, when the hip extensors work concentrically to produce hip extension, if the rectus femoris remains isometrically contracted, a secondary effect is an extensor torque exerted at the knee. In this case, it is the hip extensors that produce the knee extensor torque, since the length of the rectus femoris does not change. Research indicates that during both a vertical jump and the push-off phase of running, the rectus femoris and gastrocnemius help to extend the distal joints they cross by transferring mechanical energy from the proximal joints of the leg to the distal ones (37). During landings and the shock-absorbing phase of running, the process is reversed, with these two-joint muscles transferring energy from the distal joints to the proximal ones, thereby promoting the dissipation of mechanical energy (37). Research has shown that elderly individuals with weak leg muscles tend to increase hip and low back mechanical energy expenditures to compensate for reduced ankle and knee mechanical energies during gait (30).

It is important not to confuse the production of mechanical energy or mechanical work by the muscles of the human body with the consumption of chemical energy or caloric expenditure. Factors such as concentric versus eccentric muscular contractions, the transfer of energy between body segments, elastic storage and reuse of energy, and limitations in joint ranges of motion complicate direct quantitative calculation of the relationship between mechanical and physiological energy estimates (50). Approximately 25% of the energy consumed by the muscles is converted into work, with the remainder changed to heat or used in the body's chemical processes.

Table 12-1 summarizes the formulas used in this chapter.

414   BASIC BIOMECHANICS

TABLE 12-1
Formula Summary

DESCRIPTION	FORMULA
Force = (mass)(acceleration)	$F = ma$
Friction = (coefficient of friction)(normal reaction force)	$F = \mu R$
Linear momentum = (mass)(velocity)	$M = mv$
Coefficient of restitution = $\dfrac{\text{relative velocity after impact}}{\text{relative velocity before impact}}$	$-e = \dfrac{v_1 - v_2}{u_1 - u_2}$
Work = (force) (displacement of resistance)	$W = Fd$
Power = $\dfrac{\text{work}}{\text{time}}$	$P = \dfrac{W}{t}$
Power = (force)(velocity)	$P = Fv$
Kinetic energy = $\frac{1}{2}$ (mass)(velocity squared)	$KE = \frac{1}{2} mv^2$
Potential energy = (weight)(height)	$PE = ma_g h$
Strain energy = $\frac{1}{2}$ (spring constant)(deformation squared)	$SE = \frac{1}{2} kx^2$
Potential energy + kinetic energy = constant	$PE + KE = C$
Work = change in energy	$W = \Delta KE + \Delta PE + \Delta TE$

SUMMARY

Linear kinetics is the study of the forces associated with linear motion. The interrelationships among many basic kinetic quantities are identified in the physical laws formulated by Sir Isaac Newton.

Friction is a force generated at the interface of two surfaces in contact when there is motion or a tendency for motion of one surface with respect to the other. The magnitudes of maximum static friction and kinetic friction are determined by the coefficient of friction between the two surfaces and by the normal reaction force pressing the two surfaces together. The direction of friction force always opposes the direction of motion or motion tendency.

Other factors that affect the behavior of two bodies in contact when a collision is involved are momentum and elasticity. Linear momentum is the product of an object's mass and its velocity. The total momentum present in a given system remains constant barring the action of external forces. Changes in momentum result from impulses, external forces acting over a time interval. The elasticity of an impact governs the amount of velocity present in the system following the impact. The relative elasticity of two impacting bodies is represented by the coefficient of restitution.

Mechanical work is the product of force and the distance through which the force acts. Mechanical power is the mechanical work done over a time interval. Mechanical energy has two major forms: kinetic and potential. When gravity is the only acting external force, the sum of the kinetic and potential energies possessed by a given body remains constant. Changes in a body's energy are equal to the mechanical work done by an external force.

INTRODUCTORY PROBLEMS

1. How much force must be applied by a kicker to give a stationary 2.5 kg ball an acceleration of 40 m/s^2? (Answer: 100 N)

2. A high jumper with a body weight of 712 N exerts a force of 3 kN against the ground during takeoff. How much force is exerted by the ground on the high jumper? (Answer: 3 kN)

3. What factors affect the magnitude of friction?

4. If m_s between a basketball shoe and a court is 0.56, and the normal reaction force acting on the shoe is 350 N, how much horizontal force is required to cause the shoe to slide? (Answer: >196 N)

5. A football player pushes a 670 N blocking sled. The coefficient of static friction between sled and grass is 0.73, and the coefficient of dynamic friction between sled and grass is 0.68.
   a. How much force must the player exert to start the sled in motion?
   b. How much force is required to keep the sled in motion?
   c. Answer the same two questions with a 100 kg coach standing on the back of the sled.
   (Answers: a. >489.1 N; b. 455.6 N; c. >1205.2 N, 1122.7 N)

6. Lineman A has a mass of 100 kg and is traveling with a velocity of 4 m/s when he collides head-on with lineman B, who has a mass of 90 kg and is traveling at 4.5 m/s. If both players remain on their feet, what will happen? (Answer: lineman B will push lineman A backward with a velocity of 0.03 m/s)

7. Two skaters gliding on ice run into each other head-on. If the two skaters hold onto each other and continue to move as a unit after the collision, what will be their resultant velocity? Skater A has a velocity of 5 m/s and a mass of 65 kg. Skater B has a velocity of 6 m/s and a mass of 60 kg. (Answer: v = 0.28 m/s in the direction originally taken by skater B)

8. A ball dropped on a surface from a 2 m height bounces to a height of 0.98 m. What is the coefficient of restitution between ball and surface? (Answer: 0.7)

9. A set of 20 stairs, each of 20 cm height, is ascended by a 700 N man in a period of 1.25 s. Calculate the mechanical work, power, and change in potential energy during the ascent. (Answer: W = 2800 J, P = 2240 W, PE = 2800 J)

10. A pitched ball with a mass of 1 kg reaches a catcher's glove traveling at a velocity of 28 m/s.
    a. How much momentum does the ball have?
    b. How much impulse is required to stop the ball?
    c. If the ball is in contact with the catcher's glove for 0.5 s during the catch, how much average force is applied by the glove?
    (Answers: a. 28 kg · m/s; b. 28 N s; c. 56 N)

ADDITIONAL PROBLEMS

1. Identify three practical examples of each of Newton's laws of motion, and clearly explain how each example illustrates the law.

2. Select one sport or daily activity, and identify the ways in which the amount of friction present between surfaces in contact affects performance outcome.

3. A 2 kg block sitting on a horizontal surface is subjected to a horizontal force of 7.5 N. If the resulting acceleration of the block is 3 m/s^2,

416   BASIC BIOMECHANICS

what is the magnitude of the friction force opposing the motion of the block? (Answer: 1.5 N)

4. Explain the interrelationships among mechanical work, power, and energy within the context of a specific human motor skill.

5. Explain in what ways mechanical work is and is not related to caloric expenditure. Include in your answer the distinction between positive and negative work and the influence of anthropometric factors.

6. A 108 cm, 0.73 kg golf club is swung for 0.5 s with a constant acceleration of 10 rad/s^2. What is the linear momentum of the club head when it impacts the ball? (Answer: 3.9 kg · m/s)

7. A 6.5 N ball is thrown with an initial velocity of 20 m/s at a 35° angle from a height of 1.5 m.
   a. What is the velocity of the ball if it is caught at a height of 1.5 m?
   b. If the ball is caught at a height of 1.5 m, how much mechanical work is required?
   (Answers: a. 20 m/s; b. 132.5 J)

8. A 50 kg person performs a maximum vertical jump with an initial velocity of 2 m/s.
   a. What is the performer's maximum kinetic energy during the jump?
   b. What is the performer's maximum potential energy during the jump?
   c. What is the performer's minimum kinetic energy during the jump?
   d. How much is the performer's center of mass elevated during the jump?
   (Answers: a. 100 J; b. 100 J; c. 0; d. 20 cm)

9. Using the principle of conservation of mechanical energy, calculate the maximum height achieved by a 7 N ball tossed vertically upward with an initial velocity of 10 m/s. (Answer: 5.1 m)

10. Select one of the following sport activities and speculate about the changes that take place between kinetic and potential forms of mechanical energy.
    a. A single leg support during running
    b. A tennis serve
    c. A pole vault performance
    d. A springboard dive

NAME _____

DATE _____

LABORATORY EXPERIENCES

1. At the *Basic Biomechanics* Online Learning Center (www.mhhe.com/hall5e), go to Student Resources, Chapter 12, Lab Manual, Lab 1, then view Newton's Laws Animation 1 and Animation 2 and Energy Animation 1. Identify the principles that are illustrated, and write explanations of what is demonstrated.

Principle in Newton's Laws Animation 1: _____

Explanation: _____

_____

Principle in Newton's Laws Animation 2: _____

Explanation: _____

_____

Principle in Energy Animation 1: _____

Explanation: _____

_____

2. Following the instructions above, go to the online lab manual and click on Collisions in One Dimension. Play this simulation with all different possible combinations of variable settings. Identify the principle that is illustrated, and write an explanation of what is demonstrated.

Principle: _____

Explanation: _____

_____

_____

_____

3. Have each member of your lab group remove one shoe. Use a spring scale to determine the magnitude of maximum static friction for each shoe on two different surfaces. (Depending on the sensitivity of the spring scale, you may need to load the shoe with weight.) Present your results in a table, and write a paragraph explaining the results.

Shoe	Shoe Weight	Applied Force	μ_s

Explanation: _____

_____

_____

_____

4. Drop five different balls from a height of 2 m on two different surfaces, and carefully observe and record the bounce heights. Calculate the coefficient of restitution for each ball on each surface, and write a paragraph explaining your results.

Ball	Drop Height	Bounce Height	e

5. Using a stopwatch, time each member of your lab group running up a flight of stairs. Use a ruler to measure the height of one stair, then multiply by the number of stairs to calculate the total change in height. Calculate work, power, and change in potential energy for each group member.

Group Member	Wt (N)	Mass (kg)	Time (s)	Av. Vel. (m/s)	Ht Δ (m)	Work (J)	Power (W)	ΔPE (J)

REFERENCES

1. Arampatzis A, Knicker A, Metzler V, and Brüggeman G: Mechanical power in running: a comparison of different approaches, J Biomech 33:457, 2000.

2. Arampatzis A, Schade F, and Brüggemann G-P: Effect of the pole–human body interaction on pole vaulting performance, J Biomech 37:1353, 2004.

3. Aura O and Komi PV: Mechanical efficiency of pure positive and pure negative work with special reference to the work intensity, Int J Sports Med 7:44, 1986.

4. Bennett MS et al: Elastic properties of the human foot and their significance for running. In Bennett MS et al: *Biomechanics in sport,* London, 1988, Mechanical Engineering Publications.

5. Biewener AA and Roberts TJ: Muscle and tendon contributions to force, work, and elastic energy savings: a comparative perspective, Exerc Sport Sci Rev 28:99, 2000.

6. Burke J: *The day the universe changed,* Boston, 1985, Little, Brown.

7. Chang YH and Kram R: Metabolic cost of generating horizontal forces during human running, J Appl Physiol 86:1657, 1999.

8. Cohen BI: Newton's discovery of gravity, Sci Am 244:166, 1981.

9. Dapena J: Biomechanics of elite high jumpers. In Terauds J et al, eds: *Sports biomechanics,* Del Mar, CA, 1984, Academic Publishers.

10. de Koning JJ, de Groot G, and van Ingen Schenau GJ: Ice friction during speed skating, J Biomech 25:565, 1992.

11. Decker MJ, Torry MR, Wyland DJ, Sterett WI, and Steadman J: Gender differences in lower extremity kinematics, kinetics and energy absorption during landing, Clin Biomech 18:662, 2003.

12. Derrick TR: The effects of knee contact angle on impact forces and accelerations, Med Sci Sports Exerc 36:832, 2004.

13. Derrick TR and Mercer JA: Ground/foot impacts: measurement, attenuation, and consequences, Med Sci Sports Exerc 36:830, 2004.

14. Dixon SJ, Collop AC, and Batt ME: Surface effects on ground reaction forces and lower extremity kinematics in running, Med Sci Sports Exerc 32:1919, 2000.

15. Gerlach KE, White SC, Burton HW, Dorn JM, Leddy JJ, and Horvath PJ: Kinetic changes with fatigue and relationship to injury in female runners, Med Sci Sports Exerc 37: 657, 2005.

16. Gottschall JS and Kram R: Ground reaction forces during downhill and uphill running, J Biomech 38:445, 2005.

17. Greenwald RM, Penna LH, and Crisco JJ: Differences in batted ball speed with wood and aluminum baseball bats: a batting cage study, J Appl Biomech 17:241, 2001.

18. Groppel JL et al: Effects of different string tension patterns and racket motion on tennis racket-ball impact, Int J Sport Biomech 3:142, 1987.

19. Groppel JL et al: The effects of string type and tension on impact in midsized and oversized tennis racquets, Int J Sport Biomech 3:40, 1987.

20. Haake SJ, Carre MJ, and Goodwill SR: The dynamic impact characteristics of tennis balls with tennis rackets, J Sports Sci 21:839, 2003.

21. Hatze H: The relationship between the coefficient of restitution and energy losses in tennis rackets, J Appl Biomech 9:124, 1993.

22. Heidt RS et al: Differences in friction and torsional resistance in athletic shoe-turf surface interfaces, Am J Sports Med 24:834, 1996.

23. Hume PA, Keogh J, and Redi D: The role of biomechanics in maximizing distance and accuracy of golf shots, Sports Med 35:429, 2005.

24. Jerome J: Pole vaulting: biomechanics at the bar. In Schrier EW and Allman WF, eds: *Newton at the bat,* New York, 1984, Macmillan/Charles Scribner's Sons.

25. Kiefer J: Bowling: the great oil debate. In Schrier EW and Allman WF, eds: *Newton at the bat,* New York, 1984, Macmillan/Charles Scribner's Sons.

26. Laws K: *The physics of dance,* New York, 1984, Schirmer Books.

27. Lees A and Barton G: The interpretation of relative momentum data to assess the contribution of the free limbs to the generation of vertical velocity in sports activities, J Sports Sci 14:503, 1996.

28. Lejeune TM, Willems PA, and Heglund NC: Mechanics and energetics of human locomotion on sand, J Exp Biol 201:2071, 1998.

29. MacWilliams BA, Choi T, Perezous MK, Chao EY, and McFarland EG: Characteristic ground-reaction forces in baseball pitching, Am J Sports Med 26:66, 1998.

30. McGibbon CA, Puniello MS, and Krebs DE: Mechanical energy transfer during gait in relation to strength impairment and pathology in elderly women, Clin Biomech 16:324, 2001.

31. Neptune RR and van den Bogert AJ: Standard mechanical energy analyses do not correlate with muscle work in cycling, J Biomech 31:239, 1998.

32. Newton RU et al: Influence of load and stretch shortening cycle on the kinematics, kinetics and muscle activation that occurs during explosive upper-body movements, Eur J Appl Physiol 75:333, 1997.

33. Nigg BM: The role of impact forces and foot pronation: a new paradigm, Clin J Sport Med 11:2, 2001.

34. Nigg BM and Wakeling JM: Impact forces and muscle tuning: a new paradigm, Exerc Sport Sci Rev 29:37, 2001.

35. Pons DJ and Vaughan CL: Mechanics of cycling. In Vaughan CL, ed: *Biomechanics of sport,* Boca Raton, FL, 1989, CRC Press.

36. Preis S, Klemms A, and Müller K: Gait analysis by measuring ground reaction forces in children: changes to an adaptive gait pattern between the ages of one and five years, Dev Med Child Neurol 39:228, 1997.

37. Prilutsky BI and Zatsiorsky VM: Tendon action of two-joint muscles: transfer of mechanical energy between joints during jumping, landing, and running, J Biomech 27:25, 1994.

38. Rand KT, Hyer MW, and Williams MH: A dynamic test for comparison of rebound characteristics of three brands of tennis balls. In Groppel JL, ed: *Proceedings of the national symposium on racquet sports,* Champaign, IL, 1979.

39. Rapoport R: Artificial turf: Is the grass greener? In Schrier EW and Allman WF, eds: *Newton at the bat,* New York, 1984, Macmillan/Charles Scribner's Sons.

40. Saikko VO: A three-axis hip joint simulator for wear and friction studies on total hip prostheses, Proc Inst Mech Eng [H] 210:175, 1996.

41. Simpson KJ and Jiang P: Foot landing position during gait influences ground reaction forces, Clin Biomech 14:396, 1999.

42. Stansfield BW et al: Normalized speed, not age, characterizes ground reaction force patterns in 5- to 12-year-old children walking at self-selected speeds, J Pediatr Orthop 21:395, 2001.

43. Stone MH, Sanborn K, O'Bryant HS, Hartman M, Stone ME, Proulx C, Ward B, and Hruby J: Maximum strength-power-performance relationships in collegiate throwers, J Strength Cond Res 17:739, 2003.

44. Thys H, Willems PA, and Saels P: Energy cost, mechanical work and muscular efficiency in swing-through gait with elbow crutches, J Biomech 29:1473, 1996.

45. Tillman MD, Criss RM, Brunt D, and Hass CJ: Landing constraints influence ground reaction forces and lower extremity EMG in female volleyball players, J Appl Biomech 20:38, 2004.

46. Torg JS, Stilwell G, and Rogers K: The effect of ambient temperature on the shoe-surface interface release coefficient, Am J Sports Med 24:79, 1996.

47. van Ingen Schenau GJ, DeBoer RW, and de Groot G: Biomechanics of speed skating. In Vaughan CL, ed: *Biomechanics of sport,* Boca Raton, FL, 1989, CRC Press.

48. Voloshin A: The influence of walking speed on dynamic loading on the human musculoskeletal system, Med Sci Sports Exerc 32:1156, 2000.

49. Whitt FR and Wilson DG: *Bicycling science: ergonomics and mechanics,* Cambridge, MA, 1974, MIT Press.
50. Williams KR: The relationship between mechanical and physiological energy estimates, Med Sci Sports Exerc 17:317, 1985.
51. Wu SK, Gross MT, Prentice WE, and Yu B: Comparison of ball-and-racquet impact force between two tennis backhand stroke techniques, J Orthop Sports Phys Ther 31:247, 2001.

ANNOTATED READINGS

Alexander R McN: Storage and release of elastic energy in the locomotor system and the stretch-shortening cycle. In Nigg BM, MacIntosh BR, and Mester J, eds: *Biomechanics and biology of human movement,* Champaign, IL, 2000, Human Kinetics.
   Discusses principles of elasticity, properties of body parts, and spring functions.
de Koning JJ, de Groot G, and van Ingen Schenau GJ: Ice friction during speed skating, J Biomech 25:565, 1992.
   Presents an interesting discussion on theories as to why the coefficient of friction between a racing skate and the ice is so small.
McMahon TA and Greene PR: Fast running tracks, Sci Am 239:148, 1978.
   Includes a fascinating discussion of the thought processes behind the degree of elasticity engineered into Harvard's indoor track; using this track, runners can better their best times by nearly 3%.
Nigg BM, Stefanyshyn D, and Denoth J: Mechanical considerations of work and energy. In Nigg BM, MacIntosh BR, and Mester J, eds: *Biomechanics and biology of human movement,* Champaign, IL, 2000, Human Kinetics.
   Discusses the concepts of mechanical work and mechanical energy, calculation of mechanical energy during human movement, and conservation of energy.

RELATED WEB SITES

Advanced Medical Technology
www.amtiweb.com
   Provides information on the AMTI force platforms, with reference to ground reaction forces in gait analysis, balance and posture, and other topics.
Answers.com: Mechanical work
www.answers.com/topic/mechanical-work
   Lists definitions and examples of mechanical work.
Exploratorium's Science of Hockey
www.exploratorium.edu/hockey/
   Explains scientific concepts related to hockey, including the friction between ice and skate and the mechanics of skating.
Fear of Physics: What Is Friction
www.fearofphysics.com/Friction/frintro.html
   Includes text and illustrations, plus a link to a simulation.
Kistler
www.kistler.com
   Describes a series of force platforms for measuring ground reaction forces.
Physics Classroom: Mechanical Energy
www.physicsclassroom.com/Class/energy/U5L1d.html
   Includes definitions, illustrations, and questions with answers related to work and energy.
Scienceworld: Friction
scienceworld.wolfram.com/physics/Friction.html
   Includes definitions and examples of friction coefficients.

422   BASIC BIOMECHANICS

KEY TERMS

coefficient of friction	number that serves as an index of the interaction between two surfaces in contact
coefficient of restitution	number that serves as an index of elasticity for colliding bodies
friction	force acting at the area of contact between two surfaces in the direction opposite that of motion or motion tendency
impact	collision characterized by the exchange of a large force during a small time interval
impulse	product of a force and the time interval over which the force acts
kinetic energy	energy of motion calculated as $\frac{1}{2} mv^2$
kinetic friction	constant magnitude friction generated between two surfaces in contact during motion
linear momentum	quantity of motion, measured as the product of a body's mass and its velocity
maximum static friction	maximum amount of friction that can be generated between two static surfaces
normal reaction force	force acting perpendicular to two surfaces in contact
perfectly elastic impact	impact during which the velocity of the system is conserved
perfectly plastic impact	impact resulting in the total loss of system velocity
potential energy	energy by virtue of a body's position or configuration, calculated as the product of weight and height
power	rate of work production, calculated as work divided by the time during which the work was done
strain energy	capacity to do work by virtue of a deformed body's return to its original shape
work	in a mechanical context, force multiplied by the displacement of the resistance in the direction of the force

13

Equilibrium and Human Movement

After completing this chapter, you will be able to:

Define torque, quantify resultant torques, and identify the factors that affect resultant joint torques.

Identify the mechanical advantages associated with the different classes of levers, and explain the concept of leverage within the human body.

Solve basic quantitative problems using the equations of static equilibrium.

Define center of gravity, and explain the significance of center of gravity location in the human body.

Explain how mechanical factors affect a body's stability.

**Visit the Online Learning Center at www.mhhe.com/hall5e
to access the Online Lab Manual and many additional resources.**

424   BASIC BIOMECHANICS

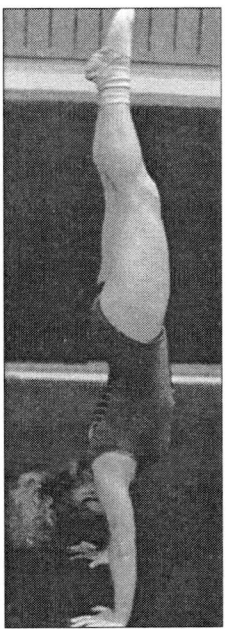

Many athletic skills require mechanical stability.

torque
the rotary effect of a force about an axis of rotation, measured as the product of the force and the perpendicular distance between the force's line of action and the axis

moment arm
shortest (perpendicular) distance between a force's line of action and an axis of rotation

W hy do long jumpers and high jumpers lower their centers of gravity before takeoff? What mechanical factors enable a wheelchair to remain stationary on a graded ramp or a Sumo wrestler to resist the attack of his opponent? A body's mechanical stability is based on its resistance to both linear and angular motion. This chapter introduces the kinetics of angular motion, along with the factors that affect mechanical stability.

EQUILIBRIUM

Torque

As discussed in Chapter 3, the rotary effect created by an applied force is known as torque, or *moment of force.* Torque, which may be thought of as *rotary force,* is the angular equivalent of linear force. Algebraically, torque is the product of force and the force's moment arm, or the perpendicular distance from the force's line of action to the axis of rotation:

$$T = Fd_\perp$$

Thus, both the magnitude of a force and the length of its moment arm equally affect the amount of torque generated (Figure 13-1). Moment arm is also sometimes referred to as *force arm* or *lever arm.*

As may be observed in Figure 13-2, the moment arm is the shortest distance between the force's line of action and the axis of rotation. A force directed through an axis of rotation produces no torque, because the force's moment arm is zero.

Within the human body, the moment arm for a muscle with respect to a joint center is the perpendicular distance between the muscle's line of action and the joint center (Figure 13-3). As a joint moves through a range of motion, there are changes in the moment arms of the muscles crossing the joint. For any given muscle, the moment arm is largest when the angle of pull on the bone is closest to 90°. At the elbow, as the angle of pull moves away from 90° in either direction, the moment arm for the elbow flexors is progressively diminished. Since torque is the product of moment arm and muscle force, changes in moment arm directly affect the joint torque that a muscle generates. For a muscle to generate a constant joint torque during an exercise, it must produce more force as its moment arm decreases.

FIGURE 13-1

Which position of force application is best for opening the swinging door? Experience should verify that position **C** is best.

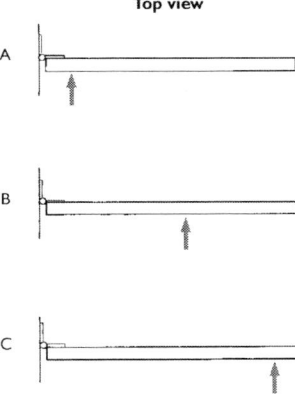

Top view

Top view

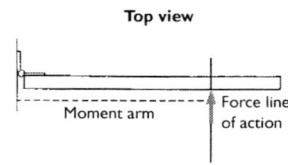

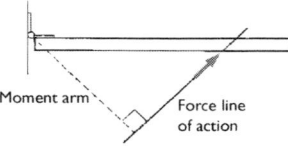

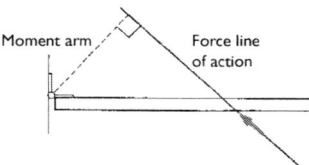

FIGURE 13-2

The moment arm of a force is the perpendicular distance from the force's line of action to the axis of rotation (the door hinge).

FIGURE 13-3

A muscle's moment arm is maximal at a 90° angle of pull. As the line of pull moves away from 90° in either direction, the moment arm becomes progressively smaller.

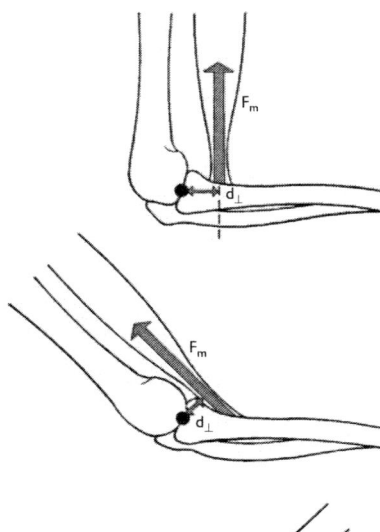

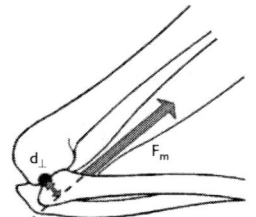

426   BASIC BIOMECHANICS

●*It is easiest to initiate rotation when force is applied perpendicularly and as far away as possible from the axis of rotation.*

In the sport of rowing, where adjacent crew members traditionally row on opposite sides of the hull, the moment arm between the force applied by the oar and the stern of the boat is a factor affecting performance (Figure 13-4). With the traditional arrangement, the rowers on one side of the boat are positioned farther from the stern than their counterparts on the other side, thus causing a net torque and a resulting lateral oscillation about the stern during rowing (28). The Italian rig eliminates this problem by positioning rowers so that no net torque is produced, assuming that the force produced by each rower with each stroke is nearly the same (Figure 13-4). Italian and German rowers have similarly developed alternative positionings for the eight-member crew (Figure 13-5).

FIGURE 13-4

A. This crew arrangement creates a net torque about the stern of the boat because the sum of the top side oar moment arms $(d_1 + d_2)$ is less than the sum of the bottom side moment arms $(d_3 + d_4)$. **B.** This arrangement eliminates the problem, assuming that all rowers stroke simultaneously and produce equal force, because $(d_1 + d_2) = (d_3 + d_4)$.

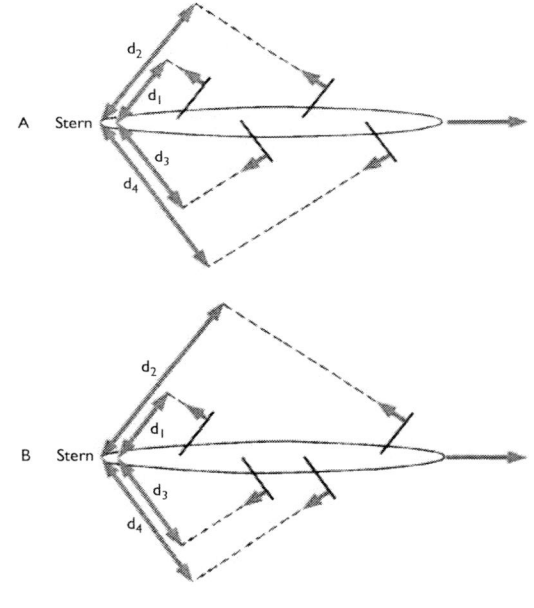

FIGURE 13-5

The Italians and Germans have used alternative positionings for eight-member crews. The torques produced by the oar forces with respect to the stern are balanced in arrangements **B** and **C,** but not in the traditional arrangement shown in **A.**

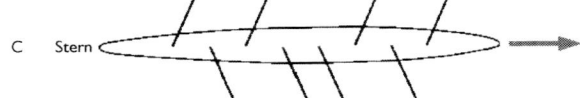

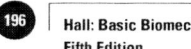
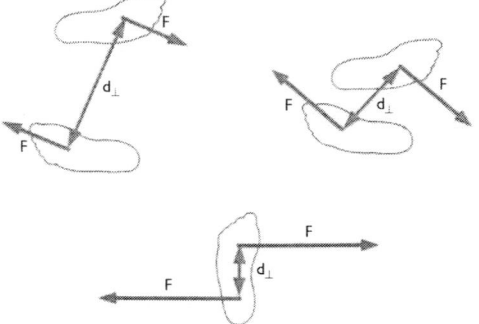

FIGURE 13-6

The wider a dancer's stance, the greater the moment arm for the force couple generated by the feet when a turn is executed. When rotation is initiated from a single-foot stance, the moment arm becomes the distance between the support points of the foot.

Another example of the significance of moment arm length is provided by a dancer's foot placement during preparation for execution of a total body rotation around the vertical axis. When a dancer initiates a turn, the torque producing the turn is provided by equal and oppositely directed forces exerted by the feet against the floor. A pair of equal and opposite forces is known as a force couple. Because the forces in a couple are positioned on opposite sides of the axis of rotation, they produce torque in the same direction. The torque generated by a couple is therefore the sum of the products of each force and its moment arm. Turning from fifth position, with a small distance between the feet, requires greater force production by a dancer than turning at the same rate from fourth position, in which the moment arms of the forces in the couple are longer (Figure 13-6). Significantly more force is required when the torque is generated by a single support foot, for which the moment arm is reduced to the distance between the metatarsals and the calcaneus (15).

couple
pair of equal, oppositely directed forces that act on opposite sides of an axis of rotation to produce torque

Torque is a vector quantity, and is therefore characterized by both magnitude and direction. The magnitude of the torque created by a given force is equal to $Fd_\perp$, and the direction of a torque may be described as clockwise or counterclockwise. As discussed in Chapter 11, the counterclockwise direction is conventionally referred to as the positive $(+)$ direction, and the clockwise direction is regarded as negative $(-)$. The magnitudes of two or more torques acting at a given axis of rotation can be added using the rules of vector composition (see Sample Problem 13.1).

Resultant Joint Torques

The concept of torque is important in the study of human movement, because torque produces movement of the body segments. As discussed in Chapter 6, when a muscle crossing a joint develops tension, it produces a force pulling on the bone to which it attaches, thereby creating torque at the joint the muscle crosses.

●*The product of muscle tension and muscle moment arm produces a torque at the joint crossed by the muscle.*

Much human movement involves simultaneous tension development in agonist and antagonist muscle groups. The tension in the antagonists controls the velocity of the movement and enhances the stability of the joint at which the movement is occurring. Since antagonist tension development creates torque in the direction opposite that of the torque produced by the agonist, the resulting movement at the joint is a function of the net torque. When net muscle torque and joint movement occur in the same direction, the torque is termed *concentric,* and muscle torque in the direction opposite joint motion is considered to be *eccentric.* Although

SAMPLE PROBLEM 13.1

Two children sit on opposite sides of a playground seesaw. If Joey, weighing
200 N, is 1.5 m from the seesaw's axis of rotation, and Susie, weighing 190 N,
is 1.6 m from the axis of rotation, which end of the seesaw will drop?

Known

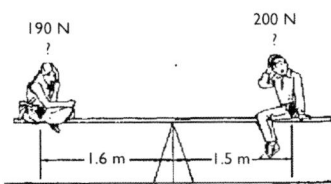

Joey: $\text{wt}(F_J) = 200$ N
        $d_{\perp J} = 1.5$ m
Susie: $\text{wt}(F_S) = 190$ N
        $d_{\perp S} = 1.6$ m

Solution

The seesaw will rotate in the direction of the resultant torque at its axis of
rotation. To find the resultant torque, the torques created by both children
are summed according to the rules of vector composition. The torque produced by Susie's body weight is in a counterclockwise (positive) direction,
and the torque produced by Joey's body weight is in a clockwise (negative)
direction.

$$T_a = (F_S)(d_{\perp S}) - (F_J)(d_{\perp J})$$
$$= (190 \text{ N})(1.6 \text{ m}) - (200 \text{ N})(1.5 \text{ m})$$
$$= 304 \text{ N-m} - 300 \text{ N-m}$$
$$= 4 \text{ N-m}$$

The resultant torque is in a positive direction, and Susie's end of the
seesaw will fall.

these terms are generally useful descriptors in analysis of muscular function, their application is complicated when two-joint or multijoint muscles
are considered, since there may be concentric torque at one joint and eccentric torque at a second joint crossed by the same muscle.

Because directly measuring the forces produced by muscles during
the execution of most movement skills is not practical, measurements
or estimates of resultant joint torques (joint moments) are often studied
to investigate the patterns of muscle contributions. A number of factors,
including the weight of body segments, the motion of the body segments,
and the action of external forces, may contribute to net joint torques.
Young infants generate irregular patterns of joint torques, possibly because of their inexperience in predicting the magnitude and direction
of external forces (14). Among adults, however, joint torque profiles are
typically matched to the requirements of the task at hand and provide at
least general estimates of muscle group contribution levels.

Interestingly, however, with advanced age there is commonly a redistribution of lower extremity joint torques during walking gait, with the
elderly using the hip extensors more and the knee extensors and plantar
flexors less than young adults walking at the same pace (5). Because hip
extension torque has been shown to be significantly related to walking
speed and stride length among the elderly, researchers have suggested

that strengthening the hip extensors may improve gait characteristics in this group (1).

To better understand muscle function during running, a number of investigators have studied resultant joint torques at the hip, knee, and ankle throughout the running stride. Figure 13-7 displays representative resultant joint torques and angular velocities for the hip, knee, and ankle during a running stride, as calculated from film and force platform data. In Figure 13-7, when the resultant joint torque curve and the angular velocity curves are on the same side of the zero line, the torque is concentric; the torque is eccentric when the reverse is true. As may be observed from Figure 13-7, both concentric and eccentric torques are present at the lower-extremity joints during running.

During both running and walking, individuals with anterior cruciate ligament (ACL) injury use greater extensor torques at the hip and ankle and lower extensor torques at the knee as compared to uninjured people (6). Research indicates that as compared to normal individuals, those with ACL injuries also display greater co-contraction of the knee flexor muscles during knee extension, which contributes to stabilization of the knee (19).

Lower-extremity joint torques during cycling at a given power are affected by pedaling rate, seat height, length of the pedal crank arm, and distance from the pedal spindle to the ankle joint. Average hip and knee torques during cycling under cruising conditions have been reported to

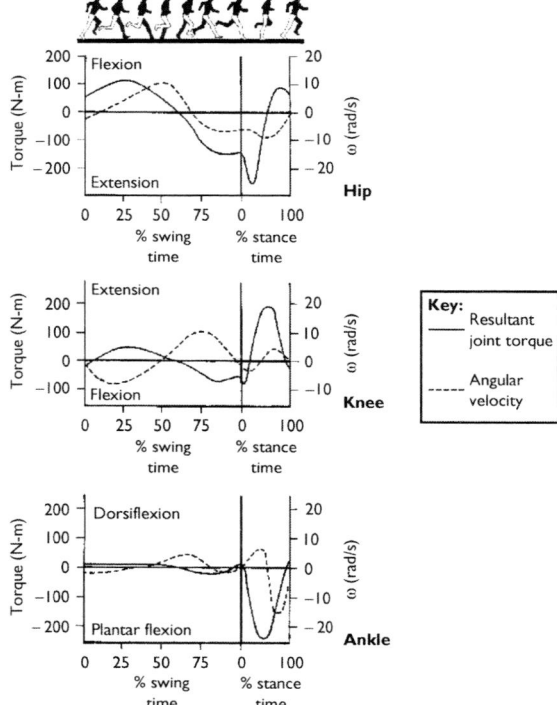

FIGURE 13-7

Representative joint torques and angular velocity curves for the lower extremity during running. Modified from Putnam CA and Kozey JW: Substantive issues in running. In Vaughan CL, ed: *Biomechanics of sport,* Boca Raton, FL, 1989, CRC Press.

430 BASIC BIOMECHANICS

FIGURE 13-8

Absolute average joint torques for the hip, knee, and ankle versus pedaling rate during cycling. Modified from Redfield R and Hull ML: On the relation between joint moments and pedalling at constant power in bicycling, J Biomech 19:317, 1986.

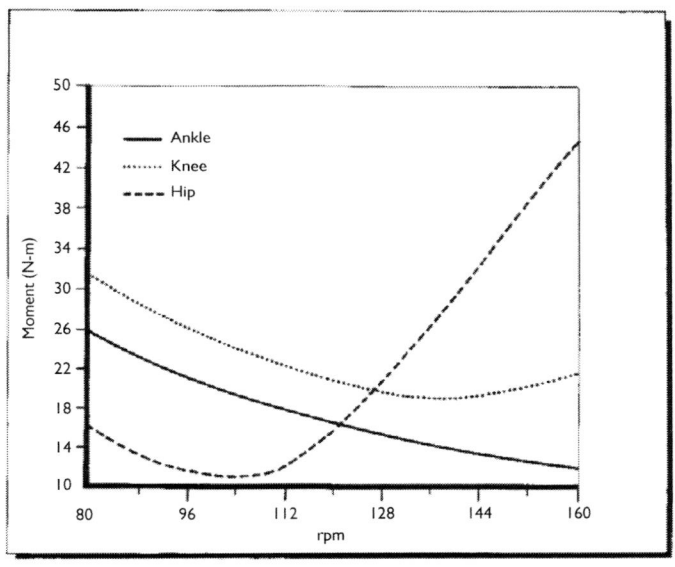

The torques required at the hip, knee, and ankle during cycling at a given power are influenced by body position and cycle dimensions.

be minimum at approximately 105 rotations per minute (24). Figure 13-8 shows the changes in average resultant torque at the hip, knee, and ankle joints with changes in pedaling rate at a constant power.

It is widely assumed that the muscular force (and subsequently, joint torque) requirements of resistance exercise increase as the amount of resistance increases. However, this is true only as long as movement kinematics remain constant. It has been shown, for example, that during the squat exercise, use of a wide stance as compared to a narrow stance produces greater torques at both the hip and the knee (7).

Another factor influencing joint torques during exercise is movement speed. When other factors remain constant, increased movement speed is associated with increased resultant joint torques during exercises such as the squat (23). However, increased movement speed during weight training is generally undesirable, because increased speed increases not only the muscle tension required but also the likelihood of incorrect technique and subsequent injury. Acceleration of the load early in the performance of a resistance exercise also generates momentum, which means that the involved muscles need not work so hard throughout the range of motion as would otherwise be the case. For these reasons, it is both safer and more effective to perform exercises at slow, controlled movement speeds.

Levers

When muscles develop tension, pulling on bones to support or move the resistance created by the weight of the body segment(s) and possibly the weight of an added load, the muscle and bone are functioning mechanically as a lever. A lever is a rigid bar that rotates about an axis, or fulcrum. Force applied to the lever moves a resistance. In the human body, the bone acts as the rigid bar; the joint is the axis, or fulcrum; and the muscles apply force. The three relative arrangements of the applied force, resistance, and axis of rotation for a lever are shown in Figure 13-9.

lever
a simple machine consisting of a relatively rigid, barlike body that may be made to rotate about an axis

fulcrum
the point of support, or axis, about which a lever may be made to rotate

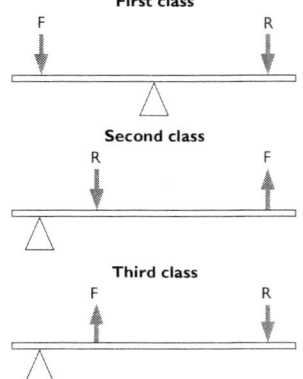

First class

Second class

Third class

FIGURE 13-9

Relative locations of the applied force, the resistance, and the fulcrum, or axis of rotation, determine lever classifications.

With a first-class lever, the applied force and resistance are located on opposite sides of the axis. The playground seesaw is an example of a first-class lever, as are a number of commonly used tools, including scissors, pliers, and crowbars (Figure 13-10). Within the human body, the simultaneous action of agonist and antagonist muscle groups on opposite sides of a joint axis is analogous to the functioning of a first-class lever, with the agonists providing the applied force and the antagonists supplying a resistance force. With a first-class lever, the applied force and resistance may be at equal distances from the axis, or one may be farther away from the axis than the other.

In a second-class lever, the applied force and the resistance are on the same side of the axis, with the resistance closer to the axis. A wheelbarrow, a lug nut wrench, and a nutcracker are examples of second-class levers, although there are no completely analogous examples in the human body (Figure 13-10).

first-class lever
lever positioned with the applied force and the resistance on opposite sides of the axis of rotation

second-class lever
lever positioned with the resistance between the applied force and the fulcrum

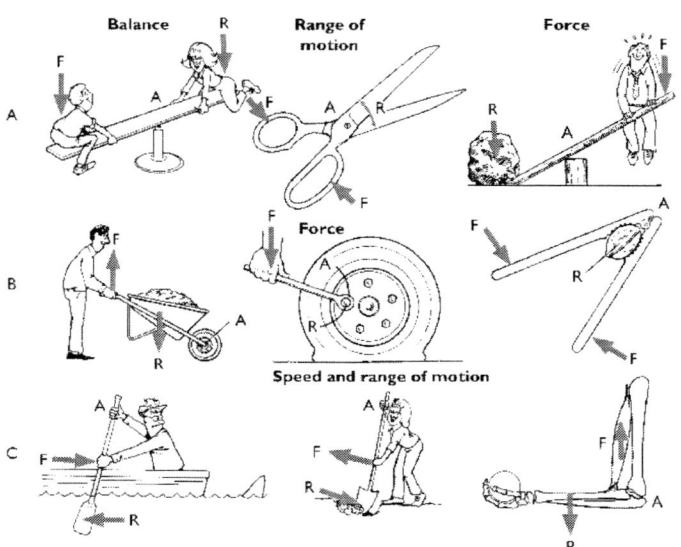

FIGURE 13-10

A. First-class levers.
B. Second-class levers.
C. Third-class levers. Note that the paddle and shovel function as third-class levers only when the top hand does not apply force but serves as a fixed axis of rotation.

432 BASIC BIOMECHANICS

third-class lever
lever positioned with the applied force between the fulcrum and the resistance

With a third-class lever, the force and the resistance are on the same side of the axis, but the applied force is closer to the axis. A canoe paddle and a shovel can serve as third-class levers (Figure 13-10). Most muscle-bone lever systems of the human body are also of the third class for concentric contractions, with the muscle supplying the applied force and attaching to the bone at a short distance from the joint center compared to the distance at which the resistance supplied by the weight of the body segment or that of a more distal body segment acts (Figure 13-11). As shown in Figure 13-12, however, during eccentric contractions, it is the muscle that supplies the resistance against the applied external force. During eccentric contractions, muscle and bone function as a second-class lever.

A lever system can serve one of two purposes (Figure 13-13). Whenever the moment arm of the applied force is greater than the moment arm of the resistance, the magnitude of the applied force needed to move a given resistance is less than the magnitude of the resistance. Whenever the resistance arm is longer than the force arm, the resistance may be moved through a relatively large distance. The mechanical effectiveness of a lever for moving a resistance may be expressed quantitatively as its mechanical advantage, which is the ratio of the moment arm of the force to the moment arm of the resistance:

mechanical advantage
ratio of force arm to resistance arm for a given lever

●*The moment arm of an applied force can also be referred to as the force arm, and the moment arm of a resistance can be referred to as the resistance arm.*

$$\text{mechanical advantage} = \frac{\text{moment arm (force)}}{\text{moment arm (resistance)}}$$

Whenever the moment arm of the force is longer than the moment arm of the resistance, the mechanical advantage ratio reduces to a number

FIGURE 13-11

Most levers within the human body are third class. **A.** The biceps at the elbow. **B.** The patellar tendon at the knee. **C.** The medial deltoid at the shoulder.

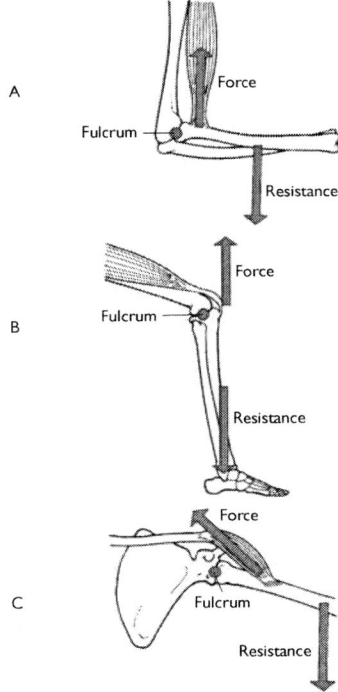

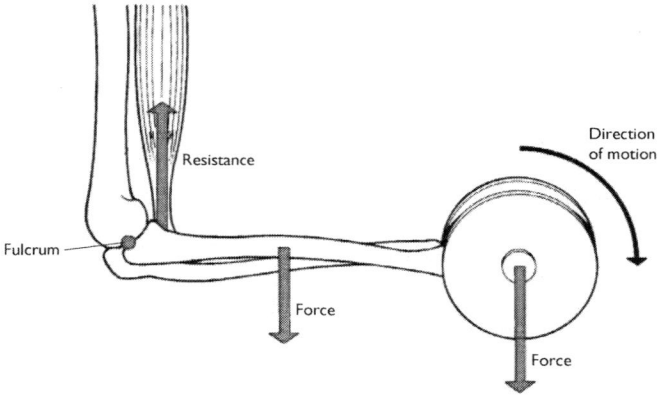

FIGURE 13-12

The elbow flexors contract eccentrically to apply a braking resistance and to control movement speed during the down phase of a curl exercise. In this case, the muscle–bone lever system is second class.

that is greater than one, and the magnitude of the applied force required to move the resistance is less than the magnitude of the resistance. The ability to move a resistance with a force that is smaller than the resistance offers a clear advantage when a heavy load must be moved. As shown in Figure 13-10, a wheelbarrow combines second-class leverage with rolling friction to facilitate transporting a load. When removing a lug nut from an automobile wheel, it is helpful to use as long an extension as is practical on the wrench to increase mechanical advantage.

Alternatively, when the mechanical advantage ratio is less than one, a force that is larger than the resistance must be applied to cause motion of the lever. Although this arrangement is less effective in the sense that

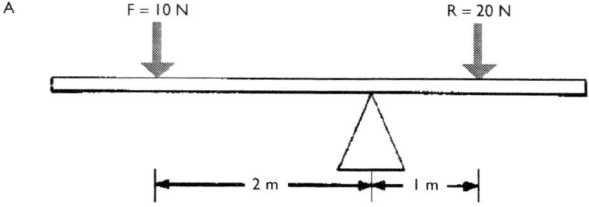

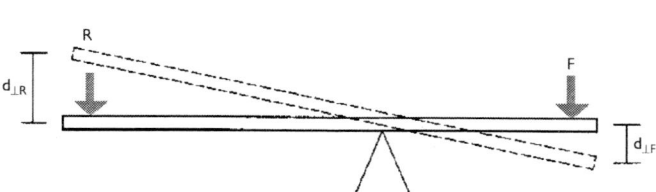

FIGURE 13-13

A. A force can balance a larger resistance when its moment arm is longer than the moment arm of the resistance. **B.** A force can move a resistance through a larger range of motion when the moment arm of the force is shorter than the moment arm of the resistance.

434   BASIC BIOMECHANICS

Skilled pitchers often maximize the length of the moment arm between the ball hand and the total-body axis of rotation during the delivery of a pitch to maximize the effect of the torque produced by the muscles.

more force is required, a small movement of the lever at the point of force application moves the resistance through a larger range of motion (see Figure 13-13).

During wheelchair propulsion, mechanical advantage is the ratio of handrim radius to wheel radius. Since handrim radius is always smaller than wheel radius, the mechanical advantage for wheelchair propulsion is always less than one. This is advantageous, because movements of the handrims translate to larger movements of the wheels, and the resistance, which is the force of rolling friction, is relatively low. For a given applied force on the pushrim, wheelchair velocity is proportional to mechanical advantage. Researchers have found that a mechanical advantage of 0.43 is more mechanically efficient than mechanical advantages ranging up to 0.87 for wheelchair propulsion, because at lower mechanical advantage (and lower velocity), the wheelchair occupant is able to apply force more directly in line with the path of handrim rotation (31). During wheelchair propulsion, mechanical advantage has been shown to have a significant effect on oxygen uptake, energy cost, mechanical efficiency, and stroke frequency (29).

Anatomical Levers

Skilled athletes in many sports intentionally maximize the length of the effective moment arm for force application to maximize the effect of the torque produced by muscles about a joint. During execution of the serve in tennis, expert players not only strike the ball with the arm fully extended but also vigorously rotate the body in the transverse plane, making the spine the axis of rotation and maximizing the length of the anatomical lever delivering the force. The same strategy is employed by accomplished baseball pitchers. As discussed in Chapter 11, the longer the radius of rotation, the greater the linear velocity of the racket head or hand delivering the pitch, and the greater the resultant velocity of the struck or thrown ball.

In the human body, most muscle–bone lever systems are of the third class, and therefore have a mechanical advantage of less than one. Although this arrangement promotes range of motion and angular speed of the body segments, the muscle forces generated must be in excess of the resistance force or forces if positive mechanical work is to be done.

The angle at which a muscle pulls on a bone also affects the mechanical effectiveness of the muscle–bone lever system. The force of muscular tension is resolved into two force components—one perpendicular to the attached bone and one parallel to the bone (Figure 13-14). As discussed in Chapter 6, only the component of muscle force acting perpendicular to the bone—the rotary component—actually causes the bone to rotate about the joint center. The component of muscle force directed parallel to the bone pulls the bone either away from the joint center (a dislocating component) or toward the joint center (a stabilizing component), depending on whether the angle between the bone and the attached muscle is less than or greater than 90°. The angle of maximum mechanical advantage for any muscle is the angle at which the most rotary force can be produced. At a joint such as the elbow, the relative angle present at the joint is close to the angles of attachment of the elbow flexors. The maximum mechanical advantages for the brachialis, biceps, and brachioradialis occur between angles at the elbow of approximately 75° and 90° (Figure 13-15).

As joint angle and mechanical advantage change, muscle length also changes. Alterations in the lengths of the elbow flexors associated with

• *The force-generating capability of a muscle is affected by muscle length, cross-sectional area, moment arm, angle of attachment, shortening velocity, and state of training.*

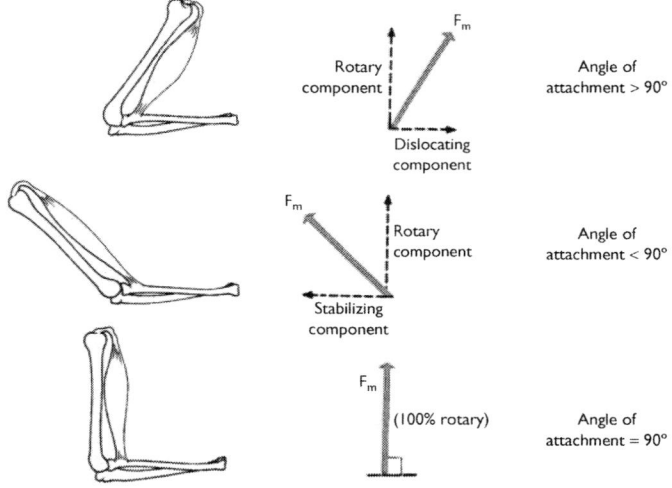

Muscle force can be resolved into rotary and dislocating components.

changes in angle at the elbow are shown in Figure 13-16. These changes affect the amount of tension a muscle can generate, as discussed in Chapter 6. The angle at the elbow at which maximum flexion torque is produced is approximately 80°, with torque capability progressively diminishing as the angle at the elbow changes in either direction (30).

The varying mechanical effectiveness of muscle groups for producing joint rotation with changes in joint angle is the underlying basis for the design of

● *Variable-resistance training devices are designed to match the resistance offered to the torque-generating capability of the muscle group as it varies throughout a range of motion.*

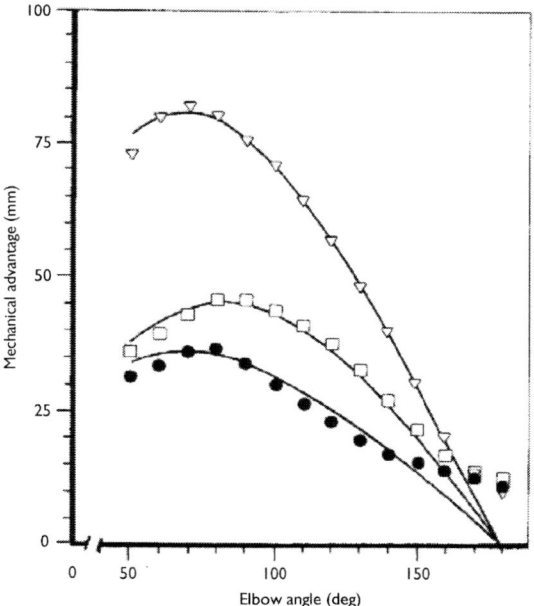

Mechanical advantage of the brachialis (●), biceps (□), and brachioradialis (▽) as a function of elbow angle. Modified from van Zuylen EJ, van Zelzen A, and van der Gon JJD: A biomechanical model for flexion torques of human arm muscles as a function of elbow angle, J Biomech 21:183, 1988.

436   BASIC BIOMECHANICS

FIGURE 13-16

Contractile length of the
brachialis (●), biceps (□),
and brachioradialis (▽) as
a function of elbow angle.
Modified from van Zuylen EJ, van
Zelzen A, and van der Gon JJD:
A biomechanical model for flexion
torques of human arm muscles as a
function of elbow angle, J Biomech
21:183, 1988.

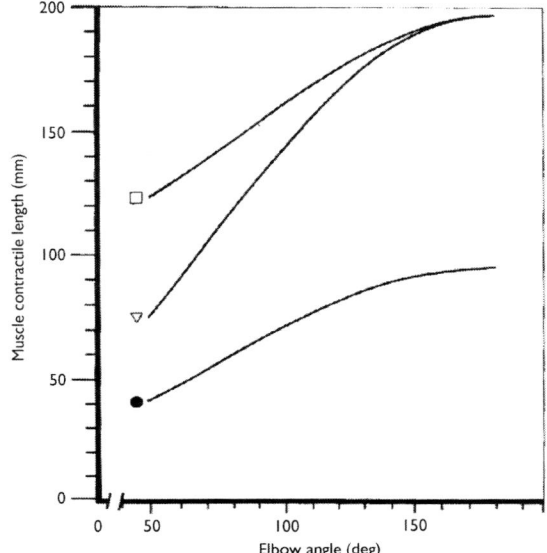

●*The term isokinetic implies
constant angular velocity at a
joint when applied to exercise
machinery.*

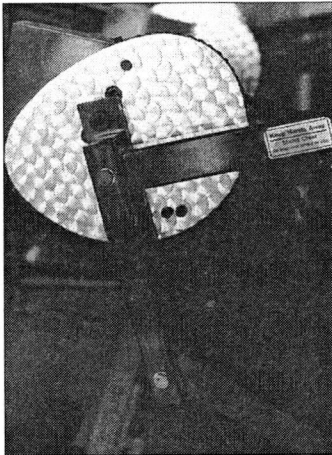

*A cam in a variable-resistance
training machine is designed
to match the resistance offered
to the mechanical advantage
of the muscle.*

modern variable-resistance strength-training devices. These machines are
designed to match the changing torque-generating capability of a muscle
group throughout the range of motion at a joint. Machines manufactured
by Universal (the Centurion) and Nautilus are examples. Although these
machines offer more relative resistance through the extremes of joint range
of motion than free weights, the resistance patterns incorporated are not an
exact match for average human strength curves (8).

Isokinetic machines represent another approach to matching torque-
generating capability with resistance. These devices are generally designed so that an individual applies force to a lever arm that rotates at a
constant angular velocity. If the joint center is aligned with the center of
rotation of the lever arm, the body segment rotates with the same (constant) angular velocity of the lever arm. If volitional torque production by
the involved muscle group is maximum throughout the range of motion,
a maximum matched resistance theoretically is achieved. However, when
force is initially applied to the lever arm of isokinetic machines, acceleration occurs, and the angular velocity of the arm fluctuates until the set rotational speed is reached (8). Because optimal use of isokinetic resistance
machines requires that the user be focused on exerting maximal effort
throughout the range of motion, some individuals prefer other modes of
resistance training.

Equations of Static Equilibrium

Equilibrium is a state characterized by balanced forces and torques (no
net forces and torques). In keeping with Newton's first law, a body in equilibrium is either motionless or moving with a constant velocity. Whenever

a body is completely motionless, it is in static equilibrium. Three conditions must be met for a body to be in a state of static equilibrium:

static equilibrium
a motionless state characterized by $\Sigma F_v = 0$, $\Sigma F_h = 0$, and $\Sigma T = 0$

1. The sum of all vertical forces (or force components) acting on the body must be zero.
2. The sum of all horizontal forces (or force components) acting on the body must be zero.
3. The sum of all torques must be zero:

$$\Sigma F_v = 0$$
$$\Sigma F_h = 0$$
$$\Sigma T = 0$$

The capital Greek letter sigma (Σ) means *the sum of,* F_v represents vertical forces, F_h represents horizontal forces, and T is torque. Whenever an object is in a static state, it may be inferred that all three conditions are in effect, since the violation of any one of the three conditions would result in motion of the body. The conditions of static equilibrium are valuable tools for solving problems relating to human movement (see Sample Problems 13.2, 13.3, and 13.4).

• *The presence of a net force acting on a body results in acceleration of the body.*

Equations of Dynamic Equilibrium

Bodies in motion are considered to be in a state of dynamic equilibrium, with all acting forces resulting in equal and oppositely directed inertial forces. This general concept was first identified by the French mathematician D'Alembert, and is known as *D'Alembert's principle.* Modified versions

dynamic equilibrium (D'Alembert's principle)
concept indicating a balance between applied forces and inertial forces for a body in motion

---

SAMPLE PROBLEM 13.2

How much force must be produced by the biceps brachii, attaching at 90° to the radius at 3 cm from the center of rotation at the elbow joint, to support a weight of 70 N held in the hand at a distance of 30 cm from the elbow joint? (Neglect the weight of the forearm and hand, and neglect any action of other muscles.)

Known

$$d_m = 3 \text{ cm}$$
$$wt = 70 \text{ N}$$
$$d_{wt} = 30 \text{ cm}$$

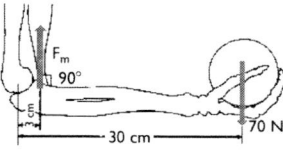

Solution

Since the situation described is static, the sum of the torques acting at the elbow must be equal to zero:

$$\Sigma T_e = 0$$
$$\Sigma T_e = (F_m)(d_m) - (wt)(d_{wt})$$
$$0 = (F_m)(0.03 \text{ m}) - (70 \text{ N})(0.30 \text{ m})$$
$$F_m = \frac{(70 \text{ N})(0.30 \text{ m})}{0.03 \text{ m}}$$

$$F_m = 700 \text{ N}$$

SAMPLE PROBLEM 13.3

Two individuals apply force to opposite sides of a frictionless swinging door. If A applies a 30 N force at a 40° angle 45 cm from the door's hinge and B applies force at a 90° angle 38 cm from the door's hinge, what amount of force is applied by B if the door remains in a static position?

Known

$$F_A = 30 \text{ N}$$
$$d_{\perp A} = (0.45 \text{ m})(\sin 40)$$
$$d_{\perp B} = 0.38 \text{ m}$$

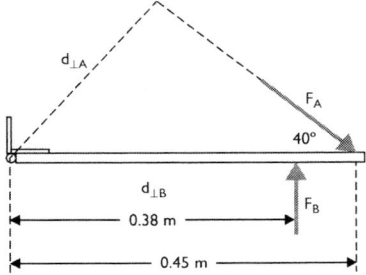

Solution

The equations of static equilibrium are used to solve for F_B. The solution may be found by summing the torques created at the hinge by both forces:

$$\Sigma T_h = 0$$
$$\Sigma T_h = (F_A)(d_{\perp A}) - (F_B)(d_{\perp B})$$
$$0 = (30 \text{ N})(0.45 \text{ m})(\sin 40) - (F_B)(0.38 \text{ m})$$
$$F_B = 22.8 \text{ N}$$

of the equations of static equilibrium, which incorporate factors known as *inertia vectors,* describe the conditions of dynamic equilibrium. The equations of dynamic equilibrium may be stated as follows:

$$\Sigma F_x - m\bar{a}_x = 0$$
$$\Sigma F_y - m\bar{a}_y = 0$$
$$\Sigma T_G - \bar{I}\alpha = 0$$

The sums of the horizontal and vertical forces acting on a body are ΣF_x and ΣF_y; $m\bar{a}_x$ and $m\bar{a}_y$ are the products of the body's mass and the horizontal and vertical accelerations of the body's center of mass; ΣT_G is the sum of torques about the body's center of mass, and is the product of the body's moment of inertia about the center of mass and the body's angular acceleration (see Sample Problem 13.5). (The concept of moment of inertia is discussed in Chapter 14.)

A familiar example of the effect of D'Alembert's principle is the change in vertical force experienced when riding in an elevator. As the elevator accelerates upward, an inertial force in the opposite direction is created, and body weight as measured on a scale in the elevator increases. As the elevator accelerates downward, an upwardly directed inertial force decreases body weight as measured on a scale in the elevator. Although body weight remains constant, the vertical inertial force changes the magnitude of the reaction force measured on the scale.

SAMPLE PROBLEM 13.4

The quadriceps tendon attaches to the tibia at a 30° angle 4 cm from the joint center at the knee. When an 80 N weight is attached to the ankle 28 cm from the knee joint, how much force is required of the quadriceps to maintain the leg in a horizontal position? What is the magnitude and direction of the reaction force exerted by the femur on the tibia? (Neglect the weight of the leg and the action of other muscles.)

$$wt = 80 \text{ N}$$
$$d_{wt} = 0.28 \text{ cm}$$
$$d_F = 0.04 \text{ cm}$$

F_m

30°

R

0.04 m

0.28 m

80 N

Solution

The equations of static equilibrium can be used to solve for the unknown quantities:

$$\Sigma T_k = 0$$
$$\Sigma T_k = (F_m \sin 30)(d_F) - (wt)(d_{wt})$$
$$0 = (F_m \sin 30)(0.04 \text{ m}) - (80 \text{ N})(0.28 \text{ m})$$
$$\boxed{F_m = 1120 \text{ N}}$$

The equations of static equilibrium can be used to solve for the vertical and horizontal components of the reaction force exerted by the femur on the tibia. Summation of vertical forces yields the following:

$$\Sigma F_v = 0$$
$$\Sigma F_v = R_v + (F_m \sin 30) - wt$$
$$0 = R_v + 1120 \sin 30 \text{ N} - 80 \text{ N}$$
$$R_v = -480 \text{ N}$$

Summation of horizontal forces yields the following:

$$\Sigma F_h = 0$$
$$\Sigma F_h = R_h - (F_m \cos 30)$$
$$0 = R_h - 1120 \cos 30 \text{ N}$$
$$R_h = 970 \text{ N}$$

The Pythagorean theorem can now be used to find the magnitude of the resultant reaction force:

$$R = \sqrt{(-480 \text{ N})^2 + (970 \text{ N})^2}$$
$$= 1082 \text{ N}$$

The tangent relationship can be used to find the angle of orientation of the resultant reaction force:

$$\tan \alpha = \frac{480 \text{ N}}{970 \text{ N}}$$
$$\alpha = 26.3$$

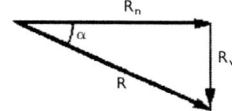

R_n

α

R_v

R

$$\boxed{R = 1082 \text{ N}, \alpha = 26.3 \text{ degrees}}$$

SAMPLE PROBLEM 13.5

A 580 N skydiver in free fall is accelerating at -8.8 m/s^2 rather than -9.81 m/s^2 because of the force of air resistance. How much drag force is acting on the skydiver?

Known

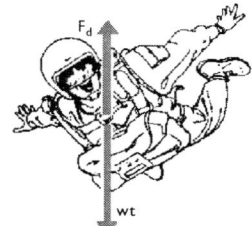

$$\text{wt} = -580 \text{ N}$$
$$a = -8.8 \text{ m/s}^2$$
$$\text{mass} = \frac{580 \text{ N}}{9.81 \text{ m/s}^2} = 59.12 \text{ kg}$$

Solution

Since the skydiver is considered to be in dynamic equilibrium, D'Alembert's principle may be used. All identified forces acting are vertical forces, so the equation of dynamic equilibrium summing the vertical forces to zero is used:

$$\Sigma F_y - \overline{m}a_y = 0$$

Given that $\Sigma F_y = -580 \text{ N} + F_d$, substitute the known information into the equation:

$$-580 \text{ N} + F_d - (59.12 \text{ kg})(-8.8 \text{ m/s}^2) = 0$$
$$\boxed{F_d = 59.7 \text{ N}}$$

CENTER OF GRAVITY

A body's mass is the matter of which it is composed. Associated with every body is a unique point around which the body's mass is equally distributed in all directions. This point is known as the center of mass, or the mass centroid, of the body. In the analysis of bodies subject to gravitational force, the center of mass may also be referred to as the center of gravity (CG), the point about which a body's weight is equally balanced in all directions, or the point about which the sum of torques produced by the weights of the body segments is equal to zero. This definition implies not that the weights positioned on opposite sides of the CG are equal, but that the torques created by the weights on opposite sides of the CG are equal. As illustrated in Figure 13-17, equal weight and equal torque generation on opposite sides of a point can be quite different. The terms *center of mass* and *center of gravity* are more commonly used for biomechanics applications than *mass centroid,* although all three terms refer to exactly the same point. Because the masses of bodies on the earth are subject to gravitational force, the center of gravity is probably the most accurately descriptive of the three to use for biomechanical applications.

The CG of a perfectly symmetrical object of homogeneous density, and therefore homogeneous mass and weight distribution, is at the exact center of the object. For example, the CG of a spherical shot or a solid rubber ball is at its geometric center. If the object is a homogeneous ring, the CG is located in the hollow center of the ring. However, when mass distribu-

center of mass
mass centroid
center of gravity
point around which the mass and weight of a body are balanced, no matter how the body is positioned

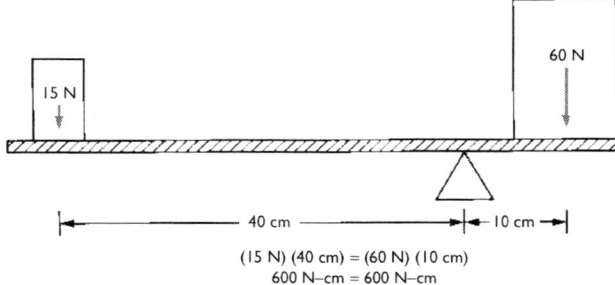

(15 N) (40 cm) = (60 N) (10 cm)
600 N–cm = 600 N–cm

FIGURE 13-17

The presence of equal torques on opposite sides of an axis of rotation does not necessitate the presence of equal weights on opposite sides of the axis.

tion within an object is not constant, the CG shifts in the direction of greater mass. It is also possible for an object's CG to be located physically outside of the object (Figure 13-18).

Locating the Center of Gravity

The location of the CG for a one-segment object such as a baseball bat, broom, or shovel can be approximately determined using a fulcrum to determine the location of a balance point for the object in three different planes. Because the CG is the point around which the mass of a body is equally distributed, it is also the point around which the body is balanced in all directions.

The location of a body's CG is of interest because, mechanically, a body behaves as though all of its mass were concentrated at the CG. For example, when the human body acts as a projectile, the body's CG follows a parabolic trajectory, regardless of any changes in the configurations of the body segments while in the air. Another implication is that when a weight vector is drawn for an object displayed in a free body diagram, the weight vector acts at the CG. Because the body's mechanical behavior can be traced by following the path of the total-body CG, this factor has been studied as a possible indicator of performance proficiency in several sports.

For example, it has been hypothesized that skilled runners display less vertical oscillation of the CG during performance. Although this has not

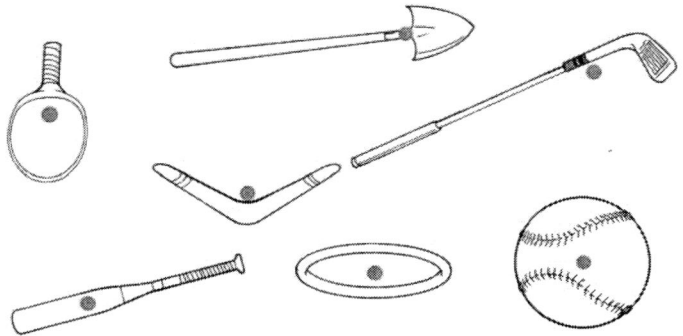

FIGURE 13-18

The center of gravity is the single point associated with a body around which the body's weight is equally balanced in all directions.

The running kinematics of a young child include noticeable vertical oscillations of the CG.

been well documented for adult runners (32), in children age 4–7, vertical oscillation of the CG decreases with age and concomitant maturation of running gait (18).

The path of the CG during takeoff in several of the jumping events is one factor believed to distinguish skilled from less-skilled performance. Research indicates that better Fosbury flop style high jumpers employ both body lean and body flexion (especially of the support leg) just before takeoff to lower the CG and prolong support foot contact time, thus resulting in increased takeoff impulse (3). In the long jump, better athletes maintain a normal sprinting stride, with CG height relatively constant, through the second-last step (11). During the last step, however, they markedly lower CG height, then increase CG height going into the jump step (11). Among better pole vaulters, there is progressive elevation of the CG from the third-last step through takeoff. This is partially due to the elevation of the arms as the vaulter prepares to plant the pole. However, research indicates that better vaulters lower their hips during the second-last step, then progressively elevate the hips (and the CG) through takeoff.

The strategy of lowering the CG prior to takeoff enables the athlete to lengthen the vertical path over which the body is accelerated during takeoff, thus facilitating a high vertical velocity at takeoff (Figure 13-19). The speed and angle of takeoff primarily determine the trajectory of the performer's CG during the jump. The only other influencing factor is air resistance, which exerts an extremely small effect on performance in the jumping events.

Locating the Human Body Center of Gravity

Locating the CG for a body containing two or more movable, interconnected segments is more difficult than doing so for a nonsegmented body, because every time the body changes configuration, its weight distribution and CG location are changed. Every time an arm, leg, or finger moves,

FIGURE 13-19

Height of the athlete's CG during preparation for takeoff in the long jump. Modified from Nixdorf E and Bruggemann P: Zur Absprungvorbereitung beim Weitsprung—Eine biomechanische Untersuchung zum problem der Korperschwerpunktsenkung, Lehre Leichtathlet p. 1539, 1983.

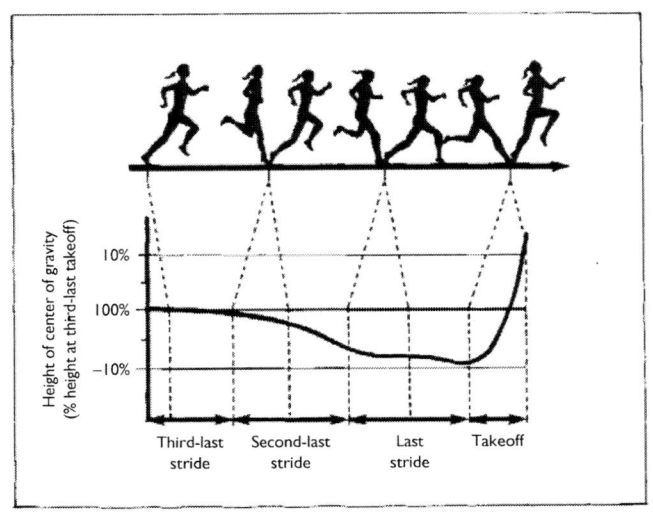

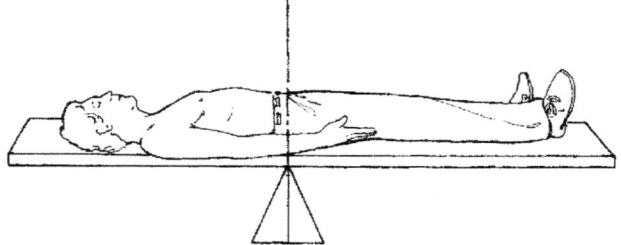

Top and bottom portions balanced

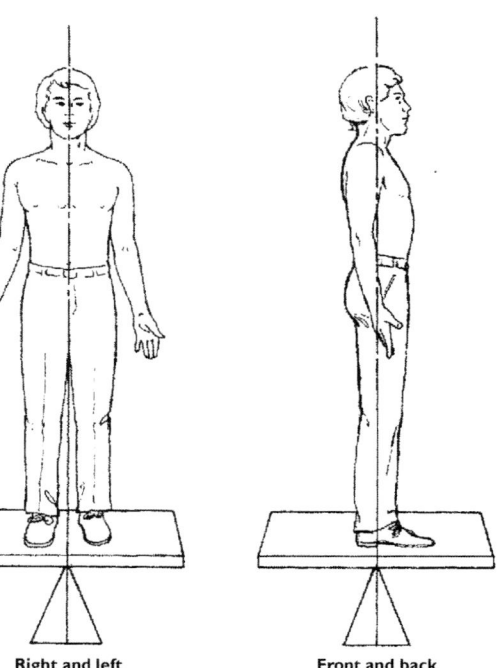

Right and left portions balanced   **Front and back portions balanced**

FIGURE 13-20

The relatively crude procedure devised by seventeenth-century mathematician Borelli for approximating the CG location of the human body.

the CG location as a whole is shifted at least slightly in the direction in which the weight is moved.

Some relatively simple procedures exist for determining the location of the CG of the human body. In the seventeenth century, the Italian mathematician Borelli used a simple balancing procedure for CG location that involved positioning a person on a wooden board (Figure 13-20). A more sophisticated version of this procedure enables calculation of the location of the plane passing through the CG of a person positioned on a reaction board. This procedure requires the use of a scale, a platform of the same height as the weighing surface of the scale, and a rigid board with sharp supports on either end (Figure 13-21). The calculation of the location of the plane containing the CG involves the summation of torques acting about the platform support. Forces creating torques at the support include the

The speed and projection angle of an athlete's total-body center of mass largely determine performance outcome in the high jump.

reaction board
specially constructed board for determining the center of gravity location of a body positioned on top of it

444   BASIC BIOMECHANICS

FIGURE 13-21

By summing torques at point a, d (the distance from a to the subject's CG) may be calculated.

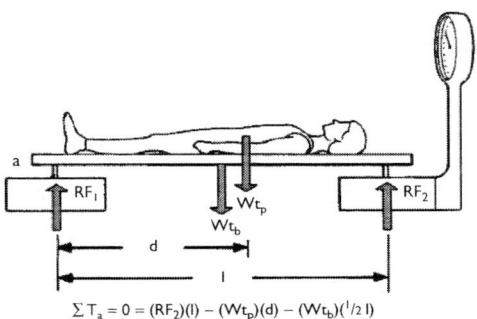

$$\Sigma T_a = 0 = (RF_2)(l) - (Wt_p)(d) - (Wt_b)(^1/_2\,l)$$

●Location of the CG of the human body is complicated by the fact that its constituents (such as bone, muscle, and fat) have different densities and are unequally distributed throughout the body.

segmental method
procedure for determining total-body center of mass location based on the masses and center of mass locations of the individual body segments

●The location of the CG of a multisegmented object is more influenced by the positions of the heavier segments than by those of the lighter segments.

●The segmental method is most commonly implemented through a computer program that reads x,y coordinates of joint centers from a file created by a digitizer.

person's body weight, the weight of the board, and the reaction force of the scale on the platform (indicated by the reading on the scale). Although the platform also exerts a reaction force on the board, it creates no torque, because the distance of that force from the platform support is zero. Since the reaction board and the subject are in static equilibrium, the sum of the three torques acting at the platform support must be zero, and the distance of the subject's CG plane to the platform may be calculated (see Sample Problem 13.6).

A commonly used procedure for estimating the location of the total body CG from projected film images of the human body is known as the segmental method. This procedure is based on the concept that since the body is composed of individual segments (each with an individual CG), the location of the total-body CG is a function of the locations of the respective segmental CGs. Some body segments, however, are much more massive than others and so have a larger influence on the location of the total-body CG. When the products of each body segment's CG location and its mass are summed and subsequently divided by the sum of all segmental masses (total body mass), the result is the location of the total-body CG. The segmental method uses data for average locations of individual body segment CGs as related to a percentage of segment length (2, 4):

$$X_{cg} = \Sigma(x_s)\,(m_s)/\Sigma m_s$$
$$Y_{cg} = \Sigma(y_s)\,(m_s)/\Sigma m_s$$

In this formula, X_{cg} and Y_{cg} are the coordinates of the total-body CG, x_s and y_s are the coordinates of the individual segment CGs, and m_s is individual segment mass. Thus, the x-coordinate of each segment's CG location is identified and multiplied by the mass of that respective segment. The $(x_s)\,(m_s)$ products for all of the body segments are then summed and subsequently divided by total body mass to yield the x-coordinate of the total-body CG location. The same procedure is followed to calculate the y-coordinate for total-body CG location (see Sample Problem 13.7).

SAMPLE PROBLEM 13.6

Find the distance from the platform support to the subject's CG, given the following information for the diagram in Figure 13-21:

Known

$$\text{mass (subject)} = 73 \text{ kg}$$
$$\text{mass (board alone)} = 44 \text{ kg}$$
$$\text{scale reading} = 66 \text{ kg}$$
$$l_b = 2m$$

Solution

$$Wt_p = (73 \text{ kg}) (9.81 \text{ m/s}^2)$$
$$= 716.13 \text{ N}$$
$$Wt_b = (44 \text{ kg}) (9.81 \text{ m/s}^2)$$
$$= 431.64 \text{ N}$$
$$RF_2 = (66 \text{ kg}) (9.81 \text{ m/s}^2)$$
$$= 647.46 \text{ N}$$

Use an equation of static equilibrium:

$$\Sigma T_a = 0 = (RF_2) (l) - (Wt_p) (d) - (Wt_b) (\tfrac{1}{2}l)$$
$$0 = (647.46 \text{ N}) (2 \text{ m}) - (716.13 \text{ N}) (d) - (431.64 \text{ N}) (\tfrac{1}{2}) (2 \text{ m})$$
$$d = 1.2 \text{ m}$$

STABILITY AND BALANCE

A concept closely related to the principles of equilibrium is stability. Stability is defined mechanically as resistance to both linear and angular acceleration, or resistance to disruption of equilibrium. In some circumstances, such as a Sumo wrestling contest or the pass protection of a quarterback by an offensive lineman, maximizing stability is desirable. In other situations, an athlete's best strategy is to intentionally minimize stability. Sprinters and swimmers in the preparatory stance before the start of a race intentionally assume a body position allowing them to accelerate quickly and easily at the sound of the starter's pistol. An individual's ability to control equilibrium is known as balance.

Different mechanical factors affect a body's stability. According to Newton's second law of motion (F = ma), the more massive an object is, the greater is the force required to produce a given acceleration. Football linemen who are expected to maintain their positions despite the forces exerted on them by opposing linemen are therefore more mechanically stable if they are more massive. In contrast, gymnasts are at a disadvantage with greater body mass, because execution of most gymnastic skills involves disruption of stability.

The greater the amount of friction is between an object and the surface or surfaces it contacts, the greater is the force requirement for initiating or maintaining motion. Toboggans and racing skates are designed so that the friction they generate against the ice will be minimal, enabling

stability
resistance to disruption of equilibrium

balance
ability to control equilibrium

446   BASIC BIOMECHANICS

SAMPLE PROBLEM 13.7

The x,y-coordinates of the CGs of the upper arm, forearm, and hand segments are provided on the diagram below. Use the segmental method to find the CG for the entire arm, using the data provided for segment masses from Appendix D.

Known

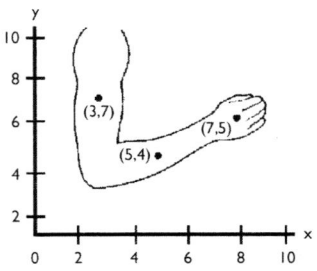

SEGMENT	MASS %	x	(x) (MASS %)	y	(y) (MASS %)
Upper arm	0.45				
Forearm	0.43				
Hand	0.12				
Σ					

Solution

First list the x- and y-coordinates in their respective columns, and then calculate and insert the product of each coordinate and the mass percentage for each segment into the appropriate columns. Sum the product columns, which yield the x,y-coordinates of the total arm CG.

SEGMENT	MASS %	x	(x) (MASS %)	y	(y) (MASS %)
Upper arm	0.45	3	1.35	7	3.15
Forearm	0.43	5	2.15	4	1.72
Hand	0.12	7	0.84	5	0.60
Σ			4.34		5.47

$$x = 4.34$$
$$y = 5.47$$

a quick disruption of stability at the beginning of a run or race. However, racquetball, golf, and batting gloves are designed to increase the stability of the player's grip on the implement.

Another factor affecting stability is the size of the base of support. This consists of the area enclosed by the outermost edges of the body in contact with the supporting surface or surfaces (Figure 13-22). When the line of action of a body's weight (directed from the CG) moves outside the base of support, a torque is created that tends to cause angular motion of the body, thereby disrupting stability, with the CG falling toward the ground. The larger the base of support is, the lower is the likelihood that this will occur.

base of support
area bound by the outermost regions of contact between a body and support surface or surfaces

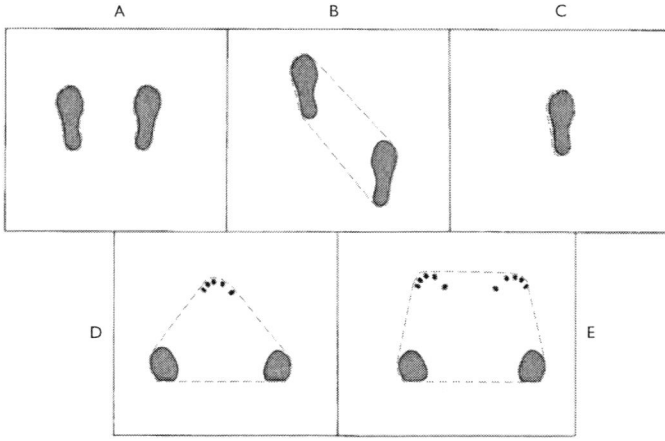

FIGURE 13-22

The base of support for (**A**) a square stance, (**B**) an angled stance, (**C**) a one-foot stance, (**D**) a three-point stance, and (**E**) a four-point stance. Areas of contact between body parts and the support surface are shaded. The base of support is the area enclosed by the dashed line.

Martial artists typically assume a wide stance during defensive situations to increase stability. Alternatively, sprinters in the starting blocks maintain a relatively small base of support so that they can quickly disrupt stability at the start of the race. Maintaining balance during an *arabesque en pointe,* in which the dancer is balanced on the toes of one foot, requires continual adjustment of CG location through subtle body movements (15).

Performing an arabesque en pointe *requires excellent balance, because lateral movement of the dancer's line of gravity outside the small base of support will result in loss of balance.*

A swimmer on the blocks positions her CG close to the front boundary of her base of support to prepare for forward acceleration.

The horizontal location of the CG relative to the base of support can also influence stability. The closer the horizontal location of the CG is to the boundary of the base of support, the smaller is the force required to push it outside the base of support, thereby disrupting equilibrium. Athletes in the starting position for a race consequently assume stances that position the CG close to the forward edge of the base of support. Alternatively, if a horizontal force must be sustained, stability is enhanced if the CG is positioned closer to the oncoming force, since the CG can be displaced farther before being moved outside the base of support. Sumo wrestlers lean toward their opponents when being pushed.

The height of the CG relative to the base of support can also affect stability. The higher the positioning of the CG, the greater the potentially disruptive torque created if the body undergoes an angular displacement (Figure 13-23). Athletes often crouch in sport situations when added stability is desirable. A common instructional cue for beginners in many sports is "Bend your knees!" Researchers have proposed a formula for an extrapolated CG position (XcoM) that relates CG height to the base of support in a dynamic situation where a person is walking or running (12). They suggest that to maintain balance, XcoM should remain within the moving base of support. They define XcoM as the vertical position of the CG plus its velocity times a factor of $(l/a_g)^{1/2}$, where l is leg length and a_g is the acceleration of gravity.

Although these principles of stability (summarized in Table 13-1) are generally true, their application to the human body should be made only with the recognition that neuromuscular factors are also influential. Changes in foot position have been found to affect two measures of standing balance: (a) the location of the line of gravity and (b) postural sway. Research has shown that frontal plane sway decreases when the base of support is widened to 15 cm, but that increasing the width of the base of support beyond 15 cm does not further reduce body sway in the frontal plane. Researchers have also found that when people stand with one foot 30 cm in front of the other, frontal plane sway increases, but a surprising increase in sagittal plane sway occurs as well. The angle of foot position during normal stance does not affect balance; however, an extreme toe-in position causes more body sway (13).

Because accidental falls are a significant problem for the growing elderly population, the issue of balance control in this age group is receiving an increasing amount of research attention. Investigators have documented a reduction in anteroposterior CG motion and an increase in mediolateral CG motion in elderly patients with balance disorders as

FIGURE 13-23

The higher the CG location, the greater the amount of torque its motion creates about the intersection of the line of gravity and the support surface.

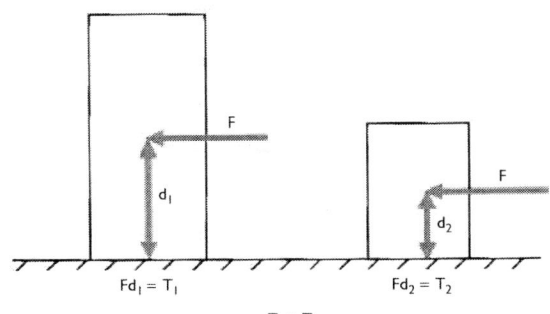

$Fd_1 = T_1$ $\qquad$ $Fd_2 = T_2$

$T_1 > T_2$

TABLE 13-1
Principles of Mechanical Stability

When other factors are held constant, a body's ability to maintain equilibrium is increased by the following:
1. Increasing body mass
2. Increasing friction between the body and the surface or surfaces contacted
3. Increasing the size of the base of support in the direction of the line of action of an external force
4. Horizontally positioning the center of gravity near the edge of the base of support on the side of the oncoming external force
5. Vertically positioning the center of gravity as low as possible

compared to young adults during walking (9, 10). This is of concern because measures of mediolateral sway have been related to the risk of falling (27). Similarly, the ability to vary step width during gait has been shown to be more important for balance control than variations in either step length or step time (20). Researchers hypothesize that difficulty with lateral balance control associated with aging may be related to impaired ability to abduct the leg at the hip with as much strength and speed as needed to maintain dynamic stability (17). Other research with young, healthy adults has shown that rapidly developed, large-magnitude moments at the hip, knee, and ankle were required in order to prevent a fall when tripping over an obstacle (22). Both weight-training and aerobic exercise programs can significantly improve postural sway among elderly individuals for whom balance is a concern (16).

Although under normal conditions the size of the base of support is a primary determiner of stability, research shows that a variety of other factors can also limit control of balance. Friction coefficient levels of less than 0.82, decreased resting muscle tension, and impairments in muscle strength, joint movement, balance, gait, hearing, vision, and cognition are all risk factors for falling (21, 25, 26). More research is needed to clarify the application of the principles of stability to human balance.

SUMMARY

Rotary motion is caused by torque, a vector quantity with magnitude and direction. When a muscle develops tension, it produces torque at the joint or joints that it crosses. Rotation of the body segment occurs in the direction of the resultant joint torque.

Mechanically, muscles and bones function as levers. Most joints function as third-class lever systems, well structured for maximizing range of motion and movement speed, but requiring muscle force of greater magnitude than that of the resistance to be overcome. The angle at which a muscle pulls on a bone also affects its mechanical effectiveness, because only the rotary component of muscle force produces joint torque.

When a body is motionless, it is in static equilibrium. The three conditions of static equilibrium are $\Sigma F_v = 0$, $\Sigma F_h = 0$, and $\Sigma T = 0$. A body in motion is in dynamic equilibrium when inertial factors are considered.

The mechanical behavior of a body subject to force or forces is greatly influenced by the location of its center of gravity: the point around which the body's weight is equally balanced in all directions. Different procedures are available for determining center of gravity location.

A body's mechanical stability is its resistance to both linear and angular acceleration. A number of factors influence a body's stability, including mass, friction, center of gravity location, and base of support.

450   BASIC BIOMECHANICS

INTRODUCTORY PROBLEMS

1. Why does a force directed through an axis of rotation not cause rotation at the axis?
2. Why does the orientation of a force acting on a body affect the amount of torque it generates at an axis of rotation within the body?
3. A 23 kg boy sits 1.5 m from the axis of rotation of a seesaw. At what distance from the axis of rotation must a 21 kg boy be positioned on the other side of the axis to balance the seesaw? (Answer: 1.6 m)
4. How much force must be produced by the biceps brachii at a perpendicular distance of 3 cm from the axis of rotation at the elbow to support a weight of 200 N at a perpendicular distance of 25 cm from the elbow? (Answer: 1667 N)
5. Two people push on opposite sides of a swinging door. If A exerts a force of 40 N at a perpendicular distance of 20 cm from the hinge and B exerts a force of 30 N at a perpendicular distance of 25 cm from the hinge, what is the resultant torque acting at the hinge, and which way will the door swing? (Answer: T_h = 0.5 N-m; in the direction that A pushes)
6. To which lever classes do a golf club, a swinging door, and a broom belong? Explain your answers, including free body diagrams.
7. Is the mechanical advantage of a first-class lever greater than, less than, or equal to one? Explain.
8. Using a diagram, identify the magnitudes of the rotary and stabilizing components of a 100 N muscle force that acts at an angle of 20° to a bone. (Answer: rotary component = 34 N, stabilizing component = 94 N)
9. A 10 kg block sits motionless on a table in spite of an applied horizontal force of 2 N. What are the magnitudes of the reaction force and friction force acting on the block? (Answer: R = 98.1 N, F = 2 N)
10. Given the following data for the reaction board procedure, calculate the distance from the platform support to the subject's CG: RF_2 = 400 N, l = 2.5 m, wt = 600 N. (Answer: 1.67 m)

ADDITIONAL PROBLEMS

1. For one joint of the lower extremity, explain why eccentric torque occurs during gait.
2. Select one human motor skill with which you are familiar, and sketch a graph showing how you would expect CG height to change during that skill.
3. A 35 N hand and forearm are held at a 45° angle to the vertically oriented humerus. The CG of the forearm and hand is located at a distance of 15 cm from the joint center at the elbow, and the elbow flexor muscles attach at an average distance of 3 cm from the joint center. (Assume that the muscles attach at an angle of 45° to the bones.)
   a. How much force must be exerted by the forearm flexors to maintain this position?
   b. How much force must the forearm flexors exert if a 50 N weight is held in the hand at a distance along the arm of 25 cm? (Answers: a. 175 N; b. 591.7 N)
4. A hand exerts a force of 90 N on a scale at 32 cm from the joint center at the elbow. If the triceps attach to the ulna at a 90° angle and at a distance of 3 cm from the elbow joint center, and if the weight of the

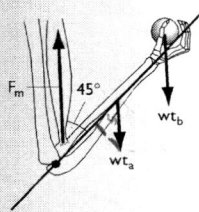

forearm and hand is 40 N with the hand/forearm CG located 17 cm from the elbow joint center, how much force is being exerted by the triceps? (Answer: 733.3 N)

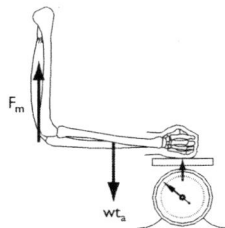

5. A patient rehabilitating a knee injury performs knee extension exercises wearing a 15 N weight boot. Calculate the amount of torque generated at the knee by the weight boot for the four positions shown, given a distance of 0.4 m between the weight boot's CG and the joint center at the knee. (Answers: a. 0; b. 3 N-m; c. 5.2 N-m; d. 6 N-m)

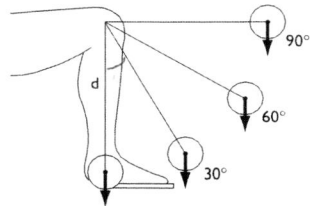

6. A 600 N person picks up a 180 N suitcase positioned so that the suitcase's CG is 20 cm lateral to the location of the person's CG before picking up the suitcase. If the person does not lean to compensate for the added load in any way, where is the combined CG location for the person and suitcase with respect to the person's original CG location? (Answer: Shifted 4.6 cm toward the suitcase)

7. A worker leans over and picks up a 90 N box at a distance of 0.7 m from the axis of rotation in her spine. Neglecting the effect of body weight, how much added force is required of the low back muscles with an average moment arm of 6 cm to stabilize the box in the position shown? (Answer: 1050 N)

8. A man carries a 3 m, 32 N board over his shoulder. If the board extends 1.8 m behind the shoulder and 1.2 m in front of the shoulder, how much force must the man apply vertically downward with his hand that rests on the board 0.2 m in front of the shoulder to stabilize the board in this position? (Assume that the weight of the board is evenly distributed throughout its length.) (Answer: 48 N)

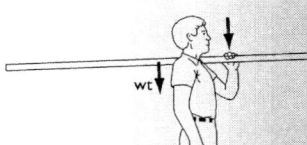

9. A therapist applies a lateral force of 80 N to the forearm at a distance of 25 cm from the axis of rotation at the elbow. The biceps attaches to the radius at a 90° angle and at a distance of 3 cm from the elbow joint center.
   a. How much force is required of the biceps to stabilize the arm in this position?
   b. What is the magnitude of the reaction force exerted by the humerus on the ulna? (Answers: a. 666.7 N; b. 586.7 N)

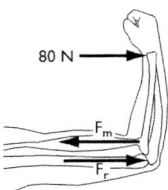

10. Tendon forces T_a and T_b are exerted on the patella. The femur exerts force F on the patella. If the magnitude of T_b is 80 N, what are the magnitudes of T_a and F, if no motion is occurring at the joint? (Answer: T_a = 44.8 N, F = 86.1 N)

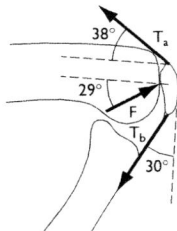

NAME _____

DATE _____

LABORATORY EXPERIENCES

1. Experiment by loosening lug nuts from an automobile tire with a lug wrench, a lug wrench with a short extension on the handle, and a lug wrench with a longer extension on the handle. Write a paragraph explaining your findings, and draw a free body diagram showing the applied force, resistance, and axis of rotation. What provides the resistance?

Explanation:_____

_____

_____

Free Body Diagram:

2. Position a pole across the back of a chair (serving as a fulcrum), and hang a 2 lb weight on one end of the pole. Position a 5 lb weight on the other side of the pole such that the weights are balanced. Measure and record the distances of the two weights from the fulcrum, and write an explanation of your results.

Distance of 5 lb weight from fulcrum: _____

Distance of 2 lb weight from fulcrum: _____

Explanation:_____

_____

_____

3. Perform curl-up exercises under the following conditions: (a) arms folded across the chest, (b) hands behind the neck, and (c) holding a 5 lb weight above the head. Write a paragraph explaining your findings, and draw a free body diagram showing the applied force, resistance, and axis of rotation.

Explanation: _____

_____

_____

_____

_____

Free Body Diagram:

454   BASIC BIOMECHANICS

4. Use the reaction board procedure to calculate the sagittal, frontal, and transverse plane positions of the center of gravity of a subject in anatomical position. Repeat the calculations with the subject (a) extending both arms overhead and (b) extending one arm to the right. Present your results in a table and write a paragraph of explanation.

Subject weight: _____

Board weight: _____

Scale reading 1: _____   Scale reading 2: _____   Scale reading 3: _____

d_1: _____ d_2: _____ d_3: _____

Calculations:

Explanation:_____

_____

_____

_____

_____

5. Using a picture of a person from a magazine or photograph and the anthropometric data from Appendix D, calculate and mark the location of total-body center of gravity using the segmental method. First draw and scale x- and y-axes around the picture. Next, mark the approximate locations of segmental centers of gravity on the picture, using the data from Appendix D. Finally, construct a table using the table in Sample Problem 13.7 as a model.

Segment	Mass %	x	(x) (Mass %)	y	(y) (Mass %)
_____	_____	_____	_____	_____	_____
_____	_____	_____	_____	_____	_____
_____	_____	_____	_____	_____	_____
_____	_____	_____	_____	_____	_____
_____	_____	_____	_____	_____	_____
_____	_____	_____	_____	_____	_____
_____	_____	_____	_____	_____	_____

REFERENCES

1. Burnfield JM, Josephson KR, Powers CM, and Rubenstein LZ: The influence of lower extremity joint torque on gait characteristics in elderly men, Arch Phys Med Rehabil 81:1153, 2000.

2. Clauser CE, McConville JT, and Young JW: Weight, volume, and center of mass of segments of the human body, AMRL Tech Rep, 1969, Wright-Patterson Air Force Base.

3. Dapena J, McDonald C, and Cappaert J: A regression analysis of high jumping technique, Int J Sport Biomech, 6:246, 1990.

4. Dempster WT: Space requirements of the seated operator, WADC Tech Rep 55-159, 1955, Wright-Patterson Air Force Base.

5. DeVita P and Hortobagyi T: Age causes a redistribution of joint torques and powers during gait, J Appl Physiol 88:1804, 2000.

6. DeVita P, Torry M, Glover KL, and Speroni DL: A functional knee brace alters joint torque and power patterns during walking and running, J Biomech 29:583, 1996.

7. Escamilla RF, Fleisig GS, Lowry TM, Barrentine SW, and Andrews JR: A three-dimensional biomechanical analysis of the squat during varying stance widths, Med Sci Sports Exerc 33:984, 2001.

8. Garhammer J: Weight lifting and training. In Vaughan CL, ed: *Biomechanics of sport,* Boca Raton, FL, 1988, CRC Press.

9. Hahn ME and Chou L-S: Can motion of individual body segments identify dynamic instability in the elderly? Clin Biomech 18:737, 2003.

10. Hahn ME and Chou L-S: Age-related reduction in sagittal plane center of mass motion during obstacle crossing, J Biomech 37:837, 2004.

11. Hay JG and Nohara H: The techniques used by elite long jumpers in preparation for take-off, J Biomech, 23:229, 1990.

12. Hof AL, Gazendam MGJ, and Sinke WE: The condition for dynamic stability, J Biomech 38:1, 2005.

13. Kirby RL, Price NA, and MacLeod DA: The influence of foot position on standing balance, J Biomech 20:423, 1987.

14. Konczak J, Borutta M, and Dichgans J: The development of goal-directed reaching in infants. II. Learning to produce task-adequate patterns of joint torque, Exp Brain Res 113:465, 1997.

15. Laws K: *The physics of dance,* New York, 1984, Schirmer Books.

16. Messier SP et al: Long-term exercise and its effect on balance in older, osteoarthitic adults: results from the Fitness, Arthritis, and Seniors Trial (FAST), J Am Geriatr Soc 48:131, 2000.

17. Mille M-L, Johnson ME, Martinez KM, and Rogers MW: Age-dependent differences in lateral balance recovery through protective stepping, Clin Biomech 20:607, 2005.

18. Miyamaru M et al: Path of the whole body center of gravity for young children in running. In Jonsson B, ed: *Biomechanics X-B,* Champaign, IL, 1987, Human Kinetics.

19. Osternig LR, James CR, and Bercades D: Effects of movement speed and joint position on knee flexor torque in healthy and post-surgical subjects, Eur J Appl Physiol Occup Physiol 80:100, 1999.

20. Owings TM and Grabiner MD: Step width variability, but not step length variability or step time variability, discriminates gait of healthy young and older adults during treadmill locomotion, J Biomech 37:935, 2004.

21. Pai YC and Patton J: Center of mass velocity-position predictions for balance control, J Biomech 30:347, 1997.

22. Pijnappels M, Bobbert M, and van Dieën JH: How early reactions in the support limb contribute to balance recovery after tripping, J Biomech 38:627, 2005.

23. Rahmani A, Viale F, Dalleau G, and Lacour JR: Force velocity and power velocity relationships in squat exercise, Eur J Appl Physiol 84:227, 2001.

24. Redfield R and Hull ML: On the relation between joint moments and pedalling rates at constant power in bicycling, J Biomech 19:317, 1986.

25. Rietdyk S, Patla AE, Winter DA, Ishac MG, and Little CE: Balance recovery from medio-lateral perturbations of the upper body during standing, J Biomech 32:1149, 1999.

26. Robinovitch SN et al: Prevention of falls and fall-related fractures through biomechanics, Exerc Sport Sci Rev 28:74, 2000.

27. Rogers MW and Mille M-L: Lateral stability and falls in older people, Exerc Sports Sci Rev 31:182, 2003.

28. Townend MS: *Mathematics in sport,* New York, 1984, John Wiley & Sons.

29. van der Woude LH, Botden E, Vriend I, and Veeger D: Mechanical advantage in wheelchair lever propulsion: effect on physical strain and efficiency, J Rehabil Res Dev 34:286, 1997.

30. van Zuylen EJ, van Zelzen A, and van der Gon JJD: A biomechanical model for flexion torques of human arm muscles as a function of elbow angle, J Biomech, 21:183, 1988.

31. Veeger HEJ, Van der Woude LHV, and Rozendal RH: Effect of handrim velocity on mechanical efficiency in wheelchair propulsion, Med Sci Sports Exerc, 24:100, 1992.

32. Williams KR: Biomechanics of running, Exerc Sport Sci Rev 13:389, 1985.

ANNOTATED READINGS

Escamilla RF, Lander JE, and Garhammer J: Biomechanics of powerlifting and weightlifting exercises. In Garrett We Jr and Kirkendall DT, eds: *Exercise and sport science,* Philadelphia, 2000, Lippincott Williams & Wilkins.
Discusses joint torques and loading during numerous lifting exercises.

Mester J: Movement control and balance in earthbound movements. In Nigg BM, MacIntosh BR, and Mester J, eds: *Biomechanics and biology of movement,* Champaign, IL, 2000, Human Kinetics.
Discusses posture and balance in the context of center of gravity location and neuromuscular control.

Rogers MW and Mille M-L: Lateral stability and falls in older people, Exerc Sports Sci Rev 31:182, 2003.
Discusses age-related changes in specific neuromusculoskeletal factors affecting protective stepping and other balance functions that may precipitate lateral instability and falls.

Winter DA: *Biomechanics and motor control of human movement* (3rd ed), New York, 2004, John Wiley & Sons.
Includes a chapter on kinetics that discusses interpreting moment of force (torque) curves and the difference between the center of gravity and center of pressure.

RELATED WEB SITES

Advanced Medical Technology, Inc.
www.amtiweb.com
Provides information on the AMTI force platforms, with reference to ground reaction forces in gait analysis, balance and posture, and other topics.

NASA: Center of Gravity
www.grc.nasa.gov/WWW/K-12/airplane/cg.html
Official site of the National Aeronautics and Space Administration; provides comprehensive discussion accompanied by slides of the relevance of the center of gravity in the design of airplanes.

NASA: Determining Center of Gravity
www.grc.nasa.gov/WWW/K-12/airplane/rktcg.html
Official site of the National Aeronautics and Space Administration; provides comprehensive discussion accompanied by slides of the relevance of the center of gravity in the design of model rockets.

Wikipedia: Center of Gravity
en.wikipedia.org/wiki/Center_of_gravity
Includes discussion of relationships among center of gravity, center of mass, and center of buoyancy.

Wikipedia: Torque
en.wikipedia.org/wiki/Torque
Discusses torque as related to other mechanical quantities and to static equilibrium, including many definitions and diagrams.

KEY TERMS

balance	ability to control equilibrium
base of support	area bound by the outermost regions of contact between a body and support surface or surfaces
center of mass mass centroid center of gravity	point around which the mass and weight of a body are balanced, no matter how the body is positioned
couple	pair of equal, oppositely directed forces that act on opposite sides of an axis of rotation to produce torque
dynamic equilibrium (D'Alembert's principle)	concept indicating a balance between applied forces and inertial forces for a body in motion
first-class lever	lever positioned with the applied force and the resistance on opposite sides of the axis of rotation
fulcrum	the point of support, or axis, about which a lever may be made to rotate
lever	a simple machine consisting of a relatively rigid, barlike body that may be made to rotate about an axis
mechanical advantage	ratio of force arm to resistance arm for a given lever
moment arm	shortest (perpendicular) distance between a force's line of action and an axis of rotation
reaction board	specially constructed board for determining the center of gravity location of a body positioned on top of it
second-class lever	lever positioned with the resistance between the applied force and the fulcrum
segmental method	procedure for determining total-body center of mass location based on the masses and center of mass locations of the individual body segments
stability	resistance to disruption of equilibrium
static equilibrium	motionless state characterized by $\Sigma SF_v = 0$, $\Sigma SF_h = 0$, and $\Sigma ST = 0$
third-class lever	lever positioned with the applied force between the fulcrum and the resistance
torque	the rotary effect of a force about an axis of rotation, measured as the product of the force and the perpendicular distance between the force's line of action and the axis

Angular Kinetics of Human Movement

14

After completing this chapter, you will be able to:

Identify the angular analogues of mass, force, momentum, and impulse.

Explain why changes in the configuration of a rotating airborne body can produce changes in the body's angular velocity.

Identify and provide examples of the angular analogues of Newton's laws of motion.

Define centripetal force, and explain where and how it acts.

Solve quantitative problems relating to the factors that cause or modify angular motion.

Visit the Online Learning Center at www.mhhe.com/hall5e to access the Online Lab Manual and many additional resources.

460   BASIC BIOMECHANICS

Why do sprinters run with more swing phase flexion at the knee than do distance runners? Why do dancers and ice skaters spin more rapidly when their arms are brought in close to the body? How do cats always land on their feet? In this chapter, we explore more concepts pertaining to angular kinetics, from the perspective of the similarities and differences between linear and angular kinetic quantities.

RESISTANCE TO ANGULAR ACCELERATION

Moment of Inertia

Inertia is a body's tendency to resist acceleration (see Chapter 3). Although inertia itself is a concept rather than a quantity that can be measured in units, a body's inertia is directly proportional to its mass (Figure 14-1). According to Newton's second law, the greater a body's mass, the greater its resistance to linear acceleration. Therefore, mass is a body's inertial characteristic for considerations relative to linear motion.

Resistance to angular acceleration is also a function of a body's mass. The greater the mass, the greater the resistance to angular acceleration. However, the relative ease or difficulty of initiating or halting angular motion depends on an additional factor: the distribution of mass with respect to the axis of rotation.

Consider the baseball bats shown in Figure 14-2. Suppose a player warming up in the on-deck circle adds a weight ring to the bat he is swinging. Will the relative ease of swinging the bat be greater with the weight positioned near the striking end of the bat or with the weight near the bat's grip? Similarly, is it easier to swing a bat held by the grip (the normal hand position) or a bat turned around and held by the barrel?

Experimentation with a baseball bat or some similar object makes it apparent that the more closely concentrated the mass is to the axis of rotation, the easier it is to swing the object. Conversely, the more mass is positioned away from the axis of rotation, the more difficult it is to initiate (or stop) angular motion. Resistance to angular acceleration, therefore, depends not only on the amount of mass possessed by an object but also on the distribution of that mass with respect to the axis of rotation. The inertial property for angular motion must therefore incorporate both factors.

The inertial property for angular motion is moment of inertia, represented as I. Every body is composed of particles of mass, each with its own particular distance from a given axis of rotation. The moment of inertia for a single particle of mass may be represented as the following:

$$I = mr^2$$

In this formula, m is the particle's mass and r is the particle's radius of rotation. The moment of inertia of an entire body is the sum of

•The more closely mass is distributed to the axis of rotation, the easier it is to initiate or stop angular motion.

moment of inertia
inertial property for rotating bodies representing resistance to angular acceleration; based on both mass and the distance the mass is distributed from the axis of rotation

FIGURE 14-1

The distribution of mass in a system does not affect its linear momentum.

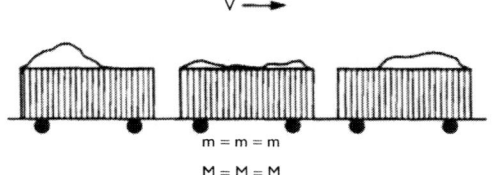

FIGURE 14-2

Although both bats have the same mass, bat A is harder to swing than bat B, because the weight ring on it is positioned farther from the axis of rotation.

the moments of inertia of all the mass particles the object contains (Figure 14-3):

$$I = \Sigma mr^2$$

The distribution of mass with respect to the axis of rotation is more important than the total amount of body mass in determining resistance to angular acceleration, because r is squared. Since r is the distance between a given particle and an axis of rotation, values of r change as the axis of rotation changes. Thus, when a player grips a baseball bat, "choking up" on the bat reduces the bat's moment of inertia with respect to the axis of rotation at the player's wrists, and concomitantly increases the relative ease of swinging the bat. Little League baseball players often unknowingly make use of this concept when swinging bats that are longer and heavier than they can effectively handle. Interestingly, research shows that when baseball players warm up with a weighted bat (with a larger moment of inertia than a regular bat) post-warm-up swing velocity is actually reduced (21).

Within the human body, the distribution of mass with respect to an axis of rotation can dramatically influence the relative ease or difficulty of moving the body limbs. For example, during gait, the distribution of a given leg's mass, and therefore its moment of inertia with respect to the primary axis of rotation at the hip, depends largely on the angle present at the knee. In sprinting, maximum angular acceleration of the legs is desired, and considerably more flexion at the knee is present during the swing phase than while running at slower speeds. This greatly reduces the moment of inertia of the leg with respect to the hip, thus reducing resistance to hip flexion. Runners who have leg morphology involving mass distribution closer to the hip, with more massive thighs and slimmer lower legs than others, have a smaller moment of inertia of the leg with respect to the hip. This is an anthropometric characteristic that contributes to running economy (3). During walking, in which minimal angular acceleration of the legs is required, flexion at the knee during the swing phase remains relatively small, and the leg's moment of inertia with respect to the hip is relatively large.

During sprinting, extreme flexion at the knee reduces the moment of inertia of the swinging leg.

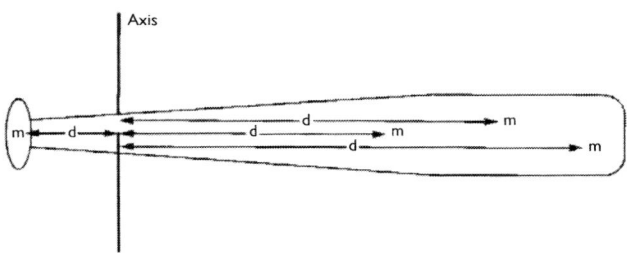

FIGURE 14-3

Moment of inertia is the sum of the products of each particle's mass and radius of rotation squared.

Modern-day golf irons are commonly constructed with the heads bottom weighted, perimeter weighted, or heel and toe weighted. These manipulations of the amount of mass and the distribution of mass within the head of the club are designed to increase club head inertia, thus reducing the tendency of the club to rotate about the shaft during an off-center hit. Research findings indicate that perimeter-weighted club heads perform best for eccentric ball contacts outside the club head center of gravity (CG), with a simple blade head club superior for contacts below the club head CG (18). The most consistent performance, however, was exhibited by a toe-and-bottom-weighted club head, which was second best for all eccentric hits (18). A golfer's individual preference, feel, and experience should ultimately determine selection of club type.

Determining Moment of Inertia

Assessing moment of inertia for a body with respect to an axis by measuring the distance of each particle of body mass from an axis of rotation and then applying the formula is obviously impractical. In practice, mathematical procedures are used to calculate moment of inertia for bodies of regular geometric shapes and known dimensions. Because the human body is composed of segments that are of irregular shapes and heterogeneous mass distributions, either experimental procedures or mathematical models are used to approximate moment-of-inertia values for individual body segments and for the body as a whole in different positions. Moment of inertia for the human body and its segments has been approximated by using average measurements from cadaver studies, measuring the acceleration of a swinging limb, employing photogrammetric methods, and applying mathematical modeling (11).

Once moment of inertia for a body of known mass has been assessed, the value may be characterized using the following formula:

$$I = mk^2$$

In this formula, I is moment of inertia with respect to an axis, m is total body mass, and k is a distance known as the radius of gyration. The radius of gyration represents the object's mass distribution with respect to a given axis of rotation. It is the distance from the axis of rotation to a point at which the mass of the body can theoretically be concentrated without altering the inertial characteristics of the rotating body. This point is *not* the same as the segmental CG (Figure 14-4). Since the radius of gyration

●*The fact that bone, muscle, and fat have different densities and are distributed dissimilarly in individuals complicates efforts to calculate human body segment moments of inertia.*

●*Because there are formulas available for calculating the moment of inertia of regularly shaped solids, some investigators have modeled the human body as a composite of various geometric shapes.*

radius of gyration
distance from the axis of rotation to a point where the body's mass could be concentrated without altering its rotational characteristics

FIGURE 14-4

Knee angle affects the moment of inertia of the swinging leg with respect to the hip because of changes in the radius of gyration for the lower leg (k_2) and foot (k_3).

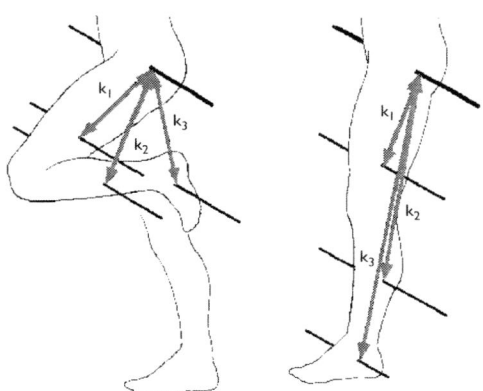

is based on r^2 for individual particles, it is always longer than the radius of rotation, the distance to the segmental CG.

The length of the radius of gyration changes as the axis of rotation changes. As mentioned earlier, it is easier to swing a baseball bat when the bat is grasped by the barrel end rather than by the bat's grip. When the bat is held by the barrel, k is much shorter than when the bat is held properly, since more mass is positioned close to the axis of rotation. Likewise, the radius of gyration for a body segment such as the forearm is greater with respect to the wrist than with respect to the elbow.

The radius of gyration is a useful index of moment of inertia when a given body's resistance to rotation with respect to different axes is discussed. Units of moment of inertia parallel the formula definition of the quantity, and therefore consist of units of mass multiplied by units of length squared$(kg \cdot m^2)$

Human Body Moment of Inertia

Moment of inertia can only be defined with respect to a specific axis of rotation. The axis of rotation for a body segment in sagittal and frontal plane motions is typically an axis passing through the center of a body segment's proximal joint. When a segment rotates around its own longitudinal axis, its moment of inertia is quite different from its moment of inertia during flexion and extension or abduction and adduction, because its mass distribution, and therefore its moment of inertia, is markedly different with respect to this axis of rotation. Figure 14-5 illustrates the difference in the lengths of the radii of gyration for the forearm with respect to the transverse and longitudinal axes of rotation.

The moment of inertia of the human body as a whole is also different with respect to different axes. When the entire human body rotates free of support, it moves around one of three principal axes: the transverse (or frontal), the anteroposterior (or sagittal), or the longitudinal (or vertical) axis, each of which passes through the total body CG. Moment of inertia with respect to one of these axes is known as a principal moment of inertia.

principal axes
three mutually perpendicular axes passing through the total body center of gravity

principal moment of inertia
total-body moment of inertia relative to one of the principal axes

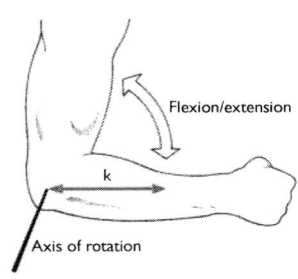

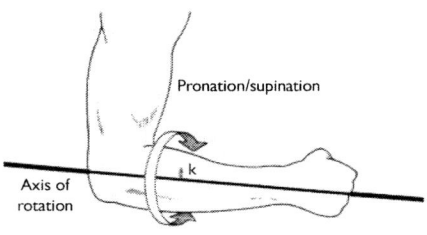

FIGURE 14-5

The radius of gyration (k) of the forearm for flexion/extension movements is much larger than for pronation/supination.

464 BASIC BIOMECHANICS

Principal moments of inertia of the human body in different positions with respect to different principal axes: (1) principal axis; (2) moment of inertia (kg · m^2). Modified from Hochmuth G: *Biomechanik sportlicher bewegungen*, Frankfurt, Germany, 1967, Wilhelm Limpert, Verlag.

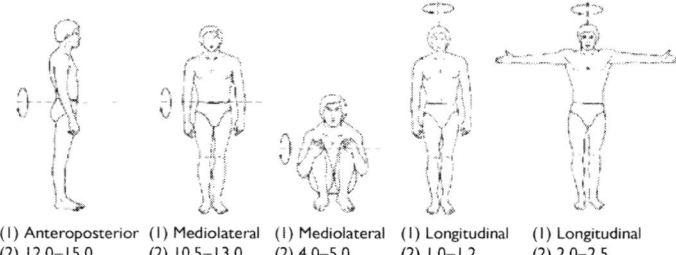

(1) Anteroposterior (2) 12.0–15.0   (1) Mediolateral (2) 10.5–13.0   (1) Mediolateral (2) 4.0–5.0   (1) Longitudinal (2) 1.0–1.2   (1) Longitudinal (2) 2.0–2.5

The ratio of muscular strength (the ability of a muscle group to produce torque about a joint) to segmental moments of inertia (resistance to rotation at a joint) is an important contributor to performance capability in gymnastic events.

Figure 14-6 shows quantitative estimates of principal moments of inertia for the human body in several different positions. When the body assumes a tucked position during a somersault, its principal moment of inertia (and resistance to angular motion) about the transverse axis is clearly less than when the body is in anatomical position. Divers performing a somersaulting dive undergo changes in principal moment of inertia about the transverse axis on the order of 15 kg · m^2 to 6.5 kg · m^2 as the body goes from a layout position to a pike position (9).

As children grow from childhood through adolescence and into adulthood, developmental changes result in changing proportions of body segment lengths, masses, and radii of gyration, all affecting segment moments of inertia (10). Segment moments of inertia affect resistance to angular rotation, and therefore performance capability, in sports such as gymnastics and diving. Because of smaller moments of inertia, smaller gymnasts have an advantage in performing skills involving whole-body rotations, despite the fact that larger gymnasts may have greater strength and be able to generate more power (1). Several prominent female gymnasts who achieved world-class status during early adolescence faded from the public view before reaching age 20 because of declines in their performance capabilities generally attributed to changes in body proportions with growth. Substantial changes in principal moments of inertia for the body segments occur with age, and large interindividual differences exist in the growth patterns of these principal moments of inertia (11). According to Jensen (10), the best predictor of moment of inertia values among children is the product of body mass and body height squared, (m) (ht)^2, rather than age.

ANGULAR MOMENTUM

Since moment of inertia is the inertial property for rotational movement, it is an important component of other angular kinetic quantities. As discussed in Chapter 12, the quantity of motion that an object possesses is referred to as its *momentum*. Linear momentum is the product of the linear inertial property (mass) and linear velocity. The quantity of angular motion that a body possesses is likewise known as angular momentum. Angular momentum, represented as H, is the product of the angular inertial property (moment of inertia) and angular velocity:

angular momentum
quantity of angular motion possessed by a body; measured as the product of moment of inertia and angular velocity

$$\text{For linear motion: } M = mv$$
$$\text{For angular motion: } H = I\omega$$
$$\text{Or: } H = mk^2\omega$$

Three factors affect the magnitude of a body's angular momentum: (a) its mass (m), (b) the distribution of that mass with respect to the axis of rotation (k), and (c) the angular velocity of the body (ω). If a body has no angular velocity, it has no angular momentum. As mass or angular velocity increases, angular momentum increases proportionally. The factor that most dramatically influences angular momentum is the distribution of mass with respect to the axis of rotation, because angular momentum is proportional to the square of the radius of gyration (see Sample Problem 14.1). Units of angular momentum result from multiplying units of mass, units of length squared, and units of angular velocity, which yields kg · m²/s.

For a multisegmented object such as the human body, angular momentum about a given axis of rotation is the sum of the angular momenta of the individual body segments. During an airborne somersault, the angular momentum of a single segment, such as the lower leg, with respect to the principal axis of rotation passing through the total body CG consists of two components: the local term and the remote term. The local term is based on the segment's angular momentum about its own segmental CG, and the remote term represents the segment's angular momentum about

SAMPLE PROBLEM 14.1

Consider a rotating 10 kg body for which k = 0.2 m and ω = 3 rad/s. What is the effect on the body's angular momentum if the mass doubles? The radius of gyration doubles? The angular velocity doubles?

Solution

The body's original angular momentum is the following:

$$H = mk^2\omega$$
$$H = (10 \text{ kg}) (0.2 \text{ m})^2 (3 \text{ rad/s})$$
$$H = 1.2 \text{ kg} \cdot \text{m}^2/\text{s}$$

With mass doubled:

$$H = mk^2\omega$$
$$H = (20 \text{ kg}) (0.2 \text{ m})^2 (3 \text{ rad/s})$$
$$H = 2.4 \text{ kg} \cdot \text{m}^2/\text{s}$$

H is doubled.

With k doubled:

$$H = mk^2\omega$$
$$H = (10 \text{ kg}) (0.4 \text{ m})^2 (3 \text{ rad/s})$$
$$H = 4.8 \text{ kg} \cdot \text{m}^2/\text{s}$$

H is quadrupled.

With ω doubled:

$$H = mk^2\omega$$
$$H = (10 \text{ kg}) (0.2 \text{ m})^2 (6 \text{ rad/s})$$
$$H = 2.4 \text{ kg} \cdot \text{m}^2/\text{s}$$

H is doubled.

the total body CG. Angular momentum for this segment about a principal axis is the sum of the local term and the remote term:

$$H = I_s \omega_s + mr^2 \omega_g$$

In the local term, I_s is the segment's moment of inertia and ω_s is the segment's angular velocity, both with respect to a transverse axis through the segment's own CG. In the remote term, m is the segment's mass, r is the distance between the total body and segmental CGs, and ω_g is the angular velocity of the segmental CG about the principal transverse axis (Figure 14-7). The sum of the angular momenta of all the body segments about a principal axis yields the total-body angular momentum about that axis.

During takeoff from a springboard or platform, a competitive diver must attain sufficient linear momentum to reach the necessary height (and safe distance from the board or platform) and sufficient angular momentum to perform the required number of rotations. For multiple-rotation, nontwisting platform dives, the angular momentum generated at takeoff increases as the rotational requirements of the dive increase (8). Angular momentum values as high as 66 kg · m²/s and 70 kg · m²/s have been reported for multiple gold medalist Greg Louganis during his back two-and-a-half and forward three-and-a-half springboard dives, respectively (15). When a twist is also incorporated into a somersaulting dive, the angular momentum required is further increased. Inclusion of a twist during forward one-and-a-half springboard dives is associated with increased angular momentum at takeoff of 6–19% (20). Adding a somersault while rotating in a tuck rather than a pike position also requires a small increase in angular momentum (16).

Conservation of Angular Momentum

Whenever gravity is the only acting external force, angular momentum is conserved. For angular motion, the principle of conservation of momentum may be stated as follows:

> The total angular momentum of a given system remains constant in the absence of external torques.

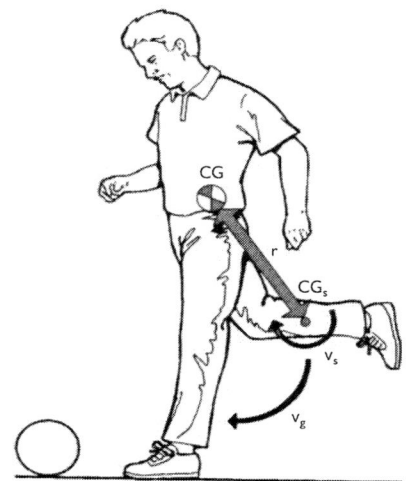

FIGURE 14-7

The angular momentum of the swinging leg is the sum of its local term, $I_s \omega_s$ and its remote term, $mr^2 \omega_g$.

Gravitational force acting at a body's CG produces no torque because $d_\perp$ equals zero and so it creates no change in angular momentum.

The principle of conservation of angular momentum is particularly useful in the mechanical analysis of diving, trampolining, and gymnastics events in which the human body undergoes controlled rotations while airborne. In a one-and-a-half front somersault dive, the diver leaves the springboard with a fixed amount of angular momentum. According to the principle of conservation of angular momentum, the amount of angular momentum present at the instant of takeoff remains constant throughout the dive. As the diver goes from an extended layout position into a tuck, the radius of gyration is decreased, thus reducing the body's principal moment of inertia about the transverse axis. Because angular momentum remains constant, a compensatory increase in angular velocity must accompany the decrease in moment of inertia (Figure 14-8). The tighter the diver's tuck, the greater the angular velocity. Once the somersault is completed, the diver extends to a full layout position, thereby increasing total-body moment of inertia with respect to the axis of rotation. Again, because angular momentum remains constant, an equivalent decrease in angular velocity occurs. For the diver to appear to enter the water perfectly vertically, minimal angular velocity is desirable. Sample Problem 14.2 quantitatively illustrates this example.

Other examples of conservation of angular momentum occur when an airborne performer has a total-body angular momentum of zero and a forceful movement such as a jump pass or volleyball spike is executed. When a volleyball player performs a spike, moving the hitting arm with a high angular velocity and a large angular momentum, there is a compensatory rotation of the lower body, producing an equal amount of angular momentum in the opposite direction (Figure 14-9). The moment of inertia of the two legs with respect to the hips is much greater than that of the spiking arm with respect to the shoulder. The angular velocity of the legs generated to counter the angular momentum of the swinging arm is therefore much less than the angular velocity of the spiking arm.

• The magnitude and direction of the angular momentum vector for an airborne performer are established at the instant of takeoff.

Transfer of Angular Momentum

Although angular momentum remains constant in the absence of external torques, transferring angular velocity at least partially from one principal axis of rotation to another is possible. This occurs when a diver changes

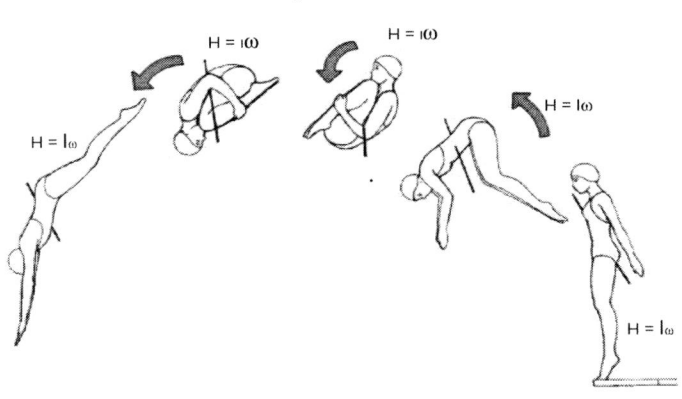

$H = I\omega$ $H = I\omega$ $H = I\omega$

$H = I\omega$

$H = I\omega$

FIGURE 14-8

When angular momentum is conserved, changes in body configuration produce a trade-off between moment of inertia and angular velocity, with a tuck position producing greater angular velocity.

SAMPLE PROBLEM 14.2

A 60 kg diver is positioned so that his radius of gyration is 0.5 m as he leaves the board with an angular velocity of 4 rad/s. What is the diver's angular velocity when he assumes a tuck position, altering his radius of gyration to 0.25 m?

Position 1

Known

$$m = 60 \text{ kg}$$
$$k = 0.5 \text{ m}$$
$$\omega = 4 \text{ rad/s}$$

$$m = 60 \text{ kg}$$
$$k = 0.25 \text{ m}$$

Position 2

Solution

To find ω, calculate the amount of angular momentum that the diver possesses when he leaves the board, since angular momentum remains constant during the airborne phase of the dive:

Position 1:

$$H = mk^2\omega$$
$$= (60 \text{ kg}) (0.5 \text{ m})^2 (4 \text{ rad/s})$$
$$= 60 \text{ kg} \cdot \text{m}^2/\text{s}$$

Use this constant value for angular momentum to determine ω when $k = 0.25$ m:

Position 2:

$$H = mk^2\omega$$
$$60 \text{ kg} \cdot \text{m}^2/\text{s} = (60 \text{ kg}) (0.25 \text{ m})^2 (\omega)$$

$$\omega = 16 \text{ rad/s}$$

from a primarily somersaulting rotation to one that is primarily twisting, and vice versa. An airborne performer's angular velocity vector does not necessarily occur in the same direction as the angular momentum vector. It is possible for a body's somersaulting angular momentum and its twisting angular momentum to be altered in midair, though the vector sum of the two (the total angular momentum) remains constant in magnitude and direction.

Researchers have observed several procedures for changing the total-body axis of rotation. Asymmetrical arm movements and rotation of the hips (termed *hula movement*) can tilt the axis of rotation out of the original plane of motion (Figure 14-10). The less-often-used hula movement can produce tilting of the principal axis of rotation when the body is som-

FIGURE 14-9

During the airborne execution of a spike in volleyball, a compensatory rotation of the lower extremity offsets the forcefully swinging arm so that total body angular momentum is conserved.

ersaulting in a piked position. These asymmetrical movements can be used to generate twist and to eliminate twist (24). The results of a study on twisting somersault performances executed from a trampoline indicate that less-skilled performers tend to rush their asymmetrical movements, detracting from performance quality (19).

Even when total-body angular momentum is zero, generating a twist in midair is possible using skillful manipulation of a body composed of at least two segments. Prompted by the observation that a domestic cat

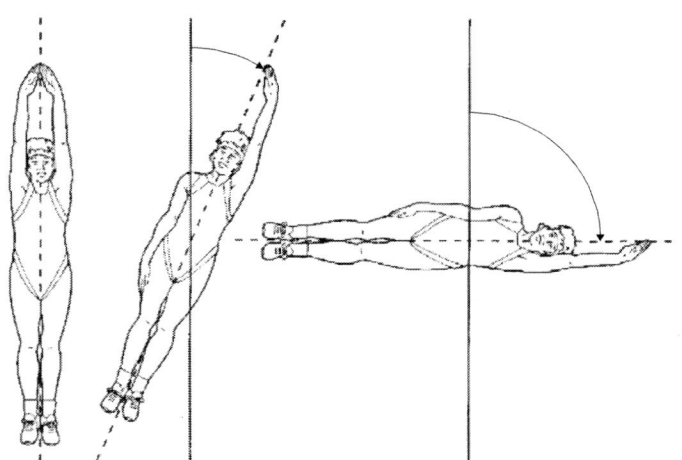

FIGURE 14-10

Asymmetrical positioning of the arms with respect to the axis of angular momentum can shift the axis of rotation.

seems always to land on its feet no matter what position it falls from, scientists have studied this apparent contradiction of the principle of conservation of angular momentum (7). Gymnasts and divers can use this procedure, referred to as *cat rotation,* without violating the conservation of angular momentum.

Cat rotation is basically a two-phase process. It is accomplished most effectively when the two body segments are in a 90° pike position, so that the radius of gyration of one segment is maximal with respect to the longitudinal axis of the other segment (Figure 14-11). The first phase consists of the internally generated rotation of Segment 1 around its longitudinal axis. Because angular momentum is conserved, there is a compensatory rotation of Segment 2 in the opposite direction around the longitudinal axis of Segment 1. However, the resulting rotation is of a relatively small velocity, because k for Segment 2 is relatively large with respect to Axis 1. The second phase of the process consists of rotation of Segment 2 around its longitudinal axis in the same direction originally taken by Segment 1. Accompanying this motion is a compensatory rotation of Segment 1 in the opposite direction around Axis 2. Again, angular velocity is relatively small, because k for Segment 1 is relatively large with respect to Axis 2. Using this procedure, a skilled diver can initiate a twist in midair and turn through as much as 450° (7). Cat rotation is performed around the longitudinal axes of the two major body segments. It is easier to initiate rotation about the longitudinal principal axis than about either the transverse or the anteroposterior principal axes, because total-body moment of inertia with respect to the longitudinal axis is much smaller than the total-body moments of inertia with respect to the other two axes.

Change in Angular Momentum

When an external torque does act, it changes the amount of angular momentum present in a system predictably. Just as with changes in linear momentum, changes in angular momentum depend not only on the mag-

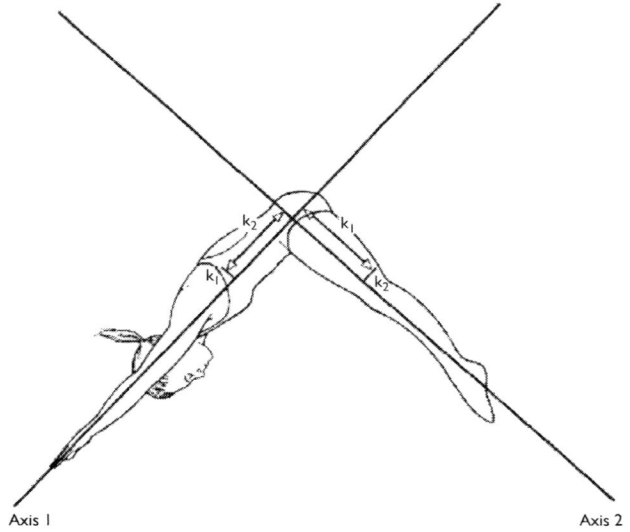

FIGURE 14-11

A skillful human performer can rotate 180° or more in the air with zero angular momentum because in a piked position there is a large discrepancy between the radii of gyration for the upper and lower extremities with respect to the longitudinal axes of these two major body segments.

Axis 1

Axis 2

nitude and direction of acting external torques but also on the length of the time interval over which each torque acts:

$$\text{linear impulse} = Ft$$
$$\text{angular impulse} = Tt$$

When an angular impulse acts on a system, the result is a change in the total angular momentum of the system. The impulse–momentum relationship for angular quantities may be expressed as the following:

$$Tt = \Delta H$$
$$= (I\omega)_2 - (I\omega)_1$$

As before, the symbols T, t, H, I, and ω represent torque, time, angular momentum, moment of inertia, and angular velocity, respectively, and subscripts 1 and 2 denote initial and second or final points in time. Because angular impulse is the product of torque and time, significant changes in an object's angular momentum may result from the action of a large torque over a small time interval or from the action of a small torque over a large time interval. Since torque is the product of a force's magnitude and the perpendicular distance to the axis of rotation, both of these factors affect angular impulse. The effect of angular impulse on angular momentum is shown in Sample Problem 14.3.

In the throwing events in track and field, the object is to maximize the angular impulse exerted on an implement before release, to maximize its momentum and the ultimate horizontal displacement following release. As discussed in Chapter 11, linear velocity is directly related to angular velocity, with the radius of rotation serving as the factor of proportionality. As long as the moment of inertia (mk^2) of a rotating body remains constant, increased angular momentum translates directly to increased linear momentum when the body is projected. This concept is particularly evident in the hammer throw, in which the athlete first swings the hammer two or three times around the body with the feet planted, and then executes the next three or four whole-body turns while facing the hammer before release. Some hammer throwers perform the first one or two of the whole body turns with the trunk in slight flexion (called *countering with the hips*), thereby enabling a farther reach with the hands (Figure 14-12).

angular impulse
change in angular momentum equal to the product of torque and time interval over which the torque acts

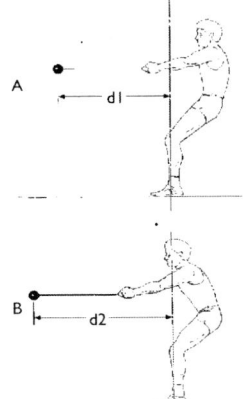

FIGURE 14-12

A hammer thrower must counter the centrifugal force of the hammer to avoid being pulled out of the throwing ring. Countering with the shoulders (**A**) results in a smaller radius of rotation for the hammer than countering with the hips (**B**).

SAMPLE PROBLEM 14.3

What average amount of force must be applied by the elbow flexors inserting at an average perpendicular distance of 1.5 cm from the axis of rotation at the elbow over a period of 0.3 s to stop the motion of the 3.5 kg arm swinging with an angular velocity of 5 rad/s when k = 20 cm?

Known

$$d = 0.015 \text{ m}$$
$$t = 0.3 \text{ s}$$
$$m = 3.5 \text{ kg}$$
$$k = 0.20 \text{ m}$$
$$\omega = 5 \text{ rad/s}$$

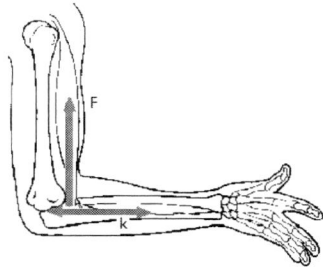

Solution

The impulse–momentum relationship for angular motion can be used.

$$Tt = \Delta H$$
$$Fdt = (mk^2\omega)_2 - (mk^2\omega)_1$$
$$F(0.015 \text{ m}) (0.3 \text{ s}) = 0 - (3.5 \text{ kg}) (0.20 \text{ m})^2 (5 \text{ rad/s})$$

$$\boxed{F = -155.56 \text{ N}}$$

This tactic increases the radius of rotation, and thus the moment of inertia of the hammer with respect to the axis of rotation, so that if angular velocity is not reduced, the angular momentum of the thrower/hammer system is increased. For this strategy, the final turns are completed with the entire body leaning away from the hammer, or *countering with the shoulders.* Researchers have suggested that although the ability to lean forward throughout the turns should increase the angular momentum imparted to the hammer, a natural tendency to protect against excessive spinal stresses or shoulder strength limitations may prevent the thrower from accomplishing this technique modification (6).

The angular momentum required for the total body rotations executed during aerial skills is primarily derived from the angular impulse created by the reaction force of the support surface during takeoff. During back dives performed from a platform, the major angular impulse is produced during the final weighting of the platform, when the diver comes out of a crouched position through extension at the hip, knee, and ankle joints and executes a vigorous arm swing simultaneously (17). The vertical component of the platform reaction force, acting in front of the diver's CG, creates most of the backward angular momentum required (Figure 14-13).

On a springboard, the position of the fulcrum with respect to the tip of the board can usually be adjusted and can influence performance. Setting the fulcrum farther back from the tip of the board results in greater downward board tip vertical velocity at the beginning of takeoff, which allows the diver more time in contact with the board to generate angular

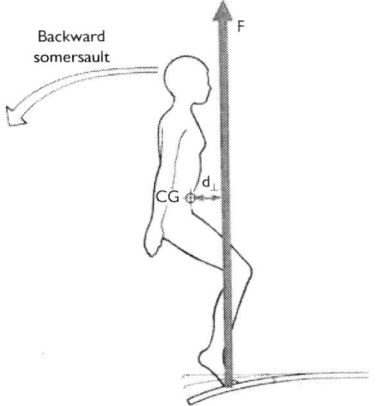

Backward somersault

FIGURE 14-13

The product of the springboard reaction force (F) and its moment arm with respect to the diver's center of gravity (d$_\perp$) creates a torque, which generates the angular impulse that produces the diver's angular momentum at takeoff.

momentum and increased vertical velocity going into the dive (12). Concomitant disadvantages, however, include the requirement of increased hurdle flight duration and the necessity of reversing downward motion from a position of greater flexion at the knees (12). In an optimum reverse dive from a springboard, peak knee extension torque is generated just prior to maximum springboard depression, so that the diver exerts force against a stiffer board (22).

The motions of the body segments during takeoff determine the magnitude and direction of the reaction force generating linear and angular impulses. During both platform and springboard dives, the rotation of the arms at takeoff generally contributes more to angular momentum than the motion of any other segment (8, 15). Highly skilled divers perform the arm swing with the arms fully extended, thus maximizing the moment of inertia of the arms and the angular momentum generated. Less-skilled divers often must use flexion at the elbow to reduce the moment of inertia of the arms about the shoulders so that arm swing can be completed during the time available (15). In contrast to the takeoff during a dive, during the takeoff for aerial somersaults performed from the floor in gymnastics, it is forceful extension of the legs that contributes the most to angular momentum (5). Optimizing performance of aerial somersaults requires generating high linear and angular velocities during the approach, as well as precise timings of body segment motions (13). During performance of the Hecht vault in gymnastics, the angular momentum produced by the forceful push-off from the horse is one of the key variables found by researchers to influence judges' scores (23).

Angular impulse produced through the support surface reaction force is also essential for performance of the *tour jeté,* a dance movement that consists of a jump accompanied by a 180° turn, with the dancer landing on the foot opposite the takeoff foot. When the movement is performed properly, the dancer appears to rise straight up and then rotate about the principal vertical axis in the air. In reality, the jump must be executed so that a reaction torque around the dancer's vertical axis is generated by the floor. The extended leg at the initiation of the jump creates a relatively large moment of inertia relative to the axis of rotation, thereby resulting in a relatively low total-body angular velocity. At the peak of the jump, the

The arm swing during takeoff contributes significantly to the diver's angular momentum.

The surface reaction force is used by the dancer to generate angular momentum during the takeoff of the tour jeté.

dancer's legs simultaneously cross the axis of rotation and the arms simultaneously come together overhead, close to the axis of rotation. These movements dramatically reduce moment of inertia, thus increasing angular velocity (14).

Similarly, when a skater performs a double or triple axel in figure skating, angular momentum is generated by the skater's movements and changes in total-body moment of inertia prior to takeoff. Over half of the angular momentum for a double axel is generated during the preparatory glide on one skate going into the jump (2). Most of this angular momentum is contributed by motion of the free leg, which is extended somewhat horizontally to increase total-body moment of inertia around the skater's vertical axis (2). As the skater becomes airborne, both legs are extended vertically, and the arms are tightly crossed to minimize moment of inertia around the vertical axis and thereby maximize rotational velocity.

In the performance of the tennis serve, although the server does not typically become airborne, the angular momentum generated plays an important role. Angular momentum is produced by the movements of the trunk, arms, and legs, with a transfer of momentum from the extending lower extremity and rotating trunk to the racket arm, and finally to the racket (3).

ANGULAR ANALOGUES OF NEWTON'S LAWS OF MOTION

Table 14-1 presents linear and angular kinetic quantities in a parallel format. With the many parallels between linear and angular motion, it is not surprising that Newton's laws of motion may also be stated in terms of angular motion. It is necessary to remember that torque and moment of inertia are the angular equivalents of force and mass in substituting terms.

Newton's First Law

The angular version of the first law of motion may be stated as follows:

> A rotating body will maintain a state of constant rotational motion unless acted on by an external torque.

In the analysis of human movement in which mass remains constant throughout, this angular analogue forms the underlying basis for the principle of conservation of angular momentum. Because angular velocity may change to compensate for changes in moment of inertia resulting from alterations in the radius of gyration, the quantity that remains constant in the absence of external torque is angular momentum.

TABLE 14-1

Linear and Angular Kinetic Quantities

LINEAR	ANGULAR
mass (m)	moment of inertia (I)
force (F)	torque (T)
momentum (M)	angular momentum (H)
impulse (Ft)	angular impulse (Tt)

Newton's Second Law

In angular terms, Newton's second law may be stated algebraically and in words as the following:

$$T = I\alpha$$

A net torque produces angular acceleration of a body that is directly proportional to the magnitude of the torque, in the same direction as the torque, and inversely proportional to the body's moment of inertia.

In accordance with Newton's second law for angular motion, the angular acceleration of the forearm is directly proportional to the magnitude of the net torque at the elbow and in the direction (flexion) of the net torque at the elbow. The greater the moment of inertia is with respect to the axis of rotation at the elbow, the smaller is the resulting angular acceleration (see Sample Problem 14.4).

Newton's Third Law

The law of reaction may be stated in angular form as the following:

For every torque exerted by one body on another, there is an equal and opposite torque exerted by the second body on the first.

When a baseball player forcefully swings a bat, rotating the mass of the upper body, a torque is created around the player's longitudinal axis. If

---

SAMPLE PROBLEM 14.4

The knee extensors insert on the tibia at an angle of 308 at a distance of 3 cm from the axis of rotation at the knee. How much force must the knee extensors exert to produce an angular acceleration at the knee of 1 rad/s^2, given a mass of the lower leg and foot of 4.5 kg and k = 23 cm?

Known

$$d = 0.03 \text{ m}$$
$$\alpha = 1 \text{ rad/s}^2$$
$$m = 4.5 \text{ kg}$$
$$k = 0.23 \text{ m}$$

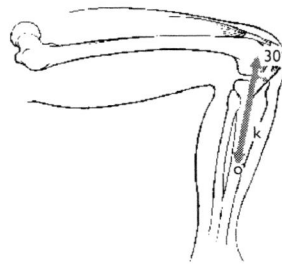

Solution

The angular analogue of Newton's second law of motion may be used to solve the problem:

$$T = I\alpha$$
$$Fd = mk^2\alpha$$
$$(F \sin 30 \text{ N}) (0.03 \text{ m}) = (4.5 \text{ kg}) (0.23 \text{ m})^2(1 \text{ rad/s}^2)$$

$$F = 15.9 \text{ N}$$

476   BASIC BIOMECHANICS

the batter's feet are not firmly planted, the lower body tends to rotate around the longitudinal axis in the opposite direction. However, since the feet usually are planted, the torque generated by the upper body is translated to the ground, where the earth generates a torque of equal magnitude and opposite direction on the cleats of the batter's shoes.

CENTRIPETAL FORCE

Bodies undergoing rotary motion around a fixed axis are also subject to a linear force. When an object attached to a line is whirled around in a circular path and then released, the object flies off on a path that forms a tangent to the circular path it was following at the point at which it was released, since this is the direction it was traveling in at the point of release (Figure 14-14). Centripetal force prevents the rotating body from leaving its circular path while rotation occurs around a fixed axis. The direction of a centripetal force is always toward the center of rotation; this is the reason it is also known as *center-seeking force*. Centripetal force produces the radial component of the acceleration of a body traveling on a curved path (see Chapter 11). The following formula quantifies the magnitude of a centripetal force in terms of the tangential linear velocity of the rotating body:

$$F_c = \frac{mv^2}{r}$$

In this formula, F_c is centripetal force, m is mass, v is the tangential linear velocity of the rotating body at a given point in time, and r is the radius of rotation. Centripetal force may also be defined in terms of angular velocity:

$$F_c = mr\omega^2$$

As is evident from both equations, the speed of rotation is the most influential factor on the magnitude of centripetal force, because centripetal force is proportional to the square of velocity or angular velocity.

When a cyclist rounds a curve, the ground exerts centripetal force on the tires of the cycle. The forces acting on the cycle/cyclist system are weight, friction, and the ground reaction force (Figure 14-15). The horizontal component of the ground reaction force and laterally directed friction provide the centripetal force, which also creates a torque about the cycle/cyclist CG. To prevent rotation toward the outside of the curve, the cyclist must lean to the inside of the curve so that the moment arm of the system's weight relative to the contact point with the ground is large enough to produce an oppositely directed torque of equal magnitude. In the absence of leaning into the curve, the cyclist would have to reduce speed to reduce the magnitude of the ground reaction force, in order to prevent loss of balance.

centripetal force
force directed toward the center of rotation for a body in rotational motion

Cyclists and runners lean into a curve to offset the torque created by centripetal force acting on the base of support.

An object swung in a circle and then released will follow a linear path tangential to the curve at the point of release, since this is the direction of motion at the point of release.

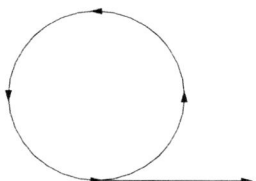

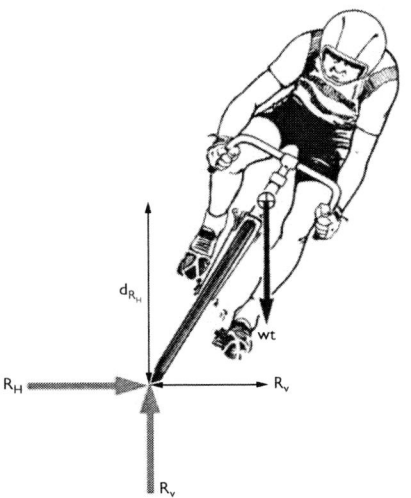

FIGURE 14-15

Free body diagram of a cyclist on a curve. R_H is centripetal force. When the cyclist is balanced, summing torques at the cyclist's CG, $(R_v)(d_{R_v}) = (R_H)(d_{R_H})$.

When rounding a corner in an automobile, there is a sensation of being pushed in the direction of the outside of the curve. What is felt has been referred to as *centrifugal force*. What is actually occurring, however, is that in accordance with Newton's first law, the body's inertia tends to cause it to continue traveling on a straight, rather than a curved, path. The car seat, the seat belt, and possibly the car door provide a reaction force that changes the direction of body motion. "Centrifugal force," then, is a fictitious force that might more appropriately be described as the absence of centripetal force acting on an object.

Table 14-2 summarizes the formulas used in this chapter.

TABLE 14-2

Formula Summary

DESCRIPTION	FORMULA
Moment of Inertia = (mass)(radius of gyration squared)	$I = mk^2$
Angular momentum = (moment of inertia)(angular velocity)	$H = I\omega$
Local term for angular momentum = (segment moment of inertia about segment CG)(segment angular velocity about segment CG)	$H_l = I_s v_s$
Remote term for angular momentum = (segment mass) (distance between total body and segment CGs, squared) (angular velocity of segment about the principal axis)	$Hr = mr^2\omega_g$
Angular impulse = change in angular momentum	$Tt = \Delta H$ $Tt = (mk^2\omega)_2 - (mk^2\omega)_1$
Newton's second law (rotational version)	$T = I\alpha$
Centripetal force = $\dfrac{(mass)\ (velocity\ squared)}{radius\ of\ rotation}$	$F_c = \dfrac{mv^2}{r}$
Centripetal force = (mass)(radius of rotation)(angular velocity squared)	$F_c = mr\omega^2$

SUMMARY

Whereas a body's resistance to linear acceleration is proportional to its mass, resistance to angular acceleration is related to both mass and the distribution of mass with respect to the axis of rotation. Resistance to angular acceleration is known as *moment of inertia,* a quantity that incorporates both the amount of mass and its distribution relative to the center of rotation.

Just as linear momentum is the product of the linear inertial property (mass) and linear velocity, angular momentum is the product of moment of inertia and angular velocity. In the absence of external torques, angular momentum is conserved. An airborne human performer can alter total-body angular velocity by manipulating moment of inertia through changes in body configuration relative to the principal axis around which rotation is occurring. Skilled performers can also alter the axis of rotation and initiate rotation when no angular momentum is present while airborne. The principle of conservation of angular momentum is based on the angular version of Newton's first law of motion. The second and third laws of motion may also be expressed in angular terms by substituting moment of inertia for mass, torque for force, and angular acceleration for linear acceleration.

A linear force that acts on all rotating bodies is centripetal (or a center-seeking) force, which is always directed toward the center of rotation. The magnitude of centripetal force depends on the mass, speed, and radius of rotation of the rotating body.

INTRODUCTORY PROBLEMS

1. If you had to design a model of the human body composed entirely of regular geometric solids, which solid shapes would you choose? Using a straightedge, sketch a model of the human body that incorporates the solid shapes you have selected.
2. Construct a table displaying common units of measure for both linear and angular quantities of the inertial property, momentum, and impulse.
3. Skilled performance of a number of sport skills is characterized by "follow-through." Explain the value of "follow-through" in terms of the concepts discussed in this chapter.
4. Explain the reason the product of body mass and body height squared is a good predictor of body moment of inertia in children.
5. A 1.1 kg racquet has a moment of inertia about a grip axis of rotation of 0.4 kg · m^2. What is its radius of gyration? (Answer: 0.6 m)
6. How much angular impulse must be supplied by the hamstrings to bring a leg swinging at 8 rad/s to a stop, given that the leg's moment of inertia is 0.7 kg · m^2? (Answer: 5.6 mg · m^2/s).
7. Given the following principal transverse axis moments of inertia and angular velocities, calculate the angular momentum of each of the following gymnasts. What body configurations do these moments of inertia represent?

	I_s(kg · m^2)	(rad/s)
A	3.5	20.00
B	7.0	10.00
C	15.0	4.67

(Answers: A = 70 kg · m^2/s; B = 70 kg · m^2/s; C = 70 kg · m^2/s)

8. A volleyball player's 3.7 kg arm moves at an average angular velocity of 15 rad/s during execution of a spike. If the average moment of inertia of the extending arm is 0.45 kg · m², what is the average radius of gyration for the arm during the spike? (Answer: 0.35 m)

9. A 50 kg diver in a full layout position, with a total body radius of gyration with respect to her transverse principal axis equal to 0.45 m, leaves a springboard with an angular velocity of 6 rad/s. What is the diver's angular velocity when she assumes a tuck position, reducing her radius of gyration to 0.25 m? (Answer: 19.4 rad/s)

10. If the centripetal force exerted on a swinging tennis racket by a player's hand is 40 N, how much reaction force is exerted on the player by the racket? (Answer: 40 N)

ADDITIONAL PROBLEMS

1. The radius of gyration of the thigh with respect to the transverse axis at the hip is 54% of the segment length. The mass of the thigh is 10.5% of total body mass, and the length of the thigh is 23.2% of total body height. What is the moment of inertia of the thigh with respect to the hip for males of the following body masses and heights?

	MASS (kg)	HEIGHT (m)
A	60	1.6
B	60	1.8
C	70	1.6
D	70	1.8

(Answers: A = 0.25 kg · m², B = 0.32 kg · m², C = 0.30 kg · m², D = 0.37 kg · m²)

2. Select three sport or daily living implements, and explain the ways in which you might modify each implement's moment of inertia with respect to the axis of rotation to adapt it for a person of impaired strength.

3. A 0.68 kg tennis ball is given an angular momentum of $2.72 \cdot 10^{-3} \cdot$ m²/s when struck by a racket. If its radius of gyration is 2 cm, what is its angular velocity? (Answer: 10 rad/s)

4. A 7.27 kg shot makes seven complete revolutions during its 2.5 s flight. If its radius of gyration is 2.54 cm, what is its angular momentum? (Answer: 0.0817 kg · m²/s)

5. What is the resulting angular acceleration of a 1.7 kg forearm and hand when the forearm flexors, attaching 3 cm from the center of rotation at the elbow, produce 10 N of tension, given a 90° angle at the elbow and a forearm and hand radius of gyration of 20 cm? (Answer: 4.41 rad/s²)

6. The patellar tendon attaches to the tibia at a 20° angle 3 cm from the axis of rotation at the knee. If the tension in the tendon is 400 N, what is the resulting acceleration of the 4.2 kg lower leg and foot given a radius of gyration of 25 cm for the lower leg/foot with respect to the axis of rotation at the knee? (Answer: 15.6 rad/s²)

7. A cavewoman swings a 0.75 m sling of negligible weight around her head with a centripetal force of 220 N. What is the initial velocity of a 9 N stone released from the sling? (Answer: 13.4 m/s)
8. A 7.27 kg hammer on a 1 m wire is released with a linear velocity of 28 m/s. What reaction force is exerted on the thrower by the hammer at the instant before release? (Answer: 5.7 kN)
9. Discuss the effect of banking a curve on a racetrack. Construct a free body diagram to assist with your analysis.
10. Using the data in Appendix D, calculate the locations of the radii of gyration of all body segments with respect to the proximal joint center for a 1.7 m tall woman.

NAME _____

DATE _____

LABORATORY EXPERIENCES

1. At the *Basic Biomechanics* Online Learning Center (www.mhhe.com/hall5e), go to Student Center, Chapter 14, Lab Manual, Lab 1, and then view the Angular Momentum Animation of a swinging ball on a rope wrapping around a pole. Answer the following questions.

   a. As the rope winds around the pole, what happens to the angular velocity of the ball?

   _____

   b. As the rope winds around the pole, what happens to the radius of rotation of the ball?

   _____

   c. As the rope winds around the pole, what happens to the angular momentum of the ball?

   Explain: _____

2. View either a video or a live performance of a long jump from the side view. Explain the motions of the jumper's arms and legs in terms of the concepts presented in this chapter.

Contributions of arms:_____

_____

_____

_____

_____

Contributions of legs: _____

_____

_____

_____

_____

3. View either a video or a live performance of a dive incorporating a pike or a somersault from the side view. Explain the motions of the diver's arms and legs in terms of the concepts presented in this chapter.

Contributions of arms:_____

_____

_____

_____

_____

Contributions of legs:_____

_____

_____

_____

_____

482   BASIC BIOMECHANICS

4. Stand on a rotating platform with both arms abducted at the shoulders at 90°, and have a partner spin you at a moderate angular velocity. Once the partner has let go, quickly fold your arms across your chest, being careful not to lose your balance. Write a paragraph explaining the change in angular velocity.

Explanation: _____

_____

_____

_____

_____

Is angular momentum in this situation constant? _____

5. Stand on a rotating platform and use a hula-hooping motion of the hips to generate rotation. Explain how total body rotation results.

Explanation:_____

_____

_____

_____

_____

REFERENCES

1. Ackland T, Elliott B, and Tichards J: Growth in body size affects rotational performance in women's gymnastics, Sports Biomech 2: 163, 2003.
2. Albert WJ and Miller DI: Takeoff characteristics of single and double axel figure skating jumps, J Appl Biomech 12:72, 1996.
3. Anderson T: Biomechanics and running economy, Sports Med 22:76, 1996.
4. Bahamonde RE: Changes in angular momentum during the tennis serve, J Sports Sci 18:579, 2000.
5. Brüggemann G-P: Biomechanics in gymnastics. In Van Gheluwe B and Atha J: Current research in sports biomechanics, Basel, 1987, Karger.
6. Dapena J and McDonald C: A three-dimensional analysis of angular momentum in the hammer throw, Med Sci Sports Exerc 21:206, 1989.
7. Frohlich C: The physics of somersaulting and twisting, Sci Am 242:154, 1980.
8. Hamill J, Ricard MD, and Golden DM: Angular momentum in multiple rotation nontwisting platform dives, Int J Sport Biomech 2:78, 1986.
9. Hay JG: The biomechanics of sports techniques (3rd ed), Englewood Cliffs, NJ, 1985, Prentice-Hall.
10. Jensen RK: The growth of children's moment of inertia, Med Sci Sports Exerc 18:440, 1987.
11. Jensen RK and Nassas G: Growth of segment principal moments of inertia between four and twenty years, Med Sci Sports Exerc 20:594, 1988.
12. Jones IC and Miller DI: Influence of fulcrum position on springboard response and takeoff performance in the running approach, J Appl Biomech 12:383, 1996.
13. King MA and Yeadon MR: Maximising somersault rotation in tumbling, J Biomech 37:471, 2004.
14. Laws K: The physics of dance, New York, 1984, Schirmer Books.
15. Miller DI, Jones IC, and Pizzimenti MA: Taking off: Greg Louganis' diving style, Soma 2:20, 1988.
16. Miller DI and Sprigings EJ: Factors influencing the performance of springboard dives of increasing difficulty, J Appl Biomech 17:217, 2001.
17. Miller DI et al: Kinetic and kinematic characteristics of 10-m platform performances of elite divers: I. back takeoffs, Int J Sport Biomech 5:60, 1989.
18. Nesbit SM et al: A discussion of iron golf club head inertia tensors and their effects on the golfer, J Appl Biomech 12:449, 1996.
19. Sanders RH: Effect of ability on twisting techniques in forward somersaults on the trampoline, J Appl Biomech 11:267, 1995.
20. Sanders RH and Wilson BD: Angular momentum requirements of the twisting and nontwisting forward $1\frac{1}{2}$ somersault dive, Int J Sport Biomech 3:47, 1988.
21. Southard D and Groomer L: Warm-up with baseball bats of varying moments of inertia: effect on bat velocity and swing pattern, Res Q Exerc Sport 74:270, 2003.
22. Sprigings EJ and Miller DI: Optimal knee extension timing in springboard and platform dives from the reverse group, J Appl Biomech 20:275, 2004.
23. Takei Y, Blucker EP, Nohara H, and Yamashita N: The Hecht vault performed at the 1995 World Gymnastics Championships: deterministic model and judges' scores, J Sports Sci 11:849, 2000.
24. Yeadon MR: The biomechanics of the human in flight, Am J Sports Med 25:575, 1997.

ANNOTATED READINGS

Frohlich C: The physics of somersaulting and twisting, Sci Am 242:154, 1980.
    Describes the way in which divers, gymnasts, astronauts, and cats perform rotational maneuvers in midair that seem to violate the conservation of angular momentum.
Miller DI, Jones IC, and Pizzimenti MA: Taking off: Greg Louganis' diving style, Soma 2:20, 1988.
    Discusses the linear and angular momentum requirements for performing total body rotations at the world-class level, and describes the methods by which these factors may be studied.

Townend MS: *Mathematics in sport*, New York, 1984, John Wiley & Sons.
Includes a chapter on running, a chapter on jumping, and sections on gymnastics and high-board diving that discuss the principle of conservation of angular momentum with respect to various applications in the identified sports.

Yeadon MR and Mikulcik EC: Stability and control of aerial movements. In Nigg BM, Stefanyshyn D, and Denoth J: *Biomechanics and biology of movement*, Champaign, IL, 2000, Human Kinetics.
Presents a detailed description of strategies and mechanical concepts related to control of rotations and twists during the execution of aerial skills in diving and gymnastics.

RELATED WEB SITES

Centrifugal Force: The False Force
regentsprep.org/Regents/physics/phys06/bcentrif/centrif.htm
Includes a description and simulation of a car going around a curve to illustrate the effect of inertia on the contents of the car.

Conceptest on Centripetal Force
motor1.physics.wayne.edu/~cinabro/cinabro/education/conceptest15.html
Poses several questions related to centripetal force with a link to an answer page.

Conservation of Angular Momentum
schutz.ucsc.edu/~josh/5A/book/torque/node15.html
Describes a demonstration, with diagrams and formulas, for conservation of angular momentum.

Exploratorium: Angular Momentum
www.exploratorium.edu/snacks/momentum_machine.html
Describes a simple experiment that illustrates angular momentum.

Model of a Carousel
www.walter-fendt.de/ph11e/carousel.htm
Displays an applet allowing user control of a rotating carousel to illustrate centripetal force.

NASA: The Conservation of Angular Momentum
liftoff.msfc.nasa.gov/Academy/ROCKET_SCI/ORBMECH/angular_momentum.html
Provides a Java applet illustrating the concept of conservation of angular momentum with a swinging pendulum.

KEY TERMS

angular impulse	change in angular momentum equal to the product of torque and time interval over which the torque acts
angular momentum	quantity of angular motion possessed by a body; measured as the product of moment of inertia and angular velocity
centripetal force	force directed toward the center of rotation for a body in rotational motion
moment of inertia	inertial property for rotating bodies representing resistance to angular acceleration; based on both mass and the distance the mass is distributed from the axis of rotation
principal axes	three mutually perpendicular axes passing through the total body center of gravity
principal moment of inertia	total-body moment of inertia relative to one of the principal axes
radius of gyration	distance from the axis of rotation to a point where the body's mass could be concentrated without altering its rotational characteristics

Human Movement in a Fluid Medium

15

After completing this chapter, you will be able to:

Explain the ways in which the composition and flow characteristics of a fluid affect fluid forces.

Define *buoyancy* and explain the variables that determine whether a human body will float.

Define *drag*, identify the components of drag, and identify the factors that affect the magnitude of each component.

Define *lift* and explain the ways in which it can be generated.

Discuss the theories regarding propulsion of the human body in swimming.

**Visit the Online Learning Center at www.mhhe.com/hall5e
to access the Online Lab Manual and many additional resources.**

The ability to control the action of fluid forces differentiates elite from average swimmers.

Why are there dimples in a golf ball? Why are some people able to float while others cannot? Why are cyclists, swimmers, downhill skiers, and speed skaters concerned with streamlining their bodies during competition?

Both air and water are fluid mediums that exert forces on bodies moving through them. Some of these forces slow the progress of a moving body; others provide support or propulsion. A general understanding of the actions of fluid forces on human movement activities is an important component of the study of the biomechanics of human movement. This chapter introduces the effects of fluid forces on both human and projectile motion.

THE NATURE OF FLUIDS

fluid
substance that flows when subjected to a shear stress

• *Air and water are fluids that exert forces on the human body.*

• *The velocity of a body relative to a fluid influences the magnitude of the forces exerted by the fluid on the body.*

Although in general conversation the term *fluid* is often used interchangeably with the term *liquid,* from a mechanical perspective, a fluid is any substance that tends to flow or continuously deform when acted on by a shear force (42). Both gases and liquids are fluids with similar mechanical behaviors.

Relative Motion

Because a fluid is a medium capable of flow, the influence of the fluid on a body moving through it depends not only on the body's velocity but also on the velocity of the fluid. Consider the case of waders standing in the shallow portion of a river with a moderately strong current. If they stand still,

---

FIGURE 15-1

The relative velocity of a moving body with respect to a fluid is equal to the vector subtraction of the velocity of the wind from the velocity of the body.

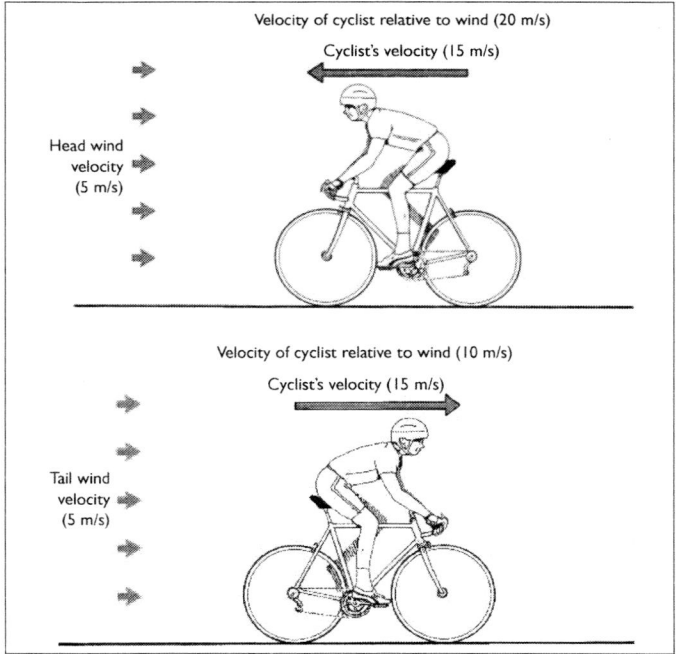

they feel the force of the current against their legs. If they walk upstream against the current, the current's force against their legs is even stronger. If they walk downstream, the current's force is reduced and perhaps even imperceptible.

When a body moves through a fluid, the relative velocity of the body with respect to the fluid influences the magnitude of the acting forces. If the direction of motion is directly opposite the direction of the fluid flow, the magnitude of the velocity of the moving body relative to the fluid is the algebraic sum of the speeds of the moving body and the fluid (Figure 15-1). If the body moves in the same direction as the surrounding fluid, the magnitude of the body's velocity relative to the fluid is the difference in the speeds of the object and the fluid. In other words, the relative velocity of a body with respect to a fluid is the vector subtraction of the absolute velocity of the fluid from the absolute velocity of the body (see Sample Problem 15.1). Likewise, the relative velocity of a fluid with respect to a

relative velocity
velocity of a body with respect to the velocity of something else, such as the surrounding fluid

SAMPLE PROBLEM 15.1

A sailboat is traveling at an absolute speed of 3 m/s against a 0.5 m/s current and with a 6 m/s tailwind. What is the velocity of the current with respect to the boat? What is the velocity of the wind with respect to the boat?

Known

$$v_b = 3 \text{ m/s} \rightarrow$$
$$v_c = 0.5 \text{ m/s} \leftarrow$$
$$v_w = 6 \text{ m/s} \rightarrow$$

Solution
The velocity of the current with respect to the boat is equal to the vector subtraction of the absolute velocity of the boat from the absolute velocity of the current.

$$v_{c/b} = v_c - v_b$$
$$= (0.5 \text{ m/s} \leftarrow) - (3 \text{ m/s} \rightarrow)$$
$$= (3.5 \text{ m/s} \leftarrow)$$

The velocity of the current with respect to the boat is 3.5 m/s in the direction opposite that of the boat.

The velocity of the wind with respect to the boat is equal to the vector subtraction of the absolute velocity of the boat from the absolute velocity of the wind.

$$v_{w/b} = v_w - v_b$$
$$= (6 \text{ m/s} \rightarrow) - (3 \text{ m/s} \rightarrow)$$
$$= (3 \text{ m/s} \rightarrow)$$

The velocity of the wind with respect to the boat is 3 m/s in the direction in which the boat is sailing.

488   BASIC BIOMECHANICS

Laminar flow is characterized by smooth, parallel layers of fluid.

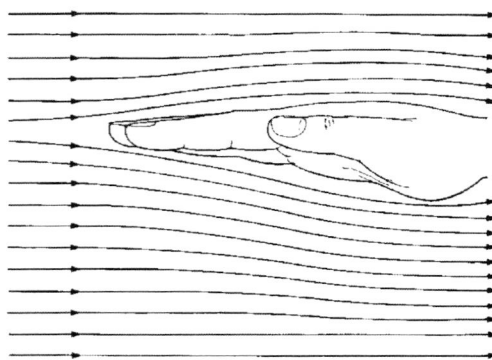

body moving through it is the vector subtraction of the velocity of the body from the velocity of the fluid.

Laminar versus Turbulent Flow

When an object such as a human hand or a canoe paddle moves through water, there is little apparent disturbance of the immediately surrounding water if the relative velocity of the object with respect to the water is low. However, if the relative velocity of motion through the water is sufficiently high, waves and eddies appear.

When an object moves with sufficiently low velocity relative to any fluid medium, the flow of the adjacent fluid is termed laminar flow. Laminar flow is characterized by smooth layers of fluid molecules flowing parallel to one another (Figure 15-2).

laminar flow
flow characterized by smooth, parallel layers of fluid

When an object moves with sufficiently high velocity relative to a surrounding fluid, the layers of fluid near the surface of the object mix, and the flow is termed *turbulent*. The rougher the surface of the body, the lower the relative velocity at which turbulence is caused. Laminar flow and turbulent flow are distinct categories. If any turbulence is present, the flow is nonlaminar. The nature of the fluid flow surrounding an object can dramatically affect the fluid forces exerted on the object. In the case of the human body during swimming, flow is neither completely laminar nor completely turbulent, but transitional between the two (34).

turbulent flow
flow characterized by mixing of adjacent fluid layers

Fluid Properties

Other factors that influence the magnitude of the forces a fluid generates are the fluid's density, specific weight, and viscosity. As discussed in Chapter 3, density (ρ) is defined as mass/volume, and the ratio of weight to volume is known as specific weight (γ). The denser and heavier the fluid medium surrounding a body, the greater the magnitude of the forces the fluid exerts on the body. The property of fluid viscosity involves the internal resistance of a fluid to flow. The greater the extent to which a fluid resists flow under an applied force, the more viscous the fluid is. A thick molasses, for example, is more viscous than a liquid honey, which is more viscous than water. Increased fluid viscosity results in increased forces exerted on bodies exposed to the fluid.

•*Atmospheric pressure and temperature influence a fluid's density, specific weight, and viscosity.*

Atmospheric pressure and temperature influence a fluid's density, specific weight, and viscosity, with more mass concentrated in a given unit of fluid volume at higher atmospheric pressures and lower temperatures.

FLUID*	DENSITY (kg/m³)	SPECIFIC WEIGHT (n/m³)	VISCOSITY (ns/m²)
Air	1.20	11.8	.000018
Water	998	9,790	.0010
Seawater⁺	1,026	10,070	.0014
Ethyl alcohol	799	7,850	.0012
Mercury	13,550.20	133,000.0	.0015

TABLE 15-1

Approximate Physical Properties of Common Fluids

*Fluids are measured at 20°C and standard atmospheric pressure.

⁺10°C, 3.3% salinity.

Because molecular motion in gases increases with temperature, the viscosity of gases also increases. The viscosity of liquids decreases with increased temperature because of a reduction in the cohesive forces among the molecules. The densities, specific weights, and viscosities of common fluids are shown in Table 15-1.

BUOYANCY

Characteristics of the Buoyant Force

Buoyancy is a fluid force that always acts vertically upward. The factors that determine the magnitude of the buoyant force were originally explained by the ancient Greek mathematician Archimedes. Archimedes' principle states that the magnitude of the buoyant force acting on a given body is equal to the weight of the fluid displaced by the body. The latter factor is calculated by multiplying the specific weight of the fluid by the volume of the portion of the body that is surrounded by the fluid. Buoyancy (F_b) is calculated as the product of the displaced volume (V_d) and the fluid's specific weight γ:

$$F_b = V_d \gamma$$

For example, if a water polo ball with a volume of 0.2 m^3 is completely submerged in water at 20°C, the buoyant force acting on the ball is equal to the ball's volume multiplied by the specific weight of water at 20°C:

$$F_b = V_d \gamma$$
$$= (0.2 \text{ m}^3)(9790 \text{ N/m}^3)$$
$$= 1958 \text{ N}$$

The more dense the surrounding fluid, the greater the magnitude of the buoyant force. Since seawater is more dense than fresh water, a given object's buoyancy is greater in seawater than in fresh water. Because the magnitude of the buoyant force is directly related to the volume of the submerged object, the point at which the buoyant force acts is the object's center of volume, which is also known as the *center of buoyancy*. The center of volume is the point around which a body's volume is equally distributed.

Flotation

The ability of a body to float in a fluid medium depends on the relationship between the body's buoyancy and its weight. When weight and the buoyant force are the only two forces acting on a body and their magnitudes

Archimedes' principle
physical law stating that the buoyant force acting on a body is equal to the weight of the fluid displaced by the body

center of volume
point around which a body's volume is equally distributed and at which the buoyant force acts

490 BASIC BIOMECHANICS

are equal, the body floats in a motionless state, in accordance with the principles of static equilibrium. If the magnitude of the weight is greater than that of the buoyant force, the body sinks, moving downward in the direction of the net force.

Most objects float statically in a partially submerged position. The volume of a freely floating object needed to generate a buoyant force equal to the object's weight is the volume that is submerged.

Flotation of the Human Body

In the study of biomechanics, buoyancy is most commonly of interest relative to the flotation of the human body in water. Some individuals cannot float in a motionless position, and others float with little effort. This difference in floatability is a function of body density. Since the density of bone and muscle is greater than the density of fat, individuals who are extremely muscular and have little body fat have higher average body densities than individuals with less muscle, less dense bones, or more body fat. If two individuals have an identical body volume, the one with the higher body density weighs more. Alternatively, if two people have the same body weight, the person with the higher body density has a smaller body volume. For flotation to occur, the body volume must be large enough to create a buoyant force greater than or equal to body weight (see Sample Problem 15.2). Many individuals can float only when holding a large volume of inspired air in the lungs, a tactic that increases body volume without altering body weight.

The orientation of the human body as it floats in water is determined by the relative position of the total-body center of gravity relative to the total-body center of volume. The exact locations of the center of gravity and center of volume vary with anthropometric dimensions and body composition. Typically, the center of gravity is inferior to the center of volume due to the relatively large volume and relatively small weight of the lungs. Because weight acts at the center of gravity and buoyancy acts at the center of volume, a torque is created that rotates the body until it is positioned so that these two acting forces are vertically aligned and the torque ceases to exist (Figure 15-3).

When beginning swimmers try to float on their backs, they typically assume a horizontal body position. Once the swimmer relaxes, the lower end of the body sinks, because of the acting torque. An experienced teacher instructs beginning swimmers to assume a more diagonal position in the water before relaxing into the back float. This position minimizes torque and the concomitant sinking of the lower extremity. Other strategies that a swimmer can use to reduce torque on the body when entering a back float position include extending the arms backward in the water above the head and flexing the knees. Both tactics elevate the location of the center of gravity, positioning it closer to the center of volume.

During swimming with the front crawl stroke, the center of buoyancy is shifted toward the feet when the recovery arm and part of the head are above the surface of the water. At this point in the stroke cycle, the buoyant torque tends to elevate the feet, rather than the reverse (55).

●In order for a body to float, the buoyant force it generates must equal or exceed its weight.

●People who cannot float in swimming pools may float in Utah's Great Salt Lake, in which the density of the water surpasses even that of seawater.

DRAG

Drag is a force caused by the dynamic action of a fluid that acts in the direction of the free-stream fluid flow. Generally, a drag is a *resistance* force: a force that slows the motion of a body moving through a fluid. The drag

| Hall: Basic Biomechanics, | 15. Human Movement in a | Text | | © The McGraw–Hill |
| Fifth Edition | Fluid Medium | | | Companies, 2007 |

SAMPLE PROBLEM 15.2

When holding a large quantity of inspired air in her lungs, a 22 kg girl
has a body volume of 0.025 m³. Can she float in fresh water if γ equals
9810 N/m³? Given her body volume, how much could she weigh and still
be able to float?

Known

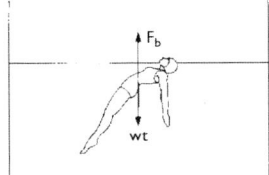

$$m = 22 \text{ kg}$$
$$V = 0.025 \text{ m}^3$$
$$\gamma = 8810 \text{ N/m}^3$$

Solution

Two forces are acting on the girl: her weight and the buoyant force. According to the conditions of static equilibrium, the sum of the vertical
forces must be equal to zero for the girl to float in a motionless position. If
the buoyant force is less than her weight, she will sink, and if the buoyant
force is equal to her weight, she will float completely submerged. If the
buoyant force is greater than her weight, she will float partly submerged.
The magnitude of the buoyant force acting on her total body volume is the
product of the volume of displaced fluid (her body volume) and the specific
weight of the fluid:

$$F_b = V_\gamma$$
$$= (0.025 \text{ m}^3)(9810 \text{ N/m}^3)$$
$$= 245.52 \text{ N}$$

Her body weight is equal to her body mass multiplied by the acceleration
of gravity:

$$wt = (22 \text{ kg})(9.81 \text{ m/s}^2)$$
$$= 215.82 \text{ N}$$

Since the buoyant force is greater than her body weight, the girl will float
partly submerged in fresh water.

> Yes, she will float.

To calculate the maximum weight that the girl's body volume can support
in fresh water, multiply the body volume by the specific weight of water.

$$wt_{max} = (0.025 \text{ m}^3)(9810 \text{ N/m}^3)$$
$$wt_{max} = 245.25 \text{ N}$$

---

force acting on a body in relative motion with respect to a fluid is defined
by the following formula:

$$F_D = \tfrac{1}{2} C_D \rho A_p v^2$$

In this formula, F_D is drag force, C_D is the coefficient of drag, ρ is the
fluid density, A_p is the projected area of the body or the surface area of
the body oriented perpendicular to the fluid flow, and v is the relative

coefficient of drag
*unitless number that is an index
of a body's ability to generate fluid
resistance*

492   BASIC BIOMECHANICS

FIGURE 15-3

A. A torque is created on a swimmer by body weight (acting at the center of gravity) and the buoyant force (acting at the center of volume). **B.** When the center of gravity and the center of volume are vertically aligned, this torque is eliminated.

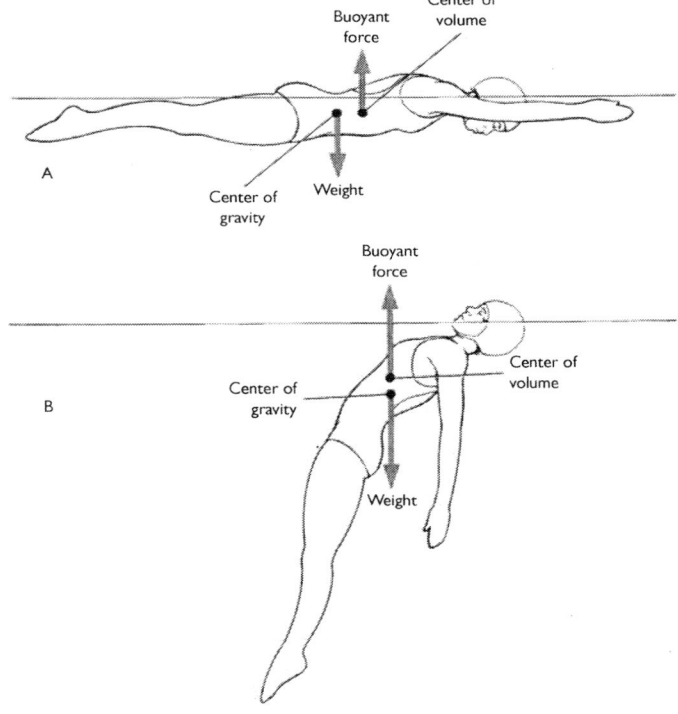

theoretical square law
drag increases approximately with the square of velocity when relative velocity is low

velocity of the body with respect to the fluid. The coefficient of drag is a unitless number that serves as an index of the amount of drag an object can generate. Its size depends on the shape and orientation of a body relative to the fluid flow, with long, streamlined bodies generally having lower coefficients of drag than blunt or irregularly shaped objects. Approximate coefficients of drag for the human body in positions commonly assumed during participation in several sports are shown in Figure 15-4.

The formula for the total drag force demonstrates the exact way in which each of the identified factors affects drag. If the coefficient of drag, the fluid density, and the projected area of the body remain constant, drag increases with the square of the relative velocity of motion. This relationship is referred to as the theoretical square law. According to this law, if cyclists double their speed and other factors remain constant, the drag force opposing them increases fourfold. The effect of drag is more consequential when a body is moving with a high velocity, which occurs in sports such as cycling, speed skating, downhill skiing, the bobsled, and the luge.

Increase or decrease in the fluid density also results in a proportional change in the drag force. Because air density decreases with increasing altitude, many world records set at the 1968 Olympic Games in Mexico City, where the elevation is 2250 m, may have been partially attributable to the reduced air resistance acting on the competitors. Mathematical model–based estimates indicate that the reduction in drag attributable to the lesser air density in Mexico City accounts for 0.08 s of performance

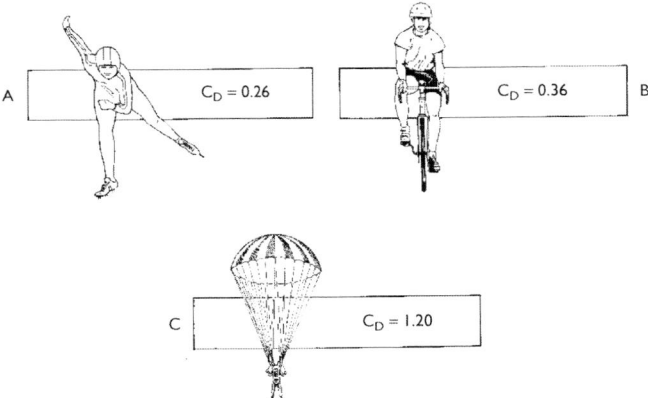

FIGURE 15-4

Approximate coefficients of drag for the human body. **A.** Frontal drag on a speed skater. **B.** Frontal drag on a cyclist in touring position. **C.** Vertical drag on a parachutist falling with the parachute fully opened. Modified from Roberson JA and Crowe CT: *Engineering fluid mechanics*, (2nd ed), Boston, 1980, Houghton Mifflin.

time in the 100 m sprint and 0.16 s of race time in the 200 m event (29). Bob Beamon's noteworthy long jump performance of 8.9 m during the games was 2.4 cm longer than if the same jump had been performed at sea level (53). Theoretical calculations indicate that because air density decreases more than VO_2max with increasing altitude, the ideal altitude for cycling performance should be 4000 m (7).

In swimming, the drag on a moving body is 500–600 times higher than it would be in the air, with the magnitude of drag varying with the anthropometric characteristics of the individual swimmer, as well as with the stroke used (46). Researchers distinguish between passive drag, which is generated by the swimmer's body size, shape, and position in the water, and active drag, which is associated with the swimming motion. Passive drag is inversely related to a swimmer's buoyancy, which has been found to have a small but important influence on sprint swimming performance (33). Passive drag on male swimmers is also significantly reduced with shoulder-to-knee and shoulder-to-ankle swimsuits as compared to briefs (34). Elite swimmers generate much less active drag than average swimmers through superior stroke technique (27). Older swimmers tend to generate more drag than younger swimmers, and sprinters tend to incur more drag than long-distance swimmers (26). Furthermore, better swimmers appear to be able to increase swimming speed while simultaneously reducing drag or showing only a small increase (26).

Three forms of resistance contribute to the total drag force. The component of resistance that predominates depends on the nature of the fluid flow immediately adjacent to the body.

Skin Friction

One component of the total drag is known as skin friction, surface drag, or viscous drag. This drag is similar to the friction force described in Chapter 12. Skin friction is derived from the sliding contacts between successive layers of fluid close to the surface of a moving body (Figure 15-5). The layer of fluid particles immediately adjacent to the moving body is slowed because of the shear stress the body exerts on the fluid. The next adjacent layer of fluid particles moves with slightly less speed because of friction between the adjacent molecules, and the next layer is affected in turn. The number of layers of affected fluid becomes progressively larger as

skin friction
surface drag
viscous drag
resistance derived from friction between adjacent layers of fluid near a body moving through the fluid

494   BASIC BIOMECHANICS

The fluid boundary layer for a thin, flat plate, shown from the side view. The laminar boundary layer gradually becomes thicker as flow progresses along the plate.

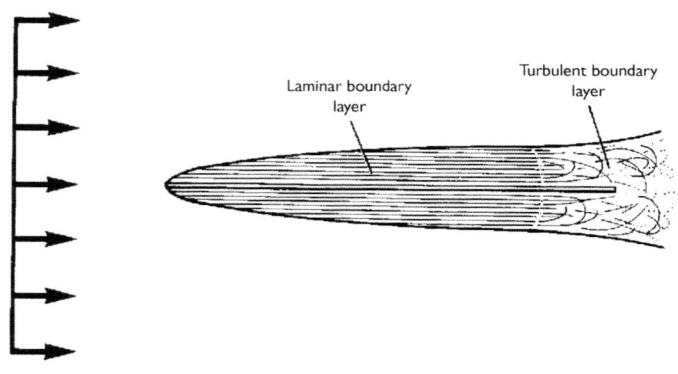

Laminar boundary layer

Turbulent boundary layer

boundary layer
layer of fluid immediately adjacent to a body

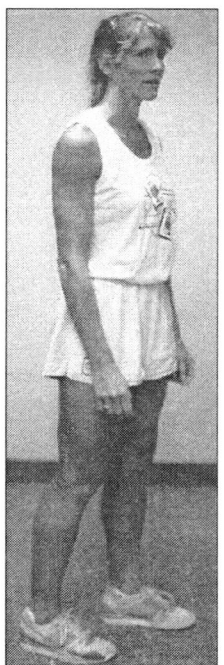

Common running attire is aerodynamically inefficient.

form drag
profile drag
pressure drag
resistance created by a pressure differential between the lead and rear sides of a body moving through a fluid

the flow moves in the downstream direction along the body. The entire region within which fluid velocity is diminished because of the shearing resistance caused by the boundary of the moving body is the boundary layer. The force the body exerts on the fluid in creating the boundary layer results in an oppositely directed reaction force exerted by the fluid on the body. This reaction force is known as *skin friction.*

Several factors affect the magnitude of skin friction drag. It increases proportionally with increases in the relative velocity of fluid flow, the surface area of the body over which the flow occurs, the roughness of the body surface, and the viscosity of the fluid. Skin friction is always one component of the total drag force acting on a body moving relative to a fluid, and it is the major form of drag present when the flow is primarily laminar. For front crawl swimming, kayaking, and rowing, skin friction drag predominates at velocities between 1 and 3 m/s (38).

Among these factors, the one that a competitive athlete can readily alter is the relative roughness of the body surface. Athletes can wear tight-fitting clothing composed of a smooth fabric rather than loose-fitting clothing or clothing made of a rough fabric. A 10% reduction of drag occurs when a speed skater wears a smooth spandex suit as opposed to the traditional wool outfit (51). A 6% decrease in air resistance results from cyclists' use of appropriate clothing, including sleeves, tights, and smooth covers over the laces of the shoes (28). The cotton socks and loose shorts and singlets commonly worn by recreational runners are particularly aerodynamically inefficient. Smoothing the running shoe and laces and either covering or shaving body hair reduces drag on runners by as much as 10% (29). Competitive male swimmers and cyclists often shave body hair to reduce skin friction.

The other factor affecting skin friction that athletes can alter in some circumstances is the amount of surface area in contact with the fluid. Carrying an extra passenger such as a coxswain in a rowing event results in a larger wetted surface area of the hull because of the added weight; as a result, skin friction drag is increased.

Form Drag

A second component of the total drag acting on a body moving through a fluid is form drag, which is also known as profile drag or pressure drag. Form drag is always one component of the drag on a body moving relative to a fluid. When the boundary layer of fluid molecules next to the surface of the moving body is primarily turbulent, form drag predominates. Form drag is the major contributor to overall drag during most human and

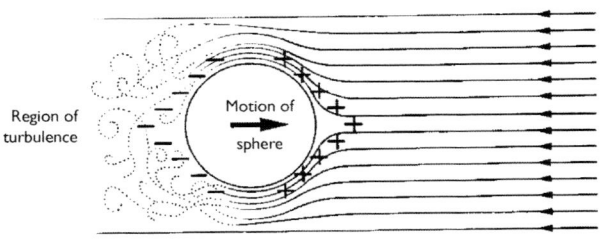

Region of
turbulence

Motion of
sphere

FIGURE 15-6

Form drag results from the suctionlike force created between the positive pressure zone on a body's leading edge and the negative pressure zone on the trailing edge when turbulence is present.

projectile motion. It is the predominant type of drag for front crawl swimming, kayaking, and rowing at velocities of less than 1 m/s (38).

When a body moves through a fluid medium with sufficient velocity to create a pocket of turbulence behind the body, an imbalance in the pressure surrounding the body—a *pressure differential*—is created (Figure 15-6). At the upstream end of the body where fluid particles meet the body head-on, a zone of relative high pressure is formed. At the downstream end of the body where turbulence is present, a zone of relative low pressure is created. Whenever a pressure differential exists, a force is directed from the region of high pressure to the region of low pressure. For example, a vacuum cleaner creates a suction force because a region of relative low pressure (the relative vacuum) exists inside the machine housing. This force, directed from front to rear of the body in relative motion through a fluid, constitutes form drag.

Several factors affect the magnitude of form drag, including the relative velocity of the body with respect to the fluid, the magnitude of the pressure gradient between the front and rear ends of the body, and the size of the surface area that is aligned perpendicular to the flow. Both the size of the pressure gradient and the amount of surface area perpendicular to the fluid flow can be reduced to minimize the effect of form drag on the human body. For example, streamlining the overall shape of the body reduces the magnitude of the pressure gradient. Streamlining minimizes the amount of turbulence created and hence minimizes the negative pressure that is created at the object's rear (Figure 15-7). Assuming a more

•*Streamlining helps to minimize form drag.*

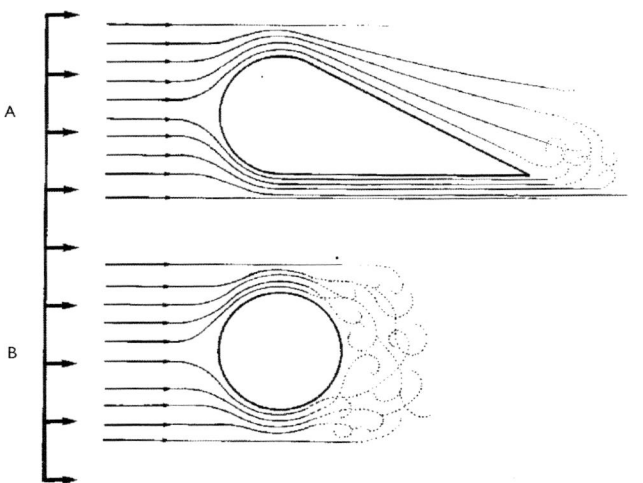

A

B

FIGURE 15-7

The effect of streamlining is a reduction in the turbulence created at the trailing edge of a body in a fluid.
A. A streamlined shape.
B. A sphere.

crouched body position also reduces the body's projected surface area oriented perpendicular to the fluid flow.

Competitive cyclists, skaters, and skiers assume a streamlined body position with the smallest possible area of the body oriented perpendicular to the oncoming airstream. Even though the low-crouched aero-position assumed by competitive cyclists increases the cyclist's metabolic cost as compared to an upright position, the aerodynamic benefit is an over tenfold reduction in drag (20). Similarly, race cars, yacht hulls, and some cycling helmets are designed with streamlined shapes. The aerodynamic frame and handlebar designs for racing cycles also reduce drag (8, 41).

Streamlining is also an effective way to reduce form drag in the water. The ability to streamline body position during freestyle swimming is a characteristic that distinguishes elite from subelite performers (9). Using a triathlon wet suit can reduce the drag on a competitor swimming at a typical triathlon race pace of 1.25 m/s by as much as 14%, because the buoyant effect of the wet suit results in reduced form drag on the swimmer (15, 48).

The nature of the boundary layer at the surface of a body moving through a fluid can also influence form drag by affecting the pressure gradient between the front and rear ends of the body. When the boundary layer is primarily laminar, the fluid separates from the boundary close to the front end of the body, creating a large turbulent pocket with a large negative pressure and thereby a large form drag (Figure 15-8). In contrast, when the boundary layer is turbulent, the point of flow separation is closer to the rear end of the body, the turbulent pocket created is smaller, and the resulting form drag is smaller.

The nature of the boundary layer depends on the roughness of the body's surface and the body's velocity relative to the flow. As the relative velocity of motion for an object such as a golf ball increases, changes in the acting drag occur (Figure 15-9). As relative velocity increases up to a certain critical point, the theoretical square law is in effect, with drag increasing with the square of velocity. After this critical velocity is reached,

A streamlined cycling helmet.

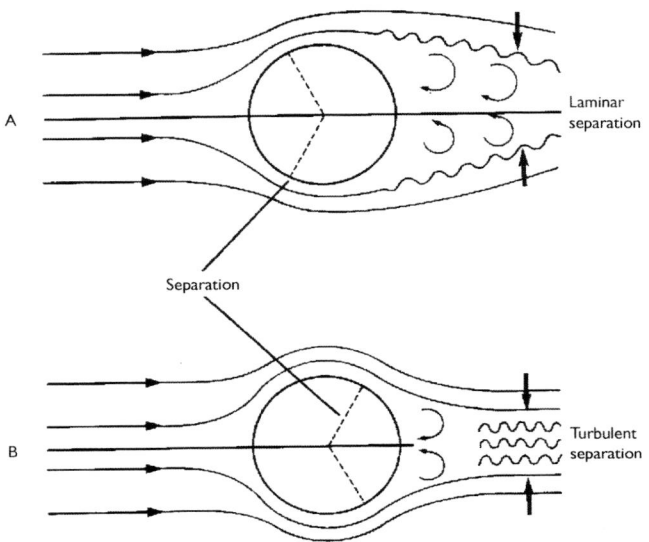

A

Laminar
separation

Separation

B

Turbulent
separation

FIGURE 15-8

A. Laminar flow results in an early separation of flow from the boundary and a larger drag producing wake as compared to **B,** turbulent boundary flow.

the boundary layer becomes more turbulent than laminar, and form drag diminishes because the pocket of reduced pressure on the trailing edge of the ball becomes smaller. As velocity increases further, the effects of skin friction and form drag grow, increasing the total drag. The dimples in a golf ball are carefully engineered to produce a turbulent boundary layer at the ball's surface that reduces form drag on the ball over the range of velocities at which a golf ball travels.

Another way in which form drag can be manipulated is through drafting, the process of following closely behind another participant in speed-based sports such as cycling and automobile racing. Drafting provides the

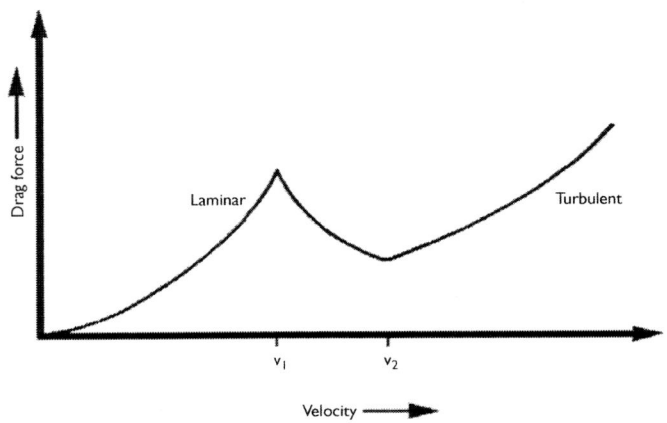

Drag force

Laminar

Turbulent

v_1 v_2

Velocity

FIGURE 15-9

Drag increases approximately with the square of velocity until there is sufficient relative velocity (v_1) to generate a turbulent boundary layer. As velocity increases beyond this point, form drag decreases. After a second critical relative velocity (v_2) is reached, the drag again increases.

498   BASIC BIOMECHANICS

Cyclists drafting to minimize form drag.

advantage of reducing form drag on the follower, since the leader partially shelters the follower's leading edge from increased pressure against the fluid. Depending on the size of the pocket of reduced pressure behind the leader, a suctionlike force may also help to propel the follower forward. In swimming, the optimal drafting distance behind another swimmer in a swimming pool is 0–50 cm from the toes of the lead swimmer (10). Drafting has even been found to improve performance during a long-distance swim, particularly for faster and leaner swimmers (11).

Wave Drag

wave drag
resistance created by the generation of waves at the interface between two different fluids, such as air and water

The third type of drag acts at the interface of two different fluids, for example, at the interface between water and air. Although bodies that are completely submerged in a fluid are not affected by wave drag, this form of drag can be a major contributor to the overall drag acting on a human swimmer, particularly when the swim is done in open water. When a swimmer moves a body segment along, near, or across the air and water interface, a wave is created in the more dense fluid (the water). The reaction force the water exerts on the swimmer constitutes wave drag.

The magnitude of wave drag increases with greater up-and-down motion of the body and increased swimming speed. The height of the bow wave generated in front of a swimmer increases proportionally with swimming velocity, although at a given velocity, skilled swimmers produce smaller waves than less-skilled swimmers, presumably due to better technique (less up-and-down motion) (47). At fast swimming speeds (over 3 m/s), wave drag is generally the largest component of the total drag acting on the swimmer (38). For this reason, competitive swimmers typically propel themselves underwater to eliminate wave drag for a small portion of the race in events in which the rules permit it. One underwater stroke is allowed following the dive or a turn in the breaststroke, and a distance of up to 15 m is allowed underwater after a turn in the backstroke. In most swimming pools, the lane lines are designed to minimize wave action by dissipating moving surface water.

The bow wave generated by a competitive swimmer.

LIFT FORCE

While drag forces act in the direction of the free-stream fluid flow, another force, known as lift, is generated perpendicular to the fluid flow. Although the name *lift* suggests that this force is directed vertically upward, it may assume any direction, as determined by the direction of the fluid flow and the orientation of the body. The factors affecting the magnitude of lift are basically the same factors that affect the magnitude of drag:

$$F_L = \frac{1}{2}\, C_L \rho A_p v^2$$

In this equation, F_L represents lift force, C_L is the coefficient of lift, ρ is the fluid density, A_p is the surface area against which lift is generated, and v is the relative velocity of a body with respect to a fluid. The factors

lift
force acting on a body in a fluid in a direction perpendicular to the fluid flow

coefficient of lift
unitless number that is an index of a body's ability to generate lift

The lane lines in modern swimming pools are designed to minimize wave action, enabling faster racing times.

500   BASIC BIOMECHANICS

TABLE 15-2

Factors Affecting the Magnitudes of Fluid Forces

FORCE	FACTORS
Buoyant force	Specific weight of the fluid Volume of fluid displaced
Skin friction	Density of the fluid Relative velocity of the fluid Amount of body surface area exposed to the flow Roughness of the body surface Viscosity of the fluid
Form drag	Density of the fluid Relative velocity of the fluid Pressure differential between leading and rear edges of the body Amount of body surface area perpendicular to the flow
Wave drag	Relative velocity of the wave Amount of surface area perpendicular to the wave Viscosity of the fluid
Lift force	Relative velocity of the fluid Density of the fluid Size, shape, and orientation of the body

TABLE 15-2

Factors Affecting the Magnitudes of Fluid Forces

affecting the magnitudes of the fluid forces discussed are summarized in Table 15-2.

Foil Shape

foil
shape capable of generating lift in the presence of a fluid flow

One way in which lift force may be created is for the shape of the moving body to resemble that of a foil (Figure 15-10). When the fluid stream encounters a foil, the fluid separates, with some flowing over the curved surface and some flowing straight back along the flat surface on the opposite side. The fluid that flows over the curved surface is positively accelerated relative to the fluid flow, creating a region of relative high-velocity flow. The difference in the velocity of flow on the curved side of the foil as opposed to the flat side of the foil creates a pressure difference in the fluid, in accordance with a relationship derived by the Italian scientist Bernoulli. According to the Bernoulli principle, regions of relative high-velocity fluid flow are associated with regions of relative low pressure, and regions of

Bernoulli principle
an expression of the inverse relationship between relative velocity and relative pressure in a fluid flow

FIGURE 15-10

Lift force generated by a foil shape is directed from the region of relative high pressure on the flat side of the foil toward the region of relative low pressure on the curved side of the foil.

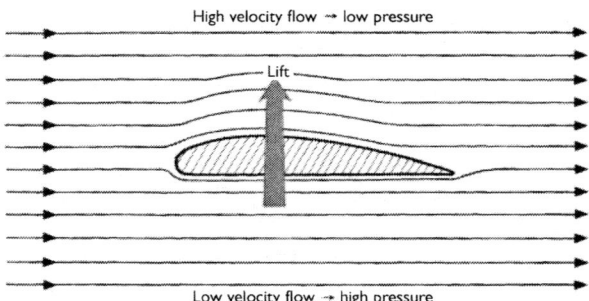

High velocity flow → low pressure

Lift

Low velocity flow → high pressure

relative low-velocity flow are associated with regions of relative high pressure. When these regions of relative low and high pressure are created on opposite sides of the foil, the result is a lift force directed perpendicular to the foil from the zone of high pressure toward the low-pressure zone.

Different factors affect the magnitude of the lift force acting on a foil. The greater the velocity of the foil relative to the fluid, the greater the pressure differential and the lift force generated. Other contributing factors are the fluid density and the surface area of the flat side of the foil. As both of these variables increase, lift increases. An additional factor of influence is the *coefficient of lift,* which indicates a body's ability to generate lift based on its shape.

The human hand resembles a foil shape when viewed from a lateral perspective. When a swimmer slices a hand through the water, it generates lift force directed perpendicular to the palm. Synchronized swimmers use a sculling motion, rapidly slicing their hands back and forth, to maneuver their bodies through various positions in the water. The lift force generated by rapid sculling motions enables elite synchronized swimmers to support their bodies in an inverted position with both legs extended completely out of the water.

The semifoil shapes of projectiles such as the discus, javelin, football, boomerang, and frisbee generate some lift force when oriented at appropriate angles with respect to the direction of the fluid flow. Spherical projectiles such as a shot or a ball, however, do not sufficiently resemble a foil and cannot generate lift by virtue of their shape.

The angle of orientation of the projectile with respect to the fluid flow—the angle of attack—is an important factor in launching a lift-producing projectile for maximum range (horizontal displacement). A positive angle of attack is necessary to generate a lift force (Figure 15-11). As the angle of attack increases, the amount of surface area exposed perpendicularly to the fluid flow also increases, thereby increasing the amount of form drag acting. With too steep an attack angle, the fluid cannot flow along the curved side of the foil to create lift. Airplanes that assume too steep an ascent can stall and lose altitude until pilots reduce the attack angle of the wings to enable lift (32).

To maximize the flight distance of a projectile such as the discus or javelin, it is advantageous to maximize lift and minimize drag. Form drag, however, is minimum at an angle of attack of 0°, which is a poor angle for generating lift. The optimum angle of attack for maximizing range is the angle at which the lift/drag ratio is maximum. The largest lift/drag ratio for a discus traveling at a relative velocity of 24 m/s is generated at an angle of attack of 10° (19). For both the discus and the javelin, however, the single most important factor related to distance achieved is release speed (3, 21).

When the projectile is the human body during the performance of a jump, maximizing the effects of lift while minimizing the effects of drag is more complicated. In the ski jump, because of the relatively long period during which the body is airborne, the lift/drag ratio for the human body is particularly important. Research on ski jumping indicates that for optimal performance, ski jumpers should have a flattened body with a large frontal area (for generating lift) and a small body weight (for enabling greater acceleration) during takeoff. The effect of lift is immediate at takeoff, resulting in a higher initial vertical velocity than the jumper generates through impulse against the ramp surface (52). During the first part of the flight, jumpers should assume a small angle of attack to minimize drag (Figure 15-12). During the latter part of the flight, they should

angle of attack
angle between the longitudinal axis of a body and the direction of the fluid flow

lift/drag ratio
the magnitude of the lift force divided by the magnitude of the total drag force acting on a body at a given time

FIGURE 15-11

A. Drag and lift are small because the angle of attack (α) does not create a sufficiently high pressure differential across the top and bottom surfaces of the foil. **B.** An angle of attack that promotes lift. **C.** When the angle of attack is too large, the fluid cannot flow over the curved surface of the foil, and no lift is generated. **D.** When the angle of attack is below the horizontal, lift is created in a downward direction.

Modified from Maglischo E: *Swimming faster: A comprehensive guide to the science of swimming,* Palo Alto, CA, 1982, Mayfield.

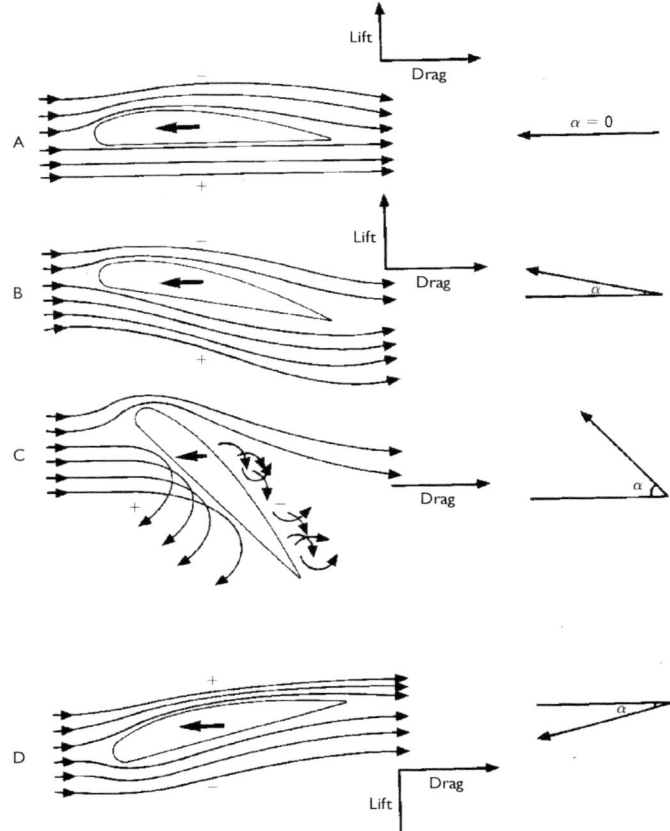

increase attack angle up to that of maximum lift. On smaller jumping hills where takeoff velocities are lower, jumpers should assume the attack angle for maximum lift earlier in the flight, because the effect of drag is not so great (40).

Other researchers investigating the ski jump have noted that the maximum length of the jump occurs neither at the body angle of attack for maximum lift nor at the attack angle for which the lift/drag is maximum, but somewhere between the two (Figure 15-13) (16). The ski jump consists of takeoff, flight, and landing, with body position during each phase influencing body position during the subsequent phase or phases. Research indicates that better performance is achieved when ski position is changed during the flight. Ski positions include the classic style, in which the skis are parallel; the V style, in which the skis are in a herringbone position in the frontal plane; and the flat V style, in which the skis are more flat in the sagittal plane than with the V style. Optimal performance results from initiating the jump in the classic style or the flat V style, and changing to the V style 1.3–1.6 s into the jump (23). This is true because the classic and flat V styles produce less drag than the V style in the first part of the jump, and the V style maximizes lift in the later part of the jump.

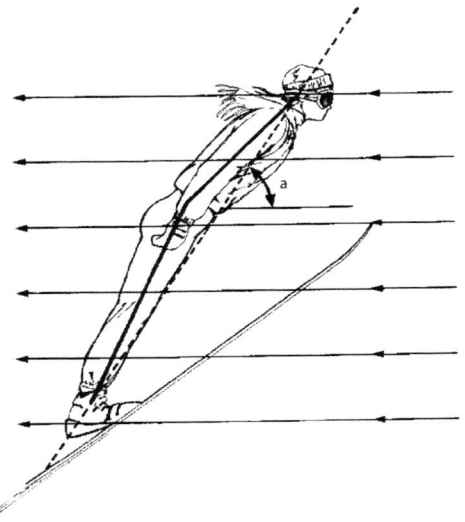

FIGURE 15-12

The angle of attack is the angle formed between the primary axis of a body and the direction of the fluid flow.

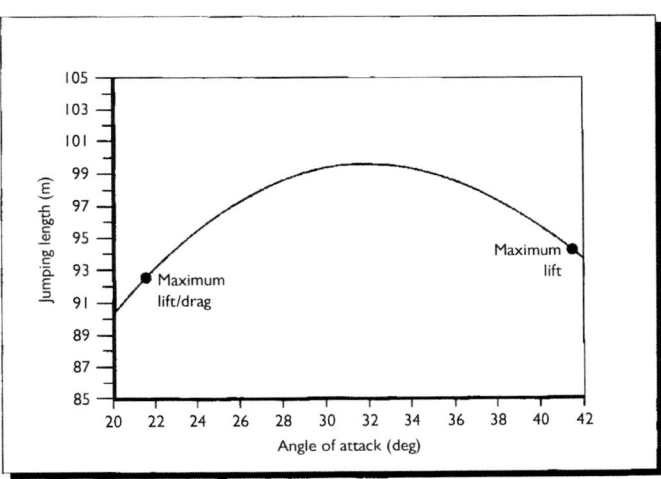

FIGURE 15-13

The relationship between ski jump length and the performer's angle of attack. Modified from Denoth J, Luethi SM, and Gasser HH: Methodological problems in optimization of the flight phase in ski jumping, Int J Sport Biomech 3:404, 1987.

Magnus Effect

Spinning objects also generate lift. When an object in a fluid medium spins, the boundary layer of fluid molecules adjacent to the object spins with it. When this happens, the fluid molecules on one side of the spinning body collide head-on with the molecules in the fluid free-stream (Figure 15-14). This creates a region of relative low velocity and high pressure. On the opposite side of the spinning object, the boundary layer moves in the same direction as the fluid flow, thereby creating a zone of relative high velocity and low pressure. The pressure differential creates what is called

504 BASIC BIOMECHANICS

Magnus force results from the pressure differential created by a spinning body.

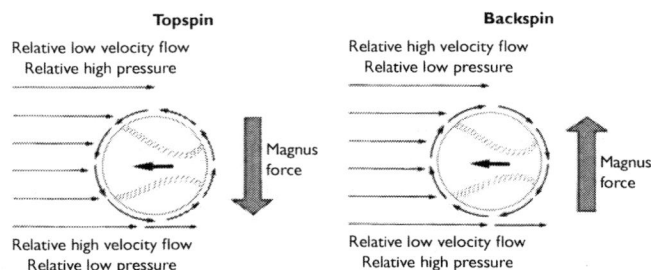

Topspin

Relative low velocity flow
Relative high pressure

Magnus force

Relative high velocity flow
Relative low pressure

Backspin

Relative high velocity flow
Relative low pressure

Magnus force

Relative low velocity flow
Relative high pressure

Magnus force
lift force created by spin

Magnus effect
deviation in the trajectory of a spinning object toward the direction of spin, resulting from the Magnus force

●*A ball projected with spin follows a trajectory that curves in the direction of the spin.*

the Magnus force, a lift force directed from the high-pressure region to the low-pressure region.

Magnus force affects the flight path of a spinning projectile as it travels through the air, causing the path to deviate progressively in the direction of the spin, a deviation known as the Magnus effect. When a tennis ball or table tennis ball is hit with topspin, the ball drops more rapidly than it would without spin, and the ball tends to rebound low and fast, often making it more difficult for the opponent to return the shot. The nap on a tennis ball traps a relatively large boundary layer of air with it as it spins, thereby accentuating the Magnus effect. The Magnus effect can also result from sidespin, as when a pitcher throws a curveball (Figure 15-15). The modern-day version of the curveball is a ball that is intentionally pitched with spin, causing it to follow a curved path in the direction of the spin throughout its flight path.

In 1982, a controversy between professional baseball players and scientists arose over the behavior of a pitched curveball. The players claimed that the path taken by a curveball was along a straight line until a certain critical point, at which the ball "broke" and suddenly curved. This appearance is enhanced when topspin is imparted to the ball, since the Magnus effect of topspin accentuates the effect of gravity. However, the actual path of a curveball is a smooth arc, which has been documented with high-speed movie film (2).

The extent to which a ball curves, or "breaks," in the horizontal and vertical planes is dependent on the orientation of the spinning ball's axis of rotation. If the axis of rotation is perfectly vertical, all of the Magnus effect occurs in the horizontal plane. Alternatively, if the axis of rotation is oriented horizontally, the Magnus effect is restricted to the vertical plane. Analysis of an actual baseball pitch thrown during the 1996 Olympic Games revealed an initial velocity of 35.9 m/s, an initial spin velocity of 18.5 rev/s, and the axis of rotation oriented nearly vertically at 85°, resulting in a horizontal deviation of 39 cm (1). Curveballs thrown by major

The trajectory of a ball thrown with sidespin follows a regular curve due to the Magnus effect. The dashed line shows the illusion seen by the players on the field.

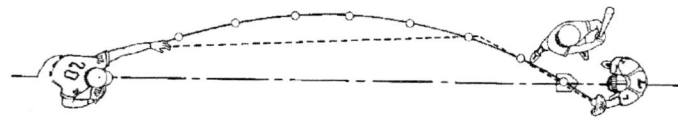

league pitchers spin as quickly as 27 revolutions per second and deviate horizontally as much as 40 cm over the pitcher-to-batter distance (49).

Soccer players also use the Magnus effect when it is advantageous for a kicked ball to follow a curved path, as may be the case when a player executing a free kick attempts to score. The "banana shot" consists of a kick executed so that the kicker places a lateral spin on the ball, curving it around the wall of defensive players in front of the goal (Figure 15-16).

The Magnus effect is maximal when the axis of spin is perpendicular to the direction of relative fluid velocity. Golf clubs are designed to impart some backspin to the struck ball, thereby creating an upwardly directed Magnus force that increases flight time and flight distance (Figure 15-17). When a golf ball is hit laterally off-center, a spin about a vertical axis is also produced, causing a laterally deviated Magnus force that causes the ball to deviate from a straight path. When backspin and side-spin have been imparted to the ball, the resultant effect of the Magnus force on the path of the ball depends on the orientation of the ball's re-sultant axis of rotation to the airstream and on the velocity with which the ball was struck. When a golf ball is struck laterally off-center by a right-handed golfer, the ball unfortunately follows a curved path to one side—commonly known as a hook (to the left) or a slice (to the right).

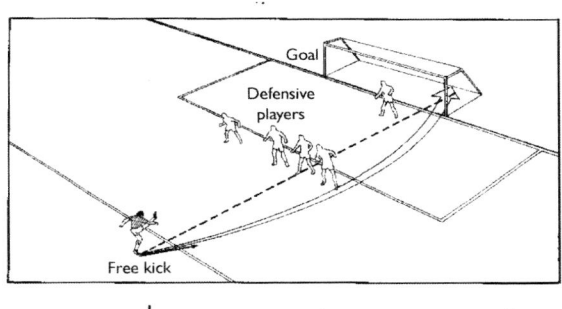

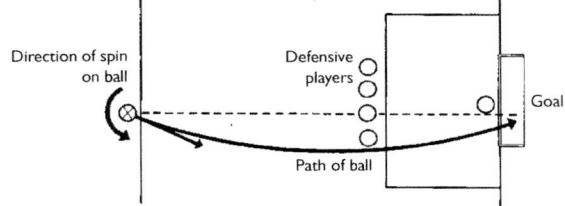

FIGURE 15-16

A banana shot in soccer results from imparting sidespin to the ball.

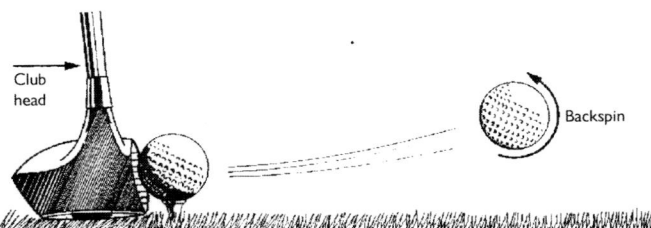

FIGURE 15-17

The loft on a golf club is designed to produce backspin on the ball. A properly hit ball rises because of the Magnus effect.

PROPULSION IN A FLUID MEDIUM

Whereas a headwind slows a runner or cyclist by increasing the acting drag force, a tailwind can actually contribute to forward propulsion. Theoretical calculations indicate that a tailwind of 2 m/s improves running time during a 100 m sprint by approximately 0.18 s (54). A tailwind affects the relative velocity of a body with respect to the air, thereby modifying the resistive drag acting on the body. Thus, a tailwind of a velocity greater than the velocity of the moving body produces a drag force in the direction of motion (Figure 15-18). This force has been termed propulsive drag.

propulsive drag
force acting in the direction of a body's motion

Analyzing the fluid forces acting on a swimmer is more complicated. Resistive drag acts on a swimmer, yet the propulsive forces exerted by the water in reaction to the swimmer's movements are responsible for the swimmer's forward motion through the water. The motions of the body segments during swimming produce a complex combination of drag and lift forces throughout each stroke cycle, and even among elite swimmers, a wide range of kinetic patterns during stroking have been observed (45). As a result, researchers have proposed several theories regarding the ways in which swimmers propel themselves through the water.

Propulsive Drag Theory

propulsive drag theory
theory attributing propulsion in swimming to propulsive drag on the swimmer

The oldest theory of swimming propulsion is the propulsive drag theory, which was proposed by Counsilman and Silvia (12) and is based on Newton's third law of motion. According to this theory, as a swimmer's hands and arms move backward through the water, the forwardly directed reaction force generated by the water produces propulsion. The theory also suggests that the horizontal components of the downward and backward motion of the foot and the upward and backward motion of the opposite foot generate a forwardly directed reaction force from the water.

When high-speed movie films of skilled swimmers revealed that swimmer's hands and feet followed a zigzag rather than a straight-back path through the water, the theory was modified. It was suggested that this type of movement pattern enabled the body segments to push against still or slowly moving water instead of water already accelerated backward, thereby creating more propulsive drag. However, propulsive drag may not be the major contributor to propulsion in swimming.

FIGURE 15-18

Drag force acting in the same direction as the body's motion may be thought of as propulsive drag because it contributes to the forward velocity of the body.

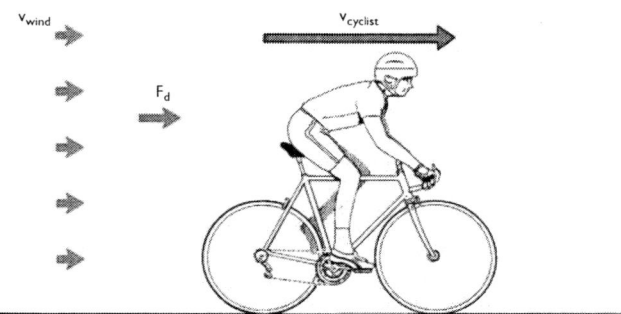

Propulsive Lift Theory

The propulsive lift theory was proposed by Counsilman in 1971 (6). According to this theory, swimmers use the foillike shape of the hand by employing rapid lateral movements through the water to generate lift. The lift is resisted by downward movement of the hand and by stabilization of the shoulder joint, which translates the forward-directed force to the body, propelling it past the hand. The theory was modified by Firby (18) in 1975, with the suggestion that swimmers use their hands and feet as propellers, constantly changing the pitches of the body segments to use the most effective angle of attack.

A number of investigators have since studied the forces generated by the body segments during swimming. It has been shown that lift does contribute to propulsion and that a combination of lift and drag forces acts throughout a stroke cycle. The relative contributions of lift and drag vary with the stroke performed, the phase within the stroke, and the individual swimmer. For example, lift is the primary force acting during the breaststroke, whereas lift and drag contribute differently to various phases of the front crawl stroke (44). Drag generated by the swimmer's hand is maximal when hand orientation is nearly perpendicular to the flow, and lift is maximal when the hand moves in the direction of either the thumb or the little finger (4).

propulsive lift theory
theory attributing propulsion in swimming at least partially to lift acting on the swimmer

Vortex Generation

Researchers have found a poor correlation between physiological and mechanical approaches to calculating propelling efficiency in swimming (5). This has led to the speculation that some unknown processes may play a role in swimming propulsion, with one possibility being the generation of vortices in the water by the swimmer. Vortex shedding has been found to play a role in the propulsion of both flying and swimming vertebrates and insects (17, 39). The generation of thrust in racing canoe and kayak paddling has also been described in terms of the mechanics of vortex–ring wakes (22). The observation that a swimmer performing the dolphin kick leaves behind a series of bound vortices, or columns of rotating water, has also been made (50). More research is needed to clarify the role of vortex generation in swimming propulsion.

Stroke Technique

Just as running speed is the product of stride length and stride rate, swimming speed is the product of stroke length (SL) and stroke rate (SR). Of the two, SL is more directly related to swimming speed among competitive freestyle swimmers (13). Comparison of male and female swimmers performing at the same competitive distances reveals nearly identical SRs, but longer SLs resulting in higher velocities for the males (37). At slower speeds, skilled freestyle swimmers are able to maintain constant, high levels of SL, with a progressive reduction in SL as exercise intensity increases due to local muscle fatigue (24). The same phenomenon has been observed over the course of distance events, with a general decrease in SL and swimming speed after the first 100 m (30). Research suggests that recreational freestyle swimmers seeking to improve swimming performance should concentrate on applying more force to the water during each stroke to increase SL, as opposed to stroking faster. Among backstrokers, although the ability to achieve a high swimming speed is related to SL at submaximal levels, increased speed is achieved through increased SR and decreased SL (25). Better performance in the breaststroke is associated with minimal vertical motion of the total body CG, but large range of hip vertical motion, during the stroke cycle (43).

508   BASIC BIOMECHANICS

Another technique variable of importance during freestyle swimming is body roll. In one study, competitive swimmers were found to roll an average of approximately 60° to the nonbreathing side (31). Research shows that body roll in swimming is caused by the turning effect of the fluid forces acting on the swimmer's body. The contribution of body roll is important, since it enables the swimmer to employ the large, powerful muscles of the trunk rather than relying solely on the muscles of the shoulder and arm. It also facilitates the breathing action without any interruption of stroke mechanics (35). Body roll can influence the path of the hand through the water almost as much as the mediolateral motions of the hand relative to the trunk (31). In particular, an increase in body roll has been shown to increase the swimmer's hand speed in the plane perpendicular to the swimming direction, thereby increasing the potential for the hand to develop propulsive lift forces (36). With increasing swimming speed, general body roll decreases, although trunk twist increases, allowing swimmers to benefit from the rolling of the upper trunk, while limiting the increase in the drag of the lower extremity (56).

SUMMARY

The relative velocity of a body with respect to a fluid and the density, specific weight, and viscosity of the fluid affect the magnitudes of fluid forces. The fluid force that enables flotation is buoyancy. The buoyant force acts vertically upward, its point of application is the body's center of volume, and its magnitude is equal to the product of the volume of the displaced fluid and the specific gravity of the fluid. A body floats in a static position only when the magnitude of the buoyant force and body weight are equal and when the center of volume and the center of gravity are vertically aligned.

Drag is a fluid force that acts in the direction of the free-stream fluid flow. Skin friction is a component of drag that is derived from the sliding contacts between successive layers of fluid close to the surface of a moving body. Form drag, another component of the total drag, is caused by a pressure differential between the lead and trailing edges of a body moving with respect to a fluid. Wave drag is created by the formation of waves at the interface between two different fluids, such as water and air.

Lift is a force that can be generated perpendicular to the free-stream fluid flow by a foil-shaped object. Lift is created by a pressure differential in the fluid on opposite sides of a body that results from differences in the velocity of the fluid flow. The lift generated by spin is known as the Magnus force. Propulsion in swimming appears to result from a complex interplay of propulsive drag and lift.

INTRODUCTORY PROBLEMS

For all problems, assume that the specific weight of fresh water equals 9810 N/m^3 and the specific weight of seawater (salt water) equals 10,070 N/m^3.

1. A boy is swimming with an absolute speed of 1.5 m/s in a river where the speed of the current is 0.5 m/s. What is the velocity of the swimmer with respect to the current when the boy swims directly upstream? Directly downstream? (Answer: 2 m/s in the upstream direction; 1 m/s in the downstream direction)

2. A cyclist is riding at a speed of 14 km/hr into a 16 km/hr headwind. What is the wind velocity relative to the cyclist? What is the cyclist's velocity with respect to the wind? (Answer: 30 km/hr in the direction of the wind; 30 km/hr in the direction of the cyclist)

3. A skier traveling at 5 m/s has a speed of 5.7 m/s relative to a head-wind. What is the absolute wind speed? (Answer 0.7 m/s)

4. A 700 N man has a body volume of 0.08 m³. If submerged in fresh water, will he float? Given his body volume, how much could he weigh and still float? (Answer: Yes; 784.8 N)

5. A racing shell has a volume of 0.38 m³. When floating in fresh water, how many 700 N people can it support? (Answer: 5)

6. How much body volume must a 60 kg person have to float in fresh water? (Answer: 0.06 m³)

7. Explain the implications for flotation due to the difference between the specific weight of fresh water and the specific weight of seawater.

8. What strategy can people use to improve their chances of floating in water? Explain your answer.

9. What types of individuals may have a difficult time floating in water? Explain your answer.

10. A beach ball weighing 1 N and with a volume of 0.03 m³ is held sub-merged in seawater. How much force must be exerted vertically down-ward to hold the ball completely submerged? To hold the ball one-half submerged? (Answer: 301.1 N; 150.05 N)

ADDITIONAL PROBLEMS

1. A cyclist riding against a 12 km/hr headwind has a velocity of 28 km/hr with respect to the wind. What is the cyclist's absolute ve-locity? (Answer: 16 km/hr)

2. A swimmer crossing a river proceeds at an absolute speed of 2.5 m/s on a course oriented at a 45° angle to the 1 m/s current. Given that the absolute velocity of the swimmer is equal to the vector sum of the velocity of the current and the velocity of the swimmer with respect to the current, what is the magnitude and direction of the velocity of the swimmer with respect to the current? (Answer: 3.3 m/s at an angle of 32.6° to the current)

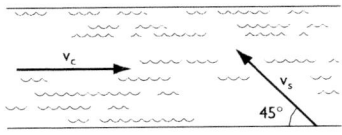

3. What maximum average density can a body possess if it is to float in fresh water? Seawater?

4. A scuba diver carries camera equipment in a cylindrical container that is 45 cm long, 20 cm in diameter, and 22 N in weight. For opti-mal maneuverability of the container under water, how much should its contents weigh? (Answer 120.36 N)

5. A 50 kg person with a body volume of 0.055 m³ floats in a motionless position. How much body volume is above the surface if the water is fresh? If the water is salt water? (Answer: 0.005 m³; 0.0063 m³)

6. A 670 N swimmer oriented horizontally in fresh water has a body volume of 0.07 m^3 and a center of volume located 3 cm superior to the center of gravity.
   a. How much torque does the swimmer's weight generate?
   b. How much torque does the buoyant force acting on the swimmer generate?
   c. What can the swimmer do to counteract the torque and maintain a horizontal position?
      (Answer: 0; 20.6 N-m)
7. Based on your knowledge of the action of fluid forces, speculate as to why a properly thrown boomerang returns to the thrower.
8. Explain the aerodynamic benefits of drafting on a bicycle or in an automobile.
9. What is the practical effect of streamlining? How does streamlining alter the fluid forces acting on a moving body?
10. Explain why a curveball curves. Include a discussion of the aerodynamic role of the seams on the ball.

NAME _____

DATE _____

LABORATORY EXPERIENCES

1. At the *Basic Biomechanics* Online Learning Center (www.mhhe.com/hall5e), go to Student Center, Chapter 15, Lab Manual, Lab 1, then view Fluids Animation 1. Identify the principle illustrated, and write an explanation of what is demonstrated.

Principle: _____

Explanation: _____

_____

_____

_____

_____

2. Slice a hollow ball such as a table tennis ball or a racquet ball in half and float one-half of the ball (concave side up) in a container of water. Gradually add lead shot to the half ball until it floats with the cut edge at the surface of the water. Remove the half ball from the water, then measure its diameter and calculate its volume. Weigh the ball along with the lead shot that was placed in the ball. Using your measurements, calculate the specific weight of the water in the container. Repeat the experiment using water at different temperatures or using different liquids.

Ball diameter: _____ ball volume: _____ weight of shot: _____

Specific weight of water: _____ specific weight of second fluid: _____

Calculations:

3. Position a container of water on a scale and record its weight. Insert your hand, fingers first, into the water until the water line is at the wrist joint. Record the weight registered on the scale. Subtract the original weight of the container from the new weight, divide the difference in half, and add the result to the original weight of the container to arrive at the target weight. Slowly elevate your hand from the water until the target weight is reached. Mark the water line on your hand. What does this line represent? _____

4. Using a stopwatch, time yourself while riding an escalator. Either measure or estimate the length of the escalator and calculate the escalator's speed. Again using a stopwatch, time yourself while carefully running up the escalator and calculate your speed. Calculate your speed relative to the speed of the escalator.

Time riding escalator: _____ time running up escalator: _____

Your speed relative to the elevator's speed: _____

Calculation:

512   BASIC BIOMECHANICS

5. Use a variable-speed fan and a spring scale to construct a mock wind tunnel. Position the fan so that it blows vertically upward, and suspend the spring scale from a rigid arm above the fan. This apparatus can be used to test the relative drag on different objects suspended from the scale. Notice that relative drag among different objects may change with fan speed.

Object	**Drag**

REFERENCES

1. Alaways LW, Mish SP, and Hubbard M: Identification of release conditions and aerodynamic forces in pitched-baseball trajectories, J Appl Biomech 17:63, 2001.

2. Allman WF: Pitching rainbows: the untold physics of the curve ball. In Schrier EW and Allman WF, eds: *Newton at the bat*, New York, 1981, Macmillan/Charles Scribner's Sons.

3. Bartlett R, Müller E, Lindinger S, Brunner F, and Morriss C: Three-dimensional evaluation of the kinematic release parameters for javelin throwers of different skill levels, J Appl Biomech 12:58, 1996.

4. Berger MA, deGroot G, and Hollander AP: Hydrodynamic drag and lift forces on human hand/arm models, J Biomech 28:125, 1995.

5. Berger MA, Hollander AP, and deGroot G: Technique and energy losses in front crawl swimming, Med Sci Sports Exerc 29:1491, 1997.

6. Brown RM and Counsilman JE: The role of lift in propelling swimmers. In Cooper JM, ed: *Biomechanics,* Chicago, 1971, Athletic Institute.

7. Capelli C and diPrampero PE: Effects of altitude on top speeds during 1 h unaccompanied cycling, Eur J Apl Physiol 71:469, 1995.

8. Capelli C et al: Energy cost and efficiency of riding aerodynamic bicycles, Eur J Appl Physiol 67:144, 1993.

9. Cappaert JM, Pease DL, and Troup JP: Three-dimensional analysis of the men's 100-m freestyle during the 1992 Olympic games, J Appl Biomech 11:103, 1995.

10. Chatard J-C and Wilson B: Drafting distance in swimming, Med Sci Sports Exerc 35:1176, 2003.

11. Chollet D, Hue O, Auclair F, Millet G, and Chatard JC: The effects of drafting on stroking variations during swimming in elite male triathletes, Eur J Appl Physiol 82:413, 2000.

12. Counsilman JE: *Science of swimming,* Englewood Cliffs, NJ, 1968, Prentice-Hall.

13. Craig AB Jr and Pendergast DR: Relationships of stroke rate, distance per stroke, and velocity in competitive swimming, Med Sci Sports Exerc 11:278, 1979.

14. Craig AB Jr. et al: Velocity, stroke rate and distance per stroke during elite swimming competition, Med Sci Sports Exerc 17:625, 1985.

15. De Lucas RD, Balikian P, Neiva CM, Greco CC, and Denadai BS: The effects of wet suits on physiological and biomechanical indices during swimming, J Sci Med Sport 3:1, 2000.

16. Denoth J, Luethi SM, and Gasser HH: Methodological problems in optimization of the flight phase in ski jumping, Int J Sport Biomech 3:404, 1987.

17. Ellington CP: Unsteady aerodynamics of insect flight, Symp Soc Exp Biol 49:109, 1995.

18. Firby H: *Howard Firby on swimming,* London, 1975, Pelham Books.

19. Ganslen RV: *Aerodynamic factors which influence discus flight,* research report, University of Arkansas, nd.

20. Gnehm P, Reichenback S, Altpeter E, Widmer H, and Hoppeler H: Influence of different racing positions on metabolic cost in elite cyclists, Med Sci Sports Exerc 29:818, 1997.

21. Hay JG and Yu B: Critical characteristics of technique in throwing the discus, J Sports Sci 13:125, 1995.

22. Jackson PS: Performance prediction for Olympic kayaks, J Sports Sci 13:239, 1995.

23. Jin H, Shimizu S, Watanuki T, Kubota H, and Kobayashi K: Desirable gliding styles and techniques in ski jumping, J Appl Biomech 11:460, 1995.

24. Keskinen KL and Komi PV: Stroking characteristics of front crawl swimming during exercise, J Appl Biomech 9:219, 1993.

25. Klentrou PP and Montpetit RR: Energetics of backstroke swimming in males and females, Med Sci Sports Exerc 24:371, 1992.

26. Kolmogorov SV and Duplishcheva OA: Active drag, useful mechanical power output and hydrodynamic force coefficient in different swimming strokes at maximal velocity, J Biomech 25:311, 1992.

27. Kolmogorov SV, Rumyantseva OA, Gordon BJ, and Cappaert JM: Hydrodynamic characteristics of competitive swimmers of different genders and performance levels, J Appl Biomech 13:88, 1997.

28. Kyle CR and Burke E: Improving the racing bicycle, Mechanical Engineering 106:34, 1984.

29. Kyle CR and Caiozzo VJ: The effect of athletic clothing aerodynamics upon running speed, Med Sci Sports Exerc 18:509, 1986.

30. Laffite LP, Vilas-Boas JP, Demarle A, Silva J, Fernandes R, and Billat VL: Changes in physiological and stroke parameters during a maximal 400-m free swimming test in elite swimmers, Can J Appl Physiol 29 Suppl:S17, 2004.

31. Liu Q, Hay JG, and Andrews JG: Body roll and handpath in freestyle swimming: an experimental study, J Appl Biomech 9:238, 1993.

32. Maglischo E: Swimming faster: a comprehensive guide to the science of swimming, Palo Alto, CA, 1982, Mayfield.

33. McLean SP and Hinrichs RN: Buoyancy, gender, and swimming performance, J Appl Biomech 16:248, 2000.

34. Mollendorf JC, Termin AC, Oppenheim E, and Pendergast DR: Effect of swim suit design on passive drag, Med Sci Sports Exerc 36:1029, 2004.

35. Payton CJ, Bartlett RM, Baltzopoulos V, and Coombs R: Upper extremity kinematics and body roll during preferred-side breathing and breath-holding front crawl swimming, J Sports Sci 17:689, 1999.

36. Payton CJ, Hay JG, and Mullineaux DR: The effect of body roll on hand speed and hand path in front crawl swimming—a simulation study, J Appl Biomech 13:300, 1997.

37. Pelayo P, Sidney M, Kherif T, Chollet D, and Tourny C: Stroking characteristics in freestyle swimming and relationships with anthropometric characteristics, J Appl Biomech 12:197, 1996.

38. Pendergast D, Mollendorf J, Zamparo P, Termin A 2nd, Bushnell D, and Paschke D: The influence of drag on human locomotion in water, Undersea Hyperb Med 32:45, 2005.

39. Rayner JM: Dynamics of the vortex wakes of flying and swimming vertebrates, Symp Soc Exp Biol 49:131, 1995.

40. Remizov LP: Biomechanics of optimal flight in ski jumping, J Biomech 17:167, 1984.

41. Richardson RS and Johnson SC: The effect of aerodynamic handlebars on oxygen consumption while cycling at a constant speed, Ergonomics 37:859, 1994.

42. Roberson JA and Crowe CT: Engineering fluid mechanics (2nd ed), Boston, 1980, Houghton Mifflin.

43. Sanders RH, Cappaert JM, and Pease DL: Wave characteristics of Olympic breaststroke swimmers, J Appl Biomech 14:40, 1998.

44. Schleihauf RE: A hydrodynamic analysis of swimming propulsion. In Terauds J and Bedingfield E, eds: Swimming III, Baltimore, 1979, University Park Press.

45. Schleihauf RE et al: Models of aquatic skill sprint front crawlstroke, N Z J Sports Med p 6, Mar 1986.

46. Taïar R, Sagnes P, Henry C, Dufour AB, and Rouard AH: Hydrodynamics optimization in butterfly swimming: position, drag coefficient and performance, J Biomech 32:803, 1999.

47. Takamoto M, Ohmichi H, and Miyashita M: Wave height in relation to swimming velocity and proficiency in front crawl stroke. In Winter D et al, eds: Biomechanics IX-B, Champaign, IL, 1985, Human Kinetics.

48. Toussaint HM et al: Effect of a triathlon wet suit on drag during swimming, Med Sci Sports Exerc 21:325, 1989.

49. Townend MS: Mathematics in sport, New York, 1984, John Wiley & Sons.

50. Ungerechts BE: On the relevance of rotating water flow for the propulsion in swimming. In Jonsson B, ed: Biomechanics X-B, Champaign, IL, 1987, Human Kinetics.

51. van Ingen Schenau GJ: The influence of air friction in speed skating, J Biomech 15:449, 1982.

52. Virmavirta M, Kivekas J, and Komi PV: Take-off aerodynamics in ski jumping, J Biomech 34:465, 2001.

53. Ward-Smith AJ: The influence of aerodynamic and biomechanical factors on long jump performance, J Biomech 16:655, 1983.
54. Ward-Smith AJ: A mathematical analysis of the influence of adverse and favourable winds on sprinting, J Biomech 18:351, 1985.
55. Yanai T: Rotational effect of buoyancy in frontcrawl: Does it really cause the legs to sink? J Biomech 34:235, 2001.
56. Yanai T: Stroke frequency in front crawl: Its mechanical link to the fluid forces required in non-propulsive directions, J Biomech 36:53, 2003.
57. Yanai T: Buoyancy is the primary source of generating bodyroll in front-crawl swimming, J Biomech 37: 605, 2004.

ANNOTATED READINGS

Kyle CR: Athletic clothing, Sci Am 254:104, 1986.
> *Presents an overview of the aerodynamic improvements that have been made in clothing for several different sports based on wind tunnel research on drag.*

Morriss C and Bartlett R: Biomechanical factors critical for performance in the men's javelin throw, Sports Med 21:438, 1996.
> *Reviews biomechanics research on the men's javelin throw to promote understanding of how elite javelin throwers achieve success.*

Toussaint HM, de Hollander AP, van den Berg C, and Vorontsov AR: Biomechanics of swimming. In Garrett WE and Kirkendall DT: *Exercise and sport science,* Philadelphia, 2000, Lippincott Williams & Wilkins.
> *Provides a comprehensive review of literature on the effects of drag in swimming and on swimming propulsion.techniques and theories.*

Townend MS: *Mathematics in sport,* New York, 1984, John Wiley & Sons.
> *Includes a chapter on sailing that provides a technical analysis of the aerodynamics and hydrodynamics of sailing and windsurfing.*

RELATED WEB SITES

Circulation and the Magnus Effect
www.phys.virginia.edu/classes/311/notes/aero/node2.html
> *Shows a diagram and includes discussion of the Magnus force with practical examples.*

Drag Force on a Sphere
www.ma.iup.edu/MathDept/Projects/CalcDEMma/drag/drag0.html
> *Provides links to pages on the graph of the drag coefficient versus Reynolds number and two models for drag force.*

Magnus Force
www.rawbw.com/~xmwang/physDemo.html#magnus
> *Provides links to a number of graphical animations of the effect of the Magnus force.*

NASA: Lift from Pressure
www.grc.nasa.gov/WWW/K-12/airplane/right1.html
> *Provides narrative, definitions of related terms, and slides illustrating lift concepts.*

NASA: Lift to Drag Ratio
www.grc.nasa.gov/WWW/K-12/airplane/ldrat.html
> *Provides narrative, definitions of related terms, and slides illustrating lift / drag ratio concepts.*

NASA: Relative Velocities
www.grc.nasa.gov/WWW/K-12/airplane/move2.html
> *Provides narrative, definitions of related terms, and slides illustrating relative velocity concepts.*

NASA: What Is Drag?
www.grc.nasa.gov/WWW/K-12/airplane/drag1.html
> *Provides narrative, definitions of related terms, and slides illustrating drag concepts.*

Open Door Website: Relativity
www.saburchill.com/physics/chapters/0083.html
Provides description of a quantitative relative velocity problem with entertaining graphics.
Physics Classroom: Relative Velocity
www.physicsclassroom.com/Class/vectors/U3L1f.html
Includes explanation, graphics, and animations demonstrating relative velocity.
Relative Velocity Applet
www.math.gatech.edu/~carlen/2507/notes/classFiles/partOne/RelVel.html
Includes an interactive application that enables control of two moving points and provides the ability to graph the absolute and relative motions of the points.
Tennis: The Magnus Effect
wings.avkids.com/Tennis/Book/magnus-01.html
Provides a description and animated drawing of the Magnus effect on a spinning tennis ball.
U.S. Centennial of Flight Commission
www.centennialofflight.gov/essay/Dictionary/four_forces/DI24.htm
Provides an illustrated discussion about the forces acting on an airplane.

KEY TERMS

angle of attack	angle between the longitudinal axis of a body and the direction of the fluid flow
Archimedes' principle	physical law stating that the buoyant force acting on a body is equal to the weight of the fluid displaced by the body
Bernoulli principle	an expression of the inverse relationship between relative velocity and relative pressure in a fluid flow
boundary layer	layer of fluid immediately adjacent to a body
center of volume	point around which a body's volume is equally balanced and at which the buoyant force acts
coefficient of drag	unitless number that is an index of a body's ability to generate fluid resistance
coefficient of lift	unitless number that is an index of a body's ability to generate lift
fluid	substance that flows when subjected to a shear stress
foil	shape capable of generating lift in the presence of a fluid flow
form drag pressure drag profile drag	resistance created by a pressure differential between the lead and rear sides of a body moving through a fluid
laminar flow	flow characterized by smooth, parallel layers of fluid
lift	force acting on a body in a fluid in a direction perpendicular to the fluid flow
lift/drag ratio	the magnitude of the lift force divided by the magnitude of the total drag force acting on a body at a given time
Magnus effect	deviation in the trajectory of a spinning object toward the direction of spin, resulting from the Magnus force
Magnus force	lift force created by spin
propulsive drag	force acting in the direction of a body's motion
propulsive drag theory	theory attributing propulsion in swimming to propulsive drag on the swimmer
propulsive lift theory	theory attributing propulsion in swimming at least partially to lift acting on the swimmer
relative velocity	velocity of a body with respect to the velocity of something else, such as the surrounding fluid
skin friction surface drag viscous drag	resistance derived from friction between adjacent layers of fluid near a body moving through the fluid
theoretical square law	drag increases approximately with the square of velocity when relative velocity is low
turbulent flow	flow characterized by mixing of adjacent fluid layers
wave drag	resistance created by the generation of waves at the interface between two different fluids, such as air and water

APPENDIX

Basic Mathematics and Related Skills

NEGATIVE NUMBERS

Negative numbers are preceded by a minus sign. Although the physical quantities used in biomechanics do not have values that are less than zero in magnitude, the minus sign is often used to indicate the direction opposite the direction regarded as positive. Therefore, it is important to recall the following rules regarding arithmetic operations involving negative numbers:

1. Addition of a negative number yields the same results as subtraction of a positive number of the same magnitude:

$$6 + (-4) = 2$$
$$10 + (-3) = 7$$
$$6 + (-8) = -2$$
$$10 + (-23) = -13$$
$$(-6) + (-3) = -9$$
$$(-10) + (-7) = -17$$

2. Subtraction of a negative number yields the same result as addition of a positive number of the same magnitude:

$$5 - (-7) = 12$$
$$8 - (-6) = 14$$
$$-5 - (-3) = -2$$
$$-8 - (-4) = -4$$
$$-5 - (-12) = 7$$
$$-8 - (-10) = 2$$

3. Multiplication or division of a number by a number of the opposite sign yields a negative result:

$$2 \times (-3) = -6$$
$$(-4) \times 5 = -20$$
$$9 \div (-3) = -3$$
$$(-10) \div 2 = -5$$

4. Multiplication or division of a number by a number of the same sign (positive or negative) yields a positive result:

$$3 \times 4 = 12$$
$$(-3) \times (-2) = 6$$
$$10 \div 5 = 2$$
$$(-15) \div (-3) = 5$$

EXPONENTS

Exponents are superscript numbers that immediately follow a base number, indicating how many times that number is to be self-multiplied to yield the result:

$$5^2 = 5 \times 5$$
$$= 25$$
$$3^2 = 3 \times 3$$
$$= 9$$
$$5^3 = 5 \times 5 \times 5$$
$$= 125$$
$$3^3 = 3 \times 3 \times 3$$
$$= 27$$

SQUARE ROOTS

Taking the square root of a number is the inverse operation of squaring a number (multiplying a number by itself). The square root of a number is the number that yields the original number when multiplied by itself. The square root of 25 is 5, and the square root of 9 is 3. Using mathematics notation, these relationships are expressed as the following:

$$\sqrt{25} = 5$$
$$\sqrt{9} = 3$$

Because -5 multiplied by itself also equals 25, -5 is also a square root of 25. The following notation is sometimes used to indicate that square roots may be either positive or negative:

$$\sqrt{25} = +5$$
$$\sqrt{9} = +3$$

ORDER OF OPERATIONS

When a computation involves more than a single operation, a set of rules must be used to arrive at the correct result. These rules may be summarized as follows:

1. Addition and subtraction are of equal precedence; these operations are carried out from left to right as they occur in an equation:

$$7 - 3 + 5 = 4 + 5$$
$$= 9$$
$$5 + 2 - 1 + 10 = 7 - 1 + 10$$
$$= 6 + 10$$
$$= 16$$

2. Multiplication and division are of equal precedence; these operations are carried out from left to right as they occur in an equation:

$$10 \div 5 \times 4 = 2 \times 4$$
$$= 8$$
$$20 \div 4 \times 3 \div 5 = 5 \times 3 \div 5$$
$$= 15 \div 5$$
$$= 3$$

3. Multiplication and division take precedence over addition and subtraction. In computations involving some combination of operations not of the same level of precedence, multiplication and division are carried out before addition and subtraction are carried out:

$$3 + 18 \div 6 = 3 + 3$$
$$= 6$$
$$9 - 2 \times 3 + 7 = 9 - 6 + 7$$
$$= 3 + 7$$
$$= 10$$
$$8 \div 4 + 5 - 2 \times 2 = 2 + 5 - 2 \times 2$$
$$= 2 + 5 - 4$$
$$= 7 - 4$$
$$= 3$$

4. When parentheses ( ), brackets [ ], or braces { } are used, the operations enclosed are performed first, before the other rules of precedence are applied:

$$2 \times 7 + (10 - 5) = 2 \times 7 + 5$$
$$= 14 + 5$$
$$= 19$$
$$20 \div (2 + 2) - 3 \times 4 = 20 \div 4 - 3 \times 4$$
$$= 5 - 3 \times 4$$
$$= 5 - 12$$
$$= -7$$

USE OF A CALCULATOR

Simple computations in biomechanics problems are often performed quickly and easily with a hand-held calculator. However, the correct result can be obtained on a calculator only when the computation is set up properly and the rules for ordering of operations are followed. Most calculators come with an instruction manual that contains sample calculations. It is worthwhile to completely familiarize yourself with your calculator's capabilities, particularly use of the memory, before using it to solve problems.

PERCENTAGES

A percentage is a part of 100. Thus, 37% represents 37 parts of 100. To find 37% of 80, multiply the number 80 by 0.37:

$$80 \times 0.37 = 29.6$$

The number 29.6 is 37% of 80. If you want to determine the percentage of the number 55 that equals 42, multiply the fraction by 100%:

$$\frac{42}{55} \times 100\% = 76.4\%$$

The number 42 is 76.4% of 55.

SIMPLE ALGEBRA

The solution of many problems involves setting up an equation containing one or more unknown quantities represented as variables such as x. An equation is a statement of equality implying that the quantities expressed on the left side of the equals sign are equal to the quantities expressed on the right side of the equals sign. Solving a problem typically requires calculation of the unknown quantity or quantities contained in the equation.

The general procedure for calculating the value of a variable in an equation is to isolate the variable on one side of the equals sign and then to carry out the operations among the numbers expressed on the other side of the equals sign. The process of isolating a variable usually involves performing a series of operations on both sides of the equals sign. As long as the same operation is carried out on both sides of the equals sign, equality is preserved and the equation remains valid:

$$x + 7 = 10$$

Subtract 7 from both sides of the equation:

$$x + 7 - 7 = 10 - 7$$
$$x + 0 = 10 - 7$$
$$x = 3$$
$$y - 3 = 12$$

Add 3 to both sides of the equation:

$$y - 3 + 3 = 12 + 3$$
$$y - 0 = 12 + 3$$
$$y = 15$$
$$z \times 3 = 18$$

Divide both sides of the equation by 3:

$$z \times 3 \div 3 = \frac{18}{3}$$
$$z \times 1 = \frac{18}{3}$$
$$z = 6$$
$$q \div 4 = 2$$

Multiply both sides of the equation by 4:

$$q \div 4 \times 4 = 2 \times 4$$
$$q = 2 \times 4$$
$$q = 8$$
$$x \div 3 + 5 = 8$$

Subtract 5 from both sides of the equation:

$$x \div 3 + 5 - 5 = 8 - 5$$
$$x \div 3 = 3$$

Multiply both sides of the equation by 3:

$$x \div 3 \times 3 = 3 \times 3$$
$$x = 9$$
$$y \div 4 - 7 = -2$$

Add 7 to both sides of the equation:

$$y \div 4 - 7 + 7 = -2 + 7$$
$$y \div 4 = 5$$

Multiply both sides of the equation by 4:

$$y \div 4 \times 4 = 5 \times 4$$
$$y = 20$$
$$z^2 = 36$$

Take the square root of both sides of the equation:

$$z = 6$$

MEASURING ANGLES

The following procedure is used for measuring an angle with a protractor:

1. Place the center of the protractor on the vertex of the angle.
2. Align the zero line on the protractor with one of the sides of the angle.
3. The size of the angle is indicated on the protractor scale where the other side of the angle intersects the scale. (Be sure to read from the correct scale on the protractor. Is the angle greater or less than 90°?)

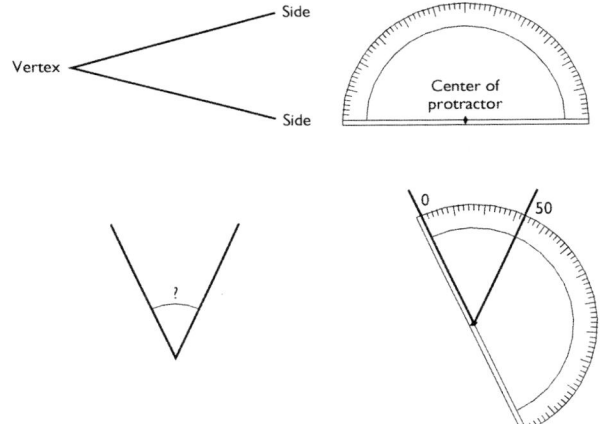

If you are unfamiliar with the use of a protractor, check yourself by verifying the sizes of the following three angles:

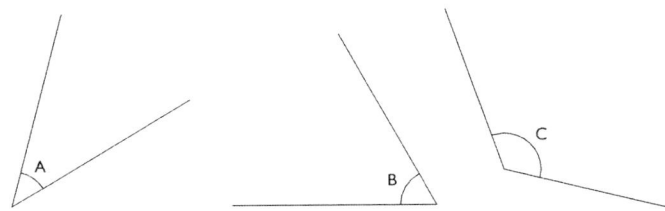

(Answer: A = 45°, B = 60°, C = 123°)

Trigonometric Functions

T rigonometric functions are based on relationships present between the sides and angles of triangles. Many functions are derived from a right triangle—a triangle containing a right (90°) angle. Consider the right triangle below with sides A, B, and C, and angles α, β, and γ.

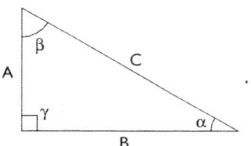

Side C, which is the longest side and the side opposite the right angle, is known as the *hypotenuse of the triangle*.

A commonly used trigonometric relationship for right triangles is the *Pythagorean theorem*. The Pythagorean theorem is an expression of the relationship between the hypotenuse and the other two sides of a right triangle:

> The sum of the squares of the lengths of the two sides of a right triangle is equal to the square of the length of the hypotenuse.

Using the sides of the labeled triangle yields the following:

$$A^2 + B^2 = C^2$$

Suppose that sides A and B are 3 and 4 units long, respectively. The Pythagorean theorem can be used to solve for the length of side C:

$$
\begin{aligned}
C^2 &= A^2 + B^2 \\
&= 3^2 + 4^2 \\
&= 9 + 16 \\
&= 25 \\
C &= 5
\end{aligned}
$$

Three trigonometric relationships are based on the ratios of the lengths of the sides of a right triangle. The sine (abbreviated *sin*) of an angle is defined as the ratio of the length of the side of the triangle opposite the angle to the length of the hypotenuse. Using the labeled triangle yields the following:

$$\sin \alpha = \frac{\text{opposite}}{\text{hypotenuse}} = \frac{A}{C}$$

$$\sin \beta = \frac{\text{opposite}}{\text{hypotenuse}} = \frac{B}{C}$$

With $A = 3$, $B = 4$, and $C = 5$:

$$\sin \alpha = \frac{A}{C} = \frac{3}{5} = 0.6$$

$$\sin \beta = \frac{B}{C} = \frac{4}{5} = 0.8$$

The cosine (abbreviated *cos*) of an angle is defined as the ratio of the length of the side of the triangle adjacent to the angle to the length of the hypotenuse. Using the labeled triangle yields the following:

$$\cos \alpha = \frac{\text{adjacent}}{\text{hypotenuse}} = \frac{B}{C}$$

$$\cos \beta = \frac{\text{adjacent}}{\text{hypotenuse}} = \frac{A}{C}$$

With $A = 3$, $B = 4$, and $C = 5$:

$$\cos \alpha = \frac{B}{C} = \frac{4}{5} = 0.8$$

$$\cos \beta = \frac{A}{C} = \frac{3}{5} = 0.6$$

The third function, the tangent (abbreviated *tan*) of an angle, is defined as the ratio of the length of the side of the triangle opposite the angle to that of the side adjacent to the angle. Using the labeled triangle yields the following:

$$\tan \alpha = \frac{\text{opposite}}{\text{adjacent}} = \frac{A}{B}$$

$$\tan \beta = \frac{\text{opposite}}{\text{adjacent}} = \frac{B}{A}$$

With $A = 3$, $B = 4$, and $C = 5$:

$$\tan \alpha = \frac{A}{B} = \frac{3}{4} = 0.75$$

$$\tan \beta = \frac{B}{A} = \frac{4}{3} = 1.33$$

Two useful trigonometric relationships are applicable to *all* triangles. The first is known as the law of sines:

> The ratio between the length of any side of a triangle and the angle opposite that side is equal to the ratio between the length of any other side of the triangle and the angle opposite that side.

With respect to the labeled triangle, this may be stated as the following:

$$\frac{A}{\sin \alpha} = \frac{B}{\sin \beta} = \frac{C}{\sin \gamma}$$

A second trigonometric relationship applicable to *all* triangles is the law of cosines:

> The square of the length of any side of a triangle is equal to the sum of the squares of the lengths of the other two sides of the triangle minus two times the product of the lengths of the other two sides and the cosine of the angle opposite the original side.

This relationship yields the following for each of the sides of the labeled triangle:

$$A^2 = B^2 + C^2 - 2BC \cos \alpha$$
$$B^2 = A^2 + C^2 - 2AC \cos \beta$$
$$C^2 = A^2 + B^2 - 2AB \cos \gamma$$

A table of the values of the basic trigonometric functions follows.

Table of Basic Trigonometric Function Values

DEG	SIN	COS	TAN	DEG	SIN	COS	TAN
00	.0000	1.0000	.0000	—	—	—	—
01	.0175	.9998	.0175	46	.7193	.6947	1.0355
02	.0349	.9994	.0349	47	.7314	.6820	1.0723
03	.0523	.9986	.0524	48	.7431	.6691	1.1106
04	.0698	.9976	.0699	49	.7547	.6561	1.1504
05	.0872	.9962	.0875	50	.7660	.6428	1.1918
06	.1045	.9945	.1051	51	.7771	.6293	1.2349
07	.1219	.9925	.1228	52	.7880	.6157	1.2799
08	.1392	.9903	.1405	53	.7986	.6018	1.3270
09	.1564	.9877	.1584	54	.8090	.5878	1.3764
10	.1736	.9848	.1763	55	.8192	.5736	1.4281
11	.1908	.9816	.1944	56	.8290	.5592	1.4826
12	.2079	.9781	.2126	57	.8387	.5446	1.5399
13	.2250	.9744	.2309	58	.8480	.5299	1.6003
14	.2419	.9703	.2493	59	.8572	.5150	1.6643
15	.2588	.9659	.2679	60	.8660	.5000	1.7321
16	.2756	.9613	.2867	61	.8746	.4848	1.8040
17	.2924	.9563	.3057	62	.8829	.4695	1.8807
18	.3090	.9511	.3249	63	.8910	.4540	1.9626
19	.3256	.9455	.3443	64	.8988	.4384	2.0503
20	.3420	.9397	.3640	65	.9063	.4226	2.1445
21	.3584	.9336	.3839	66	.9135	.4067	2.2460
22	.3746	.9272	.4040	67	.9205	.3907	2.3559
23	.3907	.9205	.4245	68	.9279	.3746	2.4751
24	.4067	.9135	.4452	69	.9336	.3584	2.6051
25	.4226	.9063	.4663	70	.9397	.3420	2.7475
26	.4384	.8988	.4877	71	.9456	.3256	2.9042
27	.4540	.8910	.5095	72	.9511	.3090	3.0779
28	.4695	.8829	.5317	73	.9563	.2924	3.2709
29	.4848	.8746	.5543	74	.9613	.2756	3.4874
30	.5000	.8660	.5774	75	.96593	.2588	3.7321
31	.5150	.8572	.6009	76	.9703	.2419	4.0108
32	.5299	.8480	.6249	77	.9744	.2250	4.3315
33	.5446	.8387	.6494	78	.9781	.2079	4.7046
34	.5592	.8290	.6745	79	.9816	.1908	5.1446
35	.5736	.8192	.7002	80	.9848	.1736	5.6713
36	.5878	.8090	.7265	81	.9877	.1564	6.3138
37	.6018	.7986	.7536	82	.9903	.1391	7.1154
38	.6157	.7880	.7813	83	.9925	.1219	8.1443
39	.6293	.7771	.8098	84	.9945	.1045	9.5144
40	.6428	.7660	.8391	85	.99625	.0872	11.4301
41	.6561	.7547	.8693	86	.9976	.0698	14.3007
42	.6691	.7431	.9004	87	.99866	.05239	19.0811
43	.6820	.7314	.9325	88	.9994	.0349	28.6363
44	.6947	.7193	.9657	89	.9998	.0175	57.2900
45	.7071	.7071	1.0000	90	1.0000	.0000	Infinity

A P P E N D I X

Common Units of Measurement

This appendix contains factors for converting between metric units commonly used in biomechanics and their English system equivalents. In each case, a value expressed in a metric unit can be divided by the conversion factor given to yield the approximate equivalent in an English unit, or a value expressed in an English unit can be multiplied by the conversion factor to find the metric unit equivalent. For example, to convert 100 Newtons to pounds, do the following:

$$\frac{100 \text{ N}}{4.45 \text{ N/lb}} = 22.5 \text{ lb}$$

To convert 100 pounds to Newtons, do the following:

$$(100 \text{ lb})\,(4.45 \text{ N/lb}) = 445 \text{ N}$$

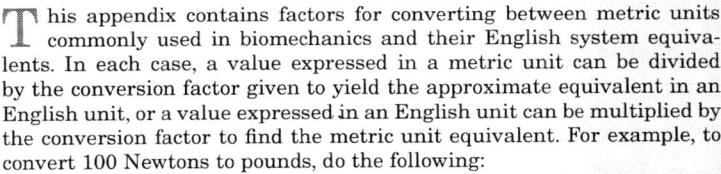

VARIABLE	METRIC UNIT	← MULTIPLY BY DIVIDE BY →	ENGLISH UNIT
Distance	Centimeters	2.54	Inches
	Meters	0.3048	Feet
	Kilometers	1.609	Miles
Speed	Meters/second	0.447	Miles/hour
Mass	Kilograms	14.59	Slugs
Force	Newtons	4.448	Pounds
Work	Joules	1.355	Foot-pounds
Power	Watts	745.63	Horsepower
Energy	Joules	1.355	Foot-pounds
Linear momentum	Kilogram-meters/second	4.448	Slug-feet/second
Impulse	Newton-seconds	4.448	Pound-seconds
Angular momentum	Kilogram-meters^2/second	1.355	Slug-feet^2/second
Moment of inertia	Kilogram-meters^2	1.355	Slug-feet^2
Torque	Newton-meters	1.355	Foot-pounds

GLOSSARY

absolute angle	angular orientation of a body segment with respect to a fixed line of reference
acromioclavicular joint	irregular joint between the acromion process of the scapula and the distal clavicle
active insufficiency	limited ability of a two-joint muscle to produce force when joint position places the muscle on slack
active stretching	stretching of muscles, tendons, and ligaments produced by active development of tension in the antagonist muscles
acute loading	application of a single force of sufficient magnitude to cause injury to a biological tissue
agonist	role played by a muscle acting to cause a movement
amenorrhea	cessation of menses
anatomical reference position	erect standing position with all body parts, including the palms of the hands, facing forward; considered the starting position for body segment movements
angle of attack	angle between the longitudinal axis of a body and the direction of the fluid flow
angle of projection	the direction at which a body is projected with respect to the horizontal
angular	involving rotation around a central line or point
angular acceleration	rate of change in angular velocity
angular displacement	change in the angular position or orientation of a line segment
angular impulse	change in angular momentum equal to the product of torque and time interval over which the torque acts
angular momentum	quantity of angular motion possessed by a body; measured as the product of moment of inertia and angular velocity
angular velocity	rate of change in the angular position or orientation of a line segment
anisotropic	exhibiting different mechanical properties in response to loads from different directions
annulus fibrosus	thick, fibrocartilaginous ring that forms the exterior of the intervertebral disc
antagonist	role played by a muscle acting to slow or stop a movement
anteroposterior axis	imaginary line around which frontal plane rotations occur
anthropometric	related to the dimensions and weights of body segments
apex	the highest point in the trajectory of a projectile
appendicular skeleton	bones composing the body appendages
Archimedes' principle	physical law stating that the buoyant force acting on a body is equal to the weight of the fluid displaced by the body
articular capsule	double-layered membrane that surrounds every synovial joint
articular cartilage	protective layer of dense white connective tissue covering the articulating bone surfaces at diarthrodial joints

articular fibrocartilage	soft-tissue discs or menisci that intervene between articulating bones
average	occurring over a designated time interval
axial	directed along the longitudinal axis of a body
axial skeleton	the skull, vertebrae, sternum, and ribs
axis of rotation	imaginary line perpendicular to the plane of rotation and passing through the center of rotation
balance	ability to control equilibrium
ballistic stretching	a series of quick, bouncing-type stretches
base of support	area bound by the outermost regions of contact between a body and support surface or surfaces
bending	asymmetric loading that produces tension on one side of a body's longitudinal axis and compression on the other side
Bernoulli principle	an expression of the inverse relationship between relative velocity and relative pressure in a fluid flow
biomechanics	application of mechanical principles in the study of living organisms
bone atrophy	decrease in bone mass resulting from a predominance of osteoclast activity
bone hypertrophy	increase in bone mass resulting from a predominance of osteoblast activity
boundary layer	layer of fluid immediately adjacent to a body
bursae	sacs secreting synovial fluid internally that lessen friction between soft tissues around joints
cardinal planes	three imaginary perpendicular reference planes that divide the body in half by mass
carpal tunnel syndrome	overuse condition caused by compression of the median nerve in the carpal tunnel and involving numbness, tingling, and pain in the hand
center of gravity	point around which a body's weight is equally balanced, no matter how the body is positioned
center of mass (mass centroid, center of gravity)	point around which the mass and weight of a body are balanced, no matter how the body is positioned
center of volume	point around which a body's volume is equally balanced and at which the buoyant force acts
centripetal force	force directed toward the center of rotation for a body in rotational motion
close-packed position	joint orientation for which the contact between the articulating bone surfaces is maximum
coefficient of drag	unitless number that is an index of a body's ability to generate fluid resistance
coefficient of friction	number that serves as an index of the interaction between two surfaces in contact
coefficient of lift	unitless number that is an index of a body's ability to generate lift
coefficient of restitution	number that serves as an index of elasticity for colliding bodies
collateral ligaments	major ligaments that cross the medial and lateral aspects of the knee
combined loading	simultaneous action of more than one of the pure forms of loading
compression	pressing or squeezing force directed axially through a body
compressive strength	ability to resist pressing or squeezing force
concentric	describing a contraction involving shortening of a muscle
contractile component	muscle property enabling tension development by stimulated muscle fibers
coracoclavicular joint	syndesmosis with the coracoid process of the scapula bound to the inferior clavicle by the coracoclavicular ligament
cortical bone	compact mineralized connective tissue with low porosity that is found in the shafts of long bones
couple	pair of equal, oppositely directed forces that act on opposite sides of an axis of rotation to produce torque

530   BASIC BIOMECHANICS

cruciate ligaments	major ligaments that cross each other in connecting the anterior and posterior aspects of the knee
curvilinear	along a curved line
deformation	change in shape
density	mass per unit of volume
dynamic equilibrium (D'Alembert's principle)	concept indicating a balance between applied forces and inertial forces for a body in motion
dynamics	branch of mechanics dealing with systems subject to acceleration
eccentric	describing a contraction involving lengthening of a muscle
electromechanical delay	time between arrival of a neural stimulus and tension development by the muscle
English system	system of weights and measures originally developed in England and used in the United States today
epicondylitis	inflammation and sometimes microrupturing of the collagenous tissues on either the lateral or the medial side of the distal humerus; believed to be an overuse injury
epiphysis	growth center of a bone that produces new bone tissue as part of the normal growth process until it closes during adolescence or early adulthood
extrinsic muscles	muscles with proximal attachments located proximal to the wrist and distal attachments located distal to the wrist
failure	loss of mechanical continuity
fast-twitch fiber	a fiber that reaches peak tension relatively quickly
first-class lever	lever positioned with the applied force and the resistance on opposite sides of the axis of rotation
flat bones	skeletal structures that are largely flat in shape, for example, the scapula
flexion relaxation phenomenon	when the spine is in full flexion, the spinal extensor muscles relax and the flexion torque is supported by the spinal ligaments
fluid	substance that flows when subjected to a shear stress
foil	shape capable of generating lift in the presence of a fluid flow
force	push or pull; the product of mass and acceleration
form drag (profile drag, pressure drag)	resistance created by a pressure differential between the lead and rear sides of a body moving through a fluid
fracture	disruption in the continuity of a bone
free body diagram	sketch that shows a defined system in isolation with all of the force vectors acting on the system
friction	force acting at the area of contact between two surfaces in the direction opposite that of motion or motion tendency
frontal plane	plane in which lateral movements of the body and body segments occur
fulcrum	the point of support, or axis, about which a lever may be made to rotate
general motion	motion involving translation and rotation simultaneously
glenohumeral joint	ball-and-socket joint in which the head of the humerus articulates with the glenoid fossa of the scapula
glenoid labrum	rim of soft tissue located on the periphery of the glenoid fossa that adds stability to the glenohumeral joint
Golgi tendon organ	sensory receptor that inhibits tension development in a muscle and initiates tension development in antagonist muscles
hamstrings	the biceps femoris, semimembranosus, and semitendinosus
humeroradial joint	gliding joint in which the capitellum of the humerus articulates with the proximal end of the radius
humeroulnar joint	hinge joint in which the humeral trochlea articulates with the trochlear fossa of the ulna
iliopsoas	the psoas major and iliacus muscles with a common insertion on the lesser trochanter of the femur

iliotibial band	thick, strong band of tissue connecting the tensor fascia lata to the lateral condyle of the femur and the lateral tuberosity of the tibia
impact	collision characterized by the exchange of a large force during a small time interval
impacted	pressed together by a compressive load
impulse	product of a force and the time interval over which the force acts
inertia	tendency of a body to resist a change in its state of motion
inference	process of forming deductions from available information
initial velocity	vector quantity incorporating both angle and speed of projection
instant center	precisely located center of rotation at a joint at a given instant in time
instantaneous	occurring during a small interval of time
intraabdominal pressure	pressure inside the abdominal cavity; believed to help stiffen the lumbar spine against buckling
intrinsic muscles	muscles with both attachments distal to the wrist
irregular bones	skeletal structures of irregular shapes, for example, the sacrum
isometric	describing a contraction involving no change in muscle length
joint flexibility	a term representing the relative ranges of motion allowed at a joint
joint stability	ability of a joint to resist abnormal displacement of the articulating bones
kinematics	the form, pattern, or sequencing of movement with respect to time
kinesiology	study of human movement
kinetic energy	energy of motion calculated as $\frac{1}{2}\ mv^2$
kinetic friction	constant magnitude friction generated between two surfaces in contact during motion
kinetics	study of the action of forces
kyphosis	extreme curvature in the thoracic region of the spine
laminar flow	flow characterized by smooth, parallel layers of fluid
laws of constant acceleration	formulas relating displacement, velocity, acceleration, and time when acceleration is unchanging
lever	a relatively rigid object that may be made to rotate about an axis by the application of force
lift	force acting on a body in a fluid in a direction perpendicular to the fluid flow
lift/drag ratio	the magnitude of the lift force divided by the magnitude of the total drag force acting on a body at a given time
ligamentum flavum	yellow ligament that connects the laminae of adjacent vertebrae; distinguished by its elasticity
linear	along a line that may be straight or curved, with all parts of the body moving in the same direction at the same speed
linear acceleration	the rate of change in linear velocity
linear displacement	change in location, or the directed distance from initial to final location
linear momentum	quantity of motion, measured as the product of a body's mass and its velocity
linear velocity	the rate of change in location
long bones	skeletal structures consisting of a long shaft with bulbous ends, for example, the femur
longitudinal axis	imaginary line around which transverse plane rotations occur
loose-packed position	any joint orientation other than the close-packed position
lordosis	extreme curvature in the lumbar region of the spine
Magnus effect	deviation in the trajectory of a spinning object toward the direction of spin, resulting from the Magnus force
Magnus force	lift force created by spin
mass	quantity of matter contained in an object

maximum static friction	maximum amount of friction that can be generated between two static surfaces
mechanical advantage	ratio of force arm to resistance arm for a given lever
mechanics	branch of physics that analyzes the actions of forces on particles and mechanical systems
mediolateral axis	imaginary line around which sagittal plane rotations occur
menisci	cartilaginous discs located between the tibial and femoral condyles
meter	the most common international unit of length, on which the metric system is based
metric system	system of weights and measures used internationally in scientific applications and adopted for daily use by every major country except the United States
moment arm	shortest (perpendicular) distance between a force's line of action and an axis of rotation
moment of inertia	inertial property for rotating bodies representing resistance to angular acceleration; based on both mass and the distance the mass is distributed from the axis of rotation
motion segment	two adjacent vertebrae and the associated soft tissues; the functional unit of the spine
motor unit	a single motor neuron and all fibers it innervates
muscle inhibition	the inability to activate all motor units of a muscle during maximal voluntary contraction
muscle spindle	sensory receptor that provokes reflex contraction in a stretched muscle and inhibits tension development in antagonist muscles
myoelectric activity	electric current or voltage produced by a muscle developing tension
net force	resultant force derived from the composition of two or more forces
neutralizer	role played by a muscle acting to eliminate an unwanted action produced by an agonist
normal reaction force	force acting perpendicular to two surfaces in contact
nucleus pulposus	colloidal gel with a high fluid content, located inside the annulus fibrosus of the intervertebral disc
osteoblasts	specialized bone cells that build new bone tissue
osteoclasts	specialized bone cells that resorb bone tissue
osteopenia	condition of reduced bone mineral density that predisposes the individual to fractures
osteoporosis	a disorder involving decreased bone mass and strength with one or more resulting fractures
parallel elastic component	passive elastic property of muscle derived from the muscle membranes
parallel fiber arrangement	pattern of fibers within a muscle in which the fibers are roughly parallel to the longitudinal axis of the muscle
passive insufficiency	inability of a two-joint muscle to stretch to the extent required to allow full range of motion at all joints crossed
passive stretching	stretching of muscles, tendons, and ligaments produced by a stretching force other than tension in the antagonist muscles
patellofemoral joint	articulation between the patella and the femur
pelvic girdle	the two hip bones plus the sacrum, which can be rotated forward, backward, and laterally to optimize positioning of the hip joint
pennate fiber arrangement	pattern of fibers within a muscle with short fibers attaching to one or more tendons
perfectly elastic impact	impact during which the velocity of the system is conserved
perfectly plastic impact	impact resulting in the total loss of system velocity
periosteum	double-layered membrane covering bone; muscle tendons attach to the outside layer, and the internal layer is a site of osteoblast activity
plantar fascia	thick bands of fascia that cover the plantar aspect of the foot
popliteus	muscle known as the unlocker of the knee because its action is lateral rotation of the femur with respect to the tibia
porous	containing pores or cavities
potential energy	energy by virtue of a body's position or configuration, calculated as the product of weight and height

power	rate of work production, calculated as work divided by the time during which the work was done
pressure	force per unit of area over which a force acts
prestress	stress on the spine created by tension in the resting ligaments
primary spinal curves	curves that are present at birth
principal axes	three mutually perpendicular axes passing through the total-body center of gravity
principal moment of inertia	total-body moment of inertia relative to one of the principal axes
projectile	a body in free fall that is subject only to the forces of gravity and air resistance
projection speed	the magnitude of projection velocity
pronation	combined conditions of dorsiflexion, eversion, and abduction
proprioceptive neuromuscular facilitation	a group of stretching procedures involving alternating contraction and relaxation of the muscles being stretched
propulsive drag	force acting in the direction of a body's motion
propulsive drag theory	theory attributing propulsion in swimming to propulsive drag on the swimmer
propulsive lift theory	theory attributing propulsion in swimming at least partially to lift acting on the swimmer
Q-angle	the angle formed between the anterior superior iliac spine, the center of the patella, and the tibial tuberosity
quadriceps	the rectus femoris, vastus lateralis, vastus medialis, and vastus intermedius
qualitative	involving nonnumeric description of quality
quantitative	involving the use of numbers
radial acceleration	component of acceleration of a body in angular motion directed toward the center of curvature; represents change in direction
radian	unit of angular measure used in angular-linear kinematic quantity conversions; equal to $57.3°$
radiocarpal joints	condyloid articulations between the radius and the three carpal bones
radioulnar joints	the proximal and distal radioulnar joints are pivot joints; the middle radioulnar joint is a syndesmosis
radius of gyration	distance from the axis of rotation to a point where the body's mass could be concentrated without altering its rotational characteristics
radius of rotation	distance from the axis of rotation to a point of interest on a rotating body
range	the horizontal displacement of a projectile at landing
range of motion	angle through which a joint moves from anatomical position to the extreme limit of segment motion in a particular direction
reaction board	a specially constructed board for determining the center of gravity location of a body positioned on top of it
reciprocal inhibition	inhibition of tension development in the antagonist muscles resulting from activation of muscle spindles
rectilinear	along a straight line
relative angle	angle at a joint formed between the longitudinal axes of adjacent body segments
relative projection height	the difference between projection height and landing height
relative velocity	velocity of a body with respect to the velocity of something else, such as the surrounding fluid
repetitive loading	repeated application of a subacute load that is usually of relatively low magnitude
resultant	single vector that results from vector composition
retinacula	fibrous bands of fascia
right hand rule	procedure for identifying the direction of an angular motion vector
rotator cuff	band of tendons of the subscapularis, supraspinatus, infraspinatus, and teres minor, which attach to the humeral head

534 BASIC BIOMECHANICS

sagittal plane	plane in which forward and backward movements of the body and body segments occur
scalar	physical quantity that is completely described by its magnitude
scapulohumeral rhythm	a regular pattern of scapular rotation that accompanies and facilitates humeral abduction
scoliosis	lateral spinal curvature
secondary spinal curves	the cervical and lumbar curves, which do not develop until the weight of the body begins to be supported in sitting and standing positions
second-class lever	lever positioned with the resistance between the applied force and the fulcrum
segmental method	a procedure for determining total-body center of mass location based on the masses and center of mass locations of the individual body segments
series elastic component	passive elastic property of muscle derived from the tendons
shear	force directed parallel to a surface
short bones	small, cubical skeletal structures, including the carpals and tarsals
skin friction (surface drag, viscous drag)	resistance derived from friction between adjacent layers of fluid near a body moving through the fluid
slow-twitch fiber	a fiber that reaches peak tension relatively slowly
specific weight	weight per unit of volume
spondylolisthesis	complete bilateral fracture of the pars interarticularis, resulting in anterior slippage of the vertebra
spondylolysis	presence of a fracture in the pars interarticularis of the vertebral neural arch
sports medicine	clinical and scientific aspects of sports and exercise
stability	resistance to disruption of equilibrium
stabilizer	role played by a muscle acting to stabilize a body part against some other force
static equilibrium	a motionless state characterized by $\Sigma SF_v = 0$, $\Sigma SF_h = 0$, and $\Sigma ST = 0$
static stretching	maintaining a slow, controlled, sustained stretch over time, usually about 30 seconds
statics	branch of mechanics dealing with systems in a constant state of motion
sternoclavicular joint	modified ball-and-socket joint between the proximal clavicle and the manubrium of the sternum
stiffness	the ratio of stress to strain in a loaded material; that is, the stress divided by the relative amount of change in the structure's shape
strain	amount of deformation divided by the original length of the structure or by the original angular orientation of the structure
strain energy	capacity to do work by virtue of a deformed body's return to its original shape
stress	distribution of force within a body, quantified as force divided by the area over which the force acts
stress fracture	fracture resulting from repeated loading of relatively low magnitude
stress reaction	progressive bone pathology associated with repeated loading
stretch reflex	monosynaptic reflex initiated by stretching of muscle spindles and resulting in immediate development of muscle tension
stretch-shortening cycle	eccentric contraction followed immediately by concentric contraction
summation	building in an additive fashion
supination	combined conditions of plantar flexion, inversion, and adduction
synovial fluid	clear, slightly yellow liquid that provides lubrication inside the articular capsule at synovial joints
system	mechanical system chosen by the analyst for study
tangential acceleration	component of acceleration of a body in angular motion directed along a tangent to the path of motion; represents change in linear speed
tensile strength	ability to resist pulling or stretching force

GLOSSARY 535

tension	pulling or stretching force directed axially through a body
tetanus	state of muscle producing sustained maximal tension resulting from repetitive stimulation
theoretical square law	drag increases approximately with the square of velocity when relative velocity is low
third-class lever	lever positioned with the applied force between the fulcrum and the resistance
tibiofemoral joint	dual condyloid articulations between the medial and lateral condyles of the tibia and the femur, composing the main hinge joint of the knee
torque	the rotary effect of a force about an axis of rotation, measured as the product of the force and the perpendicular distance between the force's line of action and the axis
torsion	load producing twisting of a body around its longitudinal axis
trabecular bone	less-compact mineralized connective tissue with high porosity that is found in the ends of long bones and in the vertebrae
trajectory	the flight path of a projectile
transducers	devices that detect signals
translation	linear motion
transverse plane	plane in which horizontal body and body segment movements occur when the body is in an erect standing position
turbulent flow	flow characterized by mixing of adjacent fluid layers
valgus	condition of outward deviation in alignment from the proximal to the distal end of a body segment
varus	condition of inward deviation in alignment from the proximal to the distal end of a body segment
vector	physical quantity that possesses both magnitude and direction
vector composition	process of determining a single vector from two or more vectors by vector addition
vector resolution	operation that replaces a single vector with two perpendicular vectors such that the vector composition of the two perpendicular vectors yields the original vector
viscoelastic	having the ability to stretch or shorten over time
volume	space occupied by a body
wave drag	resistance created by the generation of waves at the interface between two different fluids, such as air and water
weight	attractive force that the earth exerts on a body
work	in a mechanical context, force multiplied by the displacement of the resistance in the direction of the force
yield point (elastic limit)	point on the load–deformation curve past which deformation is permanent

INDEX

538   BASIC BIOMECHANICS